INTRODUCTION TO

GEOLOGY

E. B. Branson, Ph.D.
Late Professor of Geology and Paleontology
University of Missouri

W. A. Tarr, Ph.D., Sc.D.
Late Professor of Geology and Mineralogy
University of Missouri

Revised By
Carl C. Branson, Ph.D.
Professor of Geology
University of Oklahoma

W. D. Keller, Ph.D.
Professor of Geology
University of Missouri

832

THIRD EDITION

NEW YORK   TORONTO   LONDON
McGRAW-HILL BOOK COMPANY, INC.
1952

INTRODUCTION TO GEOLOGY

Library of Congress Catalog Card Number: 51-12936

IX

07239

PREFACE TO THE THIRD EDITION

A third edition of this book was planned and begun two years ago. In 1949, E. B. Branson became ill, and he died on March 12, 1950. He had made marginal notes and corrections and had discussed some of his plans for the new edition with Carl C. Branson.

This edition is thoroughly but not radically revised. The changes are chiefly attempts to bring the scientific and statistical material up to date and to meet the needs expressed by teachers who have used the book in their classrooms. It remains the objective of the present revisers to write in language understandable to the student who is not making geology his profession. The small percentage of students in elementary classes who do intend to become geologists need few technical terms before entering advanced work.

Several airplane photographs are placed in the new edition in the belief that much of future geologic work will be accomplished by the use of such photographs. One stereoscopic pair is included in order to acquaint students with the use of and value of such prints.

Mrs. W. A. Tarr and W. D. Keller revised the chapters on physical geology with the exceptions of Running Water, Snow and Ice, and Structures and Diastrophism. Carl C. Branson revised the Historical Geology section and the chapters mentioned above.

F. A. Melton kindly selected some airplane views from his collections. Kenneth Caster provided pictures from his files, and Irving G. Reimann was most helpful in providing and suggesting illustrations. Glenn A. Jepson forwarded a cut of a recently made restoration. Many other individuals and organizations gave of their time and illustrative material, and their help is acknowledged in the credit lines with the illustrations.

CARL C. BRANSON
MRS. W. A. TARR
W. D. KELLER

NORMAN, OKLA.
COLUMBIA, MO.
January, 1952

PREFACE TO THE FIRST EDITION

The authors have been associated in teaching geology for more than two decades. During this time, they have experimented with many different methods of presenting the introductory course and have had ample opportunity to observe the students' reactions while taking the work and their later opinions of the value of the subject matter. They have changed gradually the content of the beginning course from something of every phase of geology, with explanations couched in somewhat technical terms, to the outstanding principles of the subject, with a minimum of technical phraseology.

Geology at its best offers a field for thinking and enjoyment, and the beginner should not devote much time to memorizing data and becoming acquainted with terminology that is of little value after examinations have passed. The elementary student who is seeking mental training has the right to demand principles and geological reasoning rather than data that may soon be forgotten or confused. Most students have no intention of carrying their geological studies beyond the first course, and technical details tend to obscure the larger vision. As a matter of fact, the authors have observed that students who major in geology enter later courses with more enthusiasm and less feeling of repetition in subject matter if their first course is not technical.

In writing this textbook, the authors have kept before them the view that not more than one in every hundred of the readers will become a geologist. They have also thought of the text as a suitable broad foundation for later professional studies. The principles that have motivated them in the actual writing have been the selection of the most fundamental subjects and simple presentation. They have felt that it is not necessary to mention every phase of geology in order to give a broad survey of the field. They have kept in mind the outstanding need for a treatment of both physical and historical geology that may be mastered in a five-hour course of a semester's duration.

In preparing the text, Tarr wrote the chapters on physical geology, except The Work of Running Water, The Work of Snow and Ice, and Structures and Diastrophism. Branson wrote the historical part and the three chapters mentioned in the preceding sentence.

The sources of the illustrations have been acknowledged in the text, and where drawings have been modified the original drawings are mentioned.   Particular mention should be made of the illustrations procured from the United States Geological Survey, the United States Forestry Service, the United States Army Air Service, the United States Navy Air Service, the American Museum of Natural History, Professor S. W. Williston's books, Professor Charles Schuchert's paleographic maps, Professor W. B. Scott's works, Professor H. F. Osborn's works, the recent textbooks by Professor Raymond Moore, and Professors Emmons, Thiel, Stauffer, and Allison.   Most of the original drawings were made by Miss Coral Fleenor and she retouched the photographs where retouching was necessary.   Miss Grace Carter rendered efficient service in typing the manuscript and various secretarial duties.   Willard Bailey made many of the line drawings.   Mrs. Vaona Peck, Wilford Cline, James Mitchell, Robert Clark, Trusten Peery, and Philip Morey prepared the outcrop maps on which their names appear.

Our colleagues, Walter Keller, Raymond Peck, Carl Swartzlow, Sam T. Bratton, and John Quincy Adams, have helped with the work by suggestions and discussions.   Mrs. W. A. Tarr has been of invaluable service to Tarr.   Branson is under heavy obligations to his colleague M. G. Mehl for help in many ways and for his collaboration in some parts of the discussion of historical phases.

It is fitting to mention the teaching and books of S. W. Williston, Thomas C. Chamberlin, R. D. Salisbury, and Stuart Weller as having laid the foundation for this book.   Perhaps the greatest debt of the authors is to their students, who have shown them the way toward improvement in their selection and presentation of the materials.

E. B. Branson
W. A. Tarr

Columbia, Mo.
   March, 1935

CONTENTS

PART I: PHYSICAL GEOLOGY

CHAPTER 1

INTRODUCTION

Few sciences give the individual so much knowledge of the physical world about him as does geology. We are always in the presence of some of the features of which geology treats, such as hills, valleys, rivers, lakes, mountains, canyons, wind, ocean, rocks, or soil; and the person who understands the origin of these features will derive a deep satisfaction from his surroundings. How few people look upon a beautiful stream winding its way through a valley bordered by rolling hills or rugged cliffs and see in it the agent that formed both the valley and the hills! Not knowing how a stream accomplishes its work, most people, while standing upon one of the hills along the valley, could not in imagination follow the stream back through its early stages and see the valley when it was a mere gully that slowly but surely grew to its present size. Why is there a precipitous bluff at a certain point by the stream although the valley, both up- and downstream from the bluff, is bordered by gently rolling hills? Undoubtedly the character of the rock composing the bluff had something to do with it, but the person who knows nothing about the physical properties or composition of rocks cannot tell why a bluff was formed at just that point. Yet how much it would add to his appreciation of the forces of nature if he only knew that the rock forming the bluff was, for instance, volcanic in origin and once filled the throat of a volcano that has been entirely removed by the physical agents that are forever changing the surface of the earth. The inquiries might go further back, asking where this volcanic rock came from, how far down in the earth it was, what caused it to move outward, and what happened when it reached the surface. Geology seeks to answer all such queries.

But the questions could be carried still further back, inquiring how the earth originated, what was the source of the matter composing it, and whether it is like the other bodies that comprise the universe. These questions lead us into another realm of science, that of the astronomer; hence we may ask him for the answer to some of these queries. However, as geology treats of the earth, the geologist must help in answering the questions, for he knows about the composition, size, weight, and density of the earth's body, and these factors have a bearing upon its origin.

3

The discussion of the origin of the earth may be called "astronomic geology," because it makes use of both astronomy and geology.

As we travel about on the earth, we find rocks in layers or strata that are usually horizontal, though in some places they are inclined. Why? The geologic answer is that these rocks were formed by the deposition of muds and sands on the bottom of the ocean and that earth movements later caused any inclination of the strata. The study of the position of the rocks in the earth's crust we call "structural geology." We note also that rocks are different in character, each kind with its own distinguishing features that enable the geologist to name the rock and make deductions as to its history. The discussion of the different kinds of rocks is known as "petrology" (from *petros*, meaning "rock," and *logia*, meaning "to learn of").

If we examine the stratified rocks somewhat in detail, we may find other features about which we should like information, a shell, for example. It is embedded in the rock and has a fascinating story to tell, for it is evidence that life was in existence when the rock was formed. We should want to know about the conditions under which this life existed and what other creatures were on the earth at that time. The study of former life remains is known as "paleontology," and the geologist trained in that field can give us a wonderful picture of the land and seas, the climate, and the life of early times upon the earth.

There are many other fields of study in geology, but even the short sketch just given shows that a knowledge of geology can contribute a great deal to the pleasure of understanding the world about us. This knowledge can be used everywhere; in the fields; upon the highway; on the ocean; even in the cities, for in them a vast amount of earth materials is utilized for our comfort and pleasure.

Geology deals with all the features of the earth's surface and with the origin, composition, structure, and inhabitants of the earth. In this study, some of the explanations will involve physical and chemical data, and others, biological. This makes possible a logical, twofold division of geology: one division is known as "physical geology," *i.e.*, a treatment of the rocks composing the earth, the movements within it, and its surface features and the agents that form them; the other, "historical geology," traces the changing distribution of land and seas upon the earth and gives the story of the life inhabiting it.

CHAPTER 2

THE ORGANIZATION OF MATTER (OF THE EARTH)

The term *matter* is applied to the material that forms the planets, sun, stars, and everything on these bodies. All matter is composed of a relatively small number of substances called *elements*. We all are familiar with some of these elements, nine of which, copper, gold, silver, iron, lead, sulfur, mercury, carbon, and tin, were known at the dawn of history. Twenty more of the elements had been recognized by 1800; 51 were discovered during the nineteenth century; and 16 have been found or made during the first half of the present century, bringing the number to 96. Four elements of the last group of 16 were synthesized during the decade 1940 to 1950 by utilizing newly discovered nuclear reactions. The smallest structural units of ordinary matter which retain their identity when chemical reactions take place are called *atoms*, the nature of which we shall consider briefly.

The Atom. Atoms are far too small to be seen directly by any means yet devised by man. Their sizes have been measured with high accuracy, however, by means of specialized x-ray experiments, and atomic diameters thus found range from 2 to 5 angstrom units. One angstrom unit $(1 \times 10^{-8}$ centimeter) is about 0.000,000,004 (four-billionths) inch in length; hence a row of 100,000,000 atoms, laid side by side, would be about 1 inch long. It has been computed that a gram of water contains 600,000,000,000,000,000,000 (6×10^{20}) atoms and that a human body of average size contains 10,000,000,000,000,000,000,000,000,000 (10^{27}). Just what such numbers mean is beyond our understanding, but, however small the atoms may be, it is of them that the earth is built.

Atoms may be described in further detail. A nucleus at the center of each atom carries positive electric charges, which vary in number with the different kinds of atoms (elements). Electrons, which are negative charges of electricity, move rapidly in orbit-like paths around each nucleus. The number of electrons and their arrangement are characteristic of each element. Amazing discoveries have been made by physicists in their investigations of atomic architecture.

Returning to a consideration of the organization of matter that we can see or feel, we find that it may be either *crystalline* or *amorphous*. Crystalline material is characterized by the atoms' being arranged in a definite pattern that is repeated many, many times (resulting in crystals, Fig. 1). Even if crystals are broken into fragments, their atomic arrangement persists as before. One of the wonderful features of this definite arrangement of matter is that *all known crystalline compounds* can be put into 32 classes. Furthermore, all the 32 classes can be placed in 6 crystal systems. The marvelous simplicity of this arrangement is surprising, as there are thousands of crystalline compounds. In the study of these compounds, it is now possible, by passing x rays through a crystal, to determine the position of the atoms in the compound (see Figs. 2 and 3).

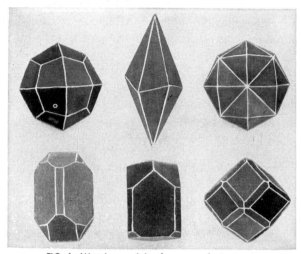

FIG. 1. Wooden models of some perfect crystals.

The discovery that x rays could be used to obtain photographs of this atomic arrangement was made in 1911, and since that time the use of this method has enabled us to understand fully the actual structure of many thousands of such compounds. *Amorphous substances* do not possess a definite arrangement of the atoms, yet the number of amorphous compounds and the different forms the material has assumed are many. Examples of amorphous substances are gases, most liquids, and some minerals.

Minerals. Atoms, in certain aggregates, go to make up what are known as *minerals*. Although most minerals are crystalline substances, a few, of which the opal is an example, are amorphous. We may define a mineral as *a naturally occurring inorganic substance having within limits a definite chemical composition and definite physical properties.* Ice on a pond occurs naturally; it has a definite chemical composition, *i.e.*, one part oxygen and two parts hydrogen, H_2O; and it has the physical property of forming six-sided crystals (this property may be observed in a perfect snowflake). We conclude, therefore, that natural ice is a mineral. From our definition of a mineral it will be seen that water is equally well a mineral, though in the popular conception only solids are accorded that name.

Minerals are very abundant, as the soil and most rocks of the earth's crust are composed of one or more of them. Minerals possess many different shapes, colors, and other physical properties. Many are beautiful, in both form and color, and so are prized as ornaments and sought after by collectors.

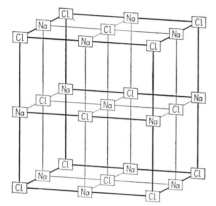

FIG. 2. Drawing showing a possible arrangement of the atoms (ions, *i.e.*, atoms with electric charges) of sodium (Na) and chlorine (Cl) in a crystal of salt (NaCl).

FIG. 3. Photograph of model showing relative size, as well as arrangement, of the atoms (ions) of sodium (small spheres) and chlorine (large spheres) in a crystal of salt. A sodium ion is about 1.9 angstrom units in diameter; a chlorine ion, about 3.6 units.

Composition of the Earth by Elements. We have learned that all matter is composed of elements. Most of these elements are so rare, however, that they have been seen by only a few people. Even such elements as platinum, gold, and copper are rare in that they form an insignificant part of the body of the earth. Our use of such substances today is made possible only by the fact that during the formation of the rocks conditions existed that favored the accumulation of these valuable metals into the deposits in which we find them.

We are reasonably certain that, through various geologic processes, rocks from depths of 10 to 12 miles have been brought to the surface of the earth. Chemical analyses of all kinds of these rocks from all parts of the world have been made and the results have been averaged. We are certain, therefore, that this average composition is representative of the composition of this thickness of the earth, which is known as the earth's *crust*. An additional thickness of 30 miles is sometimes included in the term "crust," but this lower part would be better known as the *subcrust.* By the use of the word "crust" it should not be understood that there is a solid layer over a liquid interior of the earth.

The following table gives the average composition by elements of the earth's crust, as estimated by Clarke and Washington:

COMPOSITION OF THE EARTH'S CRUST BY ELEMENTS

Element	Percentage
Oxygen (O)	46.710
Silicon (Si)	27.690
Aluminum (Al)	8.070
Iron (Fe)	5.050
Calcium (Ca)	3.650
Sodium (Na)	2.750
Potassium (K)	2.580
Magnesium (Mg)	2.080
Percentage of the 8 dominant elements	98.580
Titanium (Ti)	0.620
Hydrogen (H)	0.140
Phosphorus (P)	0.130
Carbon (C)	0.094
Manganese (Mn)	0.090
Sulfur (S)	0.082
Barium (Ba)	0.050
Chlorine (Cl)	0.045
Chromium (Cr)	0.035
Fluorine (F)	0.029
Zirconium (Zr)	0.025
Nickel (Ni)	0.019
Strontium (Sr)	0.018
Vanadium (V)	0.016
Cerium (Ce), Yttrium (Y)	0.014
Copper (Cu)	0.010
Uranium (U)	0.008
Tungsten (W)	0.005
Lithium (Li)	0.004
Zinc (Zn)	0.004
Columbium (Cb), Tantalum (Ta)	0.003
Hafnium (Hf)	0.003
Thorium (Th)	0.002
Lead (Pb)	0.002
Cobalt (Co)	0.001
Boron (B)	0.001
Glucinum (Gl)	0.001
Total	100.000

It will be seen that only eight elements make up 98.58 per cent of the crust (Fig. 4).

It should be noted that of the most common metals in use only iron, aluminum, copper, zinc, and lead are included in this table. Less commonly used metals, such as manganese, chromium, nickel, tungsten, and cobalt, are present in the table; but gold, silver, and platinum are not. Their estimated percentages in the crust are as follows: silver, 0.000,000,4; gold, 0.000,000,1; and platinum, 0.000,000,008. Such quantities can scarcely even be called traces.

Formation of the Primary Minerals. Minerals may form anywhere upon or within the earth's body, but those termed the "primary minerals" originated from a molten mass within the earth's crust. In such a mass the different atoms were free to move about and unite with one another to form various substances. The rate of movement of the atoms varied, being influenced by many factors. The most important of these factors were heat and the amount of water and gases present, as these two agents

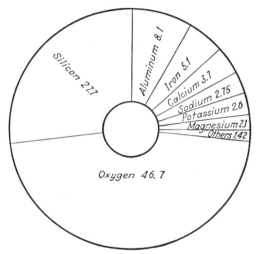

FIG. 4. Diagram showing the relative percentage amounts of the eight most abundant elements of the earth's crust.

largely controlled the fluidity of the molten material. If the liquid was very thin, like water, the atoms could travel farther to unite; if it was very thick, like tar or asphalt, they could move only short distances. Such factors influenced the size of the mineral particles formed.

Minerals contain one or more elements. Gold, silver, sulfur, and carbon (occurring as the diamond and graphite) are examples of minerals containing only one element, but these minerals do not play an important part in forming rocks. Rocks are composed, however, of primary minerals and other minerals derived from them. The eight elements (oxygen, silicon, aluminum, iron, calcium, sodium, potassium, and magnesium) that comprise 98.58 per cent of the earth's crust (see table, page 8) are the elements that formed the primary minerals.

Oxygen, the most abundant of the eight elements, exists in the atmosphere as a gas, but it combines readily with the other seven elements.   These eight elements united to form many different primary minerals, some of which are simple in composition, as, for example, *quartz*, which is composed of one atom of silicon and two atoms of oxygen, SiO_2.   Because silicon ranks next to oxygen in amount in the crust, the compound SiO_2, commonly called *silica*, is very abundant.   It readily united with other elements, and the resulting mineral is called a *silicate* because the silica is the basis of the compound, the other constituents varying.   Aluminum, the third most abundant element in the crust, is a constituent of many of the silicates.   The potassium, sodium, and calcium in the liquid mass united with silica and aluminum to form the most abundant group of primary silicate minerals, the *feldspars* (see table, page 48).   Two other common silicates, *hornblende* and *pyroxene*, were formed by making use of iron and magnesium.   There are other silicates containing iron and magnesium, but they are less common than hornblende and pyroxene.   The *micas* are two complex silicates that may also be formed as primary minerals.   Thus the eight most abundant elements in the earth's crust united in various ways to form the following most important primary minerals, named in the order of their abundance: *feldspars, quartz, hornblende* and *pyroxene, micas,* and *olivine*.

As the atoms were uniting within the molten mass, each one placed itself in a definite position relative to the other atoms like it.   In this way, a solid crystal (Fig. 1) of the mineral was built up.   The external form of the crystal was determined by this internal arrangement (Fig. 2) of the atoms.   The minerals are the "building blocks" of which we shall make use in the next chapter in explaining the formation of the rocks of the earth's crust.

CHAPTER 3

VOLCANISM AND IGNEOUS ROCKS

In the previous chapter it was pointed out that the study of minerals was a preliminary step to the study of rocks. *A rock is a substance composed of one or more minerals.* It may also be defined as *any considerable part of the earth's body.* Rocks that resulted from the solidification of a liquid mass were the first or *primary rocks,* and are known as *igneous rocks* ("igneous" comes from the Latin word *ignis,* meaning "fire"). The term *volcanism* is applied to the study of volcanic action. This chapter deals also with the source of the molten material within the earth, its movement, composition, solidification, and the final forms assumed when it becomes solid. The form and position of the igneous rock in the crust or at the surface are known as its *mode of occurrence.*

The igneous rocks owe their significant characteristics to two important factors: (1) *the composition of the original molten mass,* which controls what minerals will be formed upon solidification; and (2) *the conditions under which the mass cooled,* since the rate of cooling controls the size and arrangement of the mineral grains.

We shall begin our discussion with the consideration of a molten mass within the crust and follow it to its final stage, *i.e.,* the solid igneous rock.

THE MAGMA

A mass of liquid rock within the body of the earth is called *magma,* and when poured out upon the earth's surface, the material is called *lava.* Quite commonly, magmas and lavas contain crystals or other solid particles.

Source and Movement of a Magma. A magma is formed by the melting or solution of rocks within the earth due to the heat available there. For various reasons we are certain that temperatures within the earth are high. All deep wells and mines show an increase in temperature as they go deeper into the crust. Furthermore, from the lavas we may learn of the high temperatures, as we can measure their heat as they come from volcanoes or can heat a solid piece of lava and determine its melting point. Both methods have been used and have shown that the temperatures of magmas vary from 600 to 1200°C. Not all rocks, however, melt at the same temperature, some becoming liquid at low and others only at high temperatures. Many other factors influence the melting, but it is not necessary to consider them here.

The formation of a magma probably takes place in any portion of the earth's body where the temperature is high enough for the rocks to melt or dissolve. This melting or solution may occur 10, 50, 100 miles or more down. The liquid rock may then work its way upward to the crust or the surface by melting the rocks above it. Liquid rock is lighter in weight than solid rock and the presence of gases makes it still lighter. Therefore, as the magma is subjected to great pressures (about 1,200,000 pounds or 600 tons per square inch at a depth of 200 miles) from the surrounding solid rocks, it is forced to move, and the movement is upward because that is the direction of least pressure. The movement is aided by the great mobility of liquid rock and also by the expansive force of the gases within the magma. A steady loss in heat and, consequently, in volume accompanies the upward movement of the magma, and thus when the mass comes so near the surface that it no longer has sufficient heat to

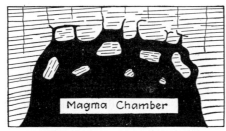

FIG. 5. Sketch showing the magma (black) prying off blocks of the surrounding rock by wedging into the cracks and fissures.

melt its way upward, it comes to rest and assumes many different forms, as shown in Fig. 10, page 17. From the upper part of the magma, portions rich in gases may find local weak places in the crust and work their way on upward, some even reaching the surface. After the magma has reached the upper zone of cracked and fissured rocks, an additional method of upward movement is available in that it may pry off blocks of the solid rock from the roof of the magma chamber (Fig. 5), and these blocks, being heavier than the liquid rock, sink into it and so cause the magma to move on upward. In this region of cracks and fissures, the magma may also move out into these openings where it is possible for it to force the cracks still wider apart, because, by its pressure on their walls, the cracks and joints in the adjoining rock are reduced in size, perhaps even practically closed. Room may thus be made in joints and other openings for a magma of considerable size to pass, and finally perhaps to solidify.

The heat of a magma may be sufficient to keep it in a liquid state for many thousands of years, during which time it may act as a source from which material moves outward from time to time to feed a volcano. Gases, by reacting with one another, may play an important part in the maintenance of this heat and in the accompanying volcanic activity.

Composition of the Magma. The composition of magmas varies in different parts of the earth; but geologists believe that, in the main, magmas originating at depths of 10 miles are of one type, those originating from 10 to 40 miles (the maximum thickness of the crust) down are of another type, and those having their origin in the layer (approximately 900 miles thick) next below the crust are of still another type. These three regions of the earth's body are known as the *granitic, gabbroid or basaltic*, and *peridotitic zones*. A magma that moved upward from a lower into a higher zone would have the composition of the lower one; but, as it melted and mingled with the rocks above, its composition would change.

We have given on page 8 the average composition of the rocks of the earth's crust. It has been estimated that 95 per cent of the crust is composed of igneous rocks, and therefore the average composition of the crust is approximately the composition of the igneous rocks. As has been pointed out also (page 10), only a few of the elements are of importance in forming the rocks. Variations in the amounts of these significant elements give rise to different kinds of rocks. Thus an abundance of iron, magnesium, calcium, and less than 60 per cent of silica give rise to the gabbroid and the peridotitic rocks; and an abundance of silica, aluminum, potassium, and sodium, to the granitic rocks. Between these two types there are all gradations.

The composition of a magma governs what minerals will be formed from it and also has a marked influence upon its movement. The basaltic lavas are more fluid than lavas rich in silica and consequently will squeeze into smaller fractures or joints in the rocks or flow farther on the surface. The fluidity of magmas influences the size of the mineral grains formed, as will be explained later. The presence of water (as a liquid or gas) and other gases in the magma greatly increases the fluidity. It should be noted in this connection that very little of the water and gases of the magma become a part of the igneous rock, as they are separated from the magma during its solidification. If this solidification occurs on the surface, the water and gases escape into the atmosphere; but, if it occurs below, they enter the surrounding rock, carrying with them much mineral matter and any metals the magma contained. These minerals and metals may later form the valuable mineral (ore) deposits from which we obtain such metals as gold, copper, and iron. These deposits will be discussed later in this chapter.

Solidification of the Magmas. The solidification of a magma is influenced by (1) *the rate at which it cools* and (2) *its composition*.

The Effect of the Rate of Cooling. We have noted the wide variance in the temperatures of magmas: from 600 to 1200°C. There is a steady decrease in heat as a magma moves upward, and when it comes to rest the heat passes into the surrounding rocks and is lost. The rate at which the cooling and solidification take place varies and depends upon many factors, of which the following are the most important:

a. Depth of the mass below the surface.

b. Size of the cooling mass.

c. Shape of the cooling mass.

a. The depth of a magma below the surface is of primary importance in the rate of cooling. A mass near the surface loses its heat much faster in this cooler area than does one that is twice as deep (Fig. 6, 1, *a* and *b*) and so becomes solid much sooner.

b. Of two similarly shaped magmas at the same depth (Fig. 6, 2, *a* and *b*), one that is twice as large as the other takes much longer to cool and so solidifies much more slowly than does the smaller one.

c. If one magma has a spherical shape (Fig. 6, 3, *b*) and another is thin and tabular (Fig. 6, 3, *a*), the thin one certainly loses its heat faster.

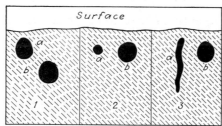

FIG. 6. Sketch illustrating some of the factors that affect the rate of cooling of magma (black areas).

The rate of cooling of a magma greatly influences the size of the mineral crystals formed during the solidification. Slow cooling keeps the magma fluid for a long period of time, which permits more atoms to get together and form large crystals; rapid cooling means small crystals; and extremely rapid cooling, such as occurs when a thick viscous lava pours out upon the surface, prevents the formation of any grains, and a glassy rock is the result.

The Effect of Composition. The composition of a magma affects its fluidity, and this fluidity, as we have already noted, becomes significant during solidification as it influences the ability of the atoms to get together to form minerals. In a thin (*i.e.*, very fluid) basaltic magma, the molecules can travel much farther during the period of cooling and, therefore, more of them can get together to form larger grains or crystals. The presence of much water, carbon dioxide, sulfur dioxide, and other gases increases the fluidity of a magma and so is favorable to the formation of large grains; in fact, the presence of these substances is so helpful in forming large mineral crystals that they are called *mineralizers*. The mineralizers are important, also, in forming deposits of valuable metals.

TEXTURE OF IGNEOUS ROCKS

We have seen how the various factors influencing the solidification of a magma combine to produce solid rocks having grains of different sizes.

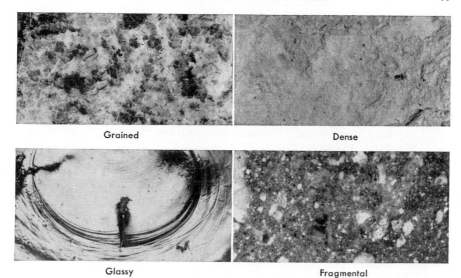

Grained   Dense

Glassy   Fragmental

FIG. 7. The principal textures of igneous rocks.

The size of the grains, together with their arrangement in a rock, is called texture.

Different Kinds of Texture. It is possible to divide rocks into four classes based upon their texture, *viz.*, *grained, dense, glassy,* and *fragmental* rocks. The lines dividing the first three classes are purely arbitrary. For our purpose we shall consider the *grained rocks* as having mineral grains or crystals larger than those of fine granulated sugar (about $\frac{1}{16}$ inch in diameter); the *dense rocks* as those with mineral grains ranging from $\frac{1}{16}$ inch in diameter to those that are invisible to the naked eye; and the *glassy rocks* as those that are devoid of grains. Figure 7 illustrates these three textures. *Fragmental* texture is not due to solidification, but to the fact that a rock is composed of fragments (see Figs. 7 and 8), which in the case of the igneous rocks were blown from a volcano.

FIG. 8. Fragmental texture in volcanic breccia, on road between Cody, Wyoming, and Yellowstone National Park. (*Photograph by Edwin R. Branson.*)

A special feature of the texture of igneous rocks, but a very common one, is that the crystals of the same rock may be of two general sizes (see Figs. 9 and 50 on page 46). This type is called *porphyritic texture* and the rock is called a "porphyry." This texture is usually the result of two periods of cooling in the magma. The first period occurred at a considerable depth, where the slow rate of cooling permitted certain minerals to grow to considerable size. Then the magma containing these solid crystals was forced up nearer the surface, where the still-liquid portion solidified rapidly, forming a fine-grained rock in which the earlier, larger crystals were embedded. The large crystals in a porphyry are

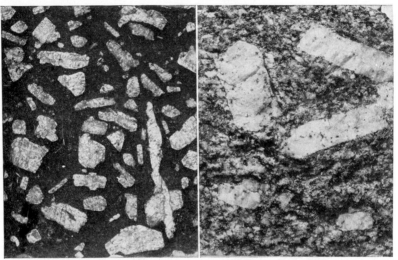

FIG. 9. Porphyry (on left) with dense groundmass, from dike in Madison County, Missouri; porphyry (on right) with grained groundmass, from Connecticut.

called *phenocrysts* and the background of uniformly sized particles is called the *groundmass*.

MODE OF OCCURRENCE OF IGNEOUS ROCKS

Study of the forms of igneous rock masses has shown that the openings followed by the magmas in their upward journey are of two dominant types: *tubular* and *tabular*. Tubular openings are rudely circular in outline; and most of them are less than a mile across, but some greatly exceed this width. Such an opening, called a *conduit* (Fig. 10), is the usual one leading up to a volcano and certain intrusive forms. The tabular type of opening is usually an enlarged fissure or joint in the rock. Some are miles in length but usually much less than a mile in width. Such openings are called *fissure openings*.

Igneous rocks have two major modes of occurrence, *viz.*, *intrusive* and *extrusive.* Intrusive rocks are those formed by the solidification of a magma below the surface; and extrusive rocks, those formed after the lava reached the surface. Many different shapes were assumed as the magma or lava solidified, and these various shapes are commonly known as *forms.* The form of an igneous rock may be due to the shape of the opening (for example, tabular) through which the magma moved; to

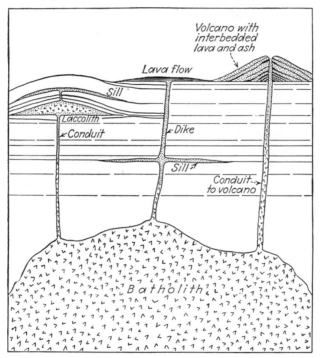

FIG. 10. Sketch of various modes of occurrence of igneous rocks.

the melting of the enclosing rock; or, it may be a surface feature. We shall describe in detail some of the more common forms of igneous rocks.

INTRUSIVE FORMS OF IGNEOUS ROCKS

The various intrusive types of igneous rocks and their relationships to one another and to the surface are shown in Fig. 10. The more common intrusive forms are *dikes, sills, laccoliths, necks* or *plugs,* and *batholiths,* though geologists recognize many other special forms.

Dikes. Dikes are thin, tabular masses of igneous rocks (see Figs. 11, *a* and *b,* 12, 13, and 14). They have essentially a vertical position, and were formed by being injected into fissures and joints in rocks. Those occurring in sedimentary rocks usually cut across the bedding planes. Some dikes are no thicker than a sheet of paper and some have a thickness of hundreds of feet, but the vast majority are less than 10 feet thick. They may be miles in length. Dikes are the most common form of intrusive igneous rocks seen at the surface. They occur in great abundance in many areas, especially in the vicinity of volcanoes. There

(a)   (b)

FIG. 11. Basalt dike in granite from southeastern Missouri. (a) Front view; (b) back view showing inclusion of granite in dike.

are, for example, hundreds of dikes around the Spanish Peaks in southern Colorado (Fig. 15).

Sills. Sills also are tabular masses of igneous rocks, but their position is essentially horizontal. Sills are thickest over or adjacent to the

FIG. 12. Dikes in the Highwood Mountains, central Montana. (*Photograph by W. A. Tarr.*)

opening through which they are fed and they thin out laterally. In very large sills the top and bottom are essentially parallel. Sills are formed by the squeezing in of magma between the beds or bands of a rock. They may cross the beds from one plane to another (Figs. 16 and 17). Like the dikes, sills have a wide range in size and extent. Most sills are thin sheets, though some are hundreds of feet thick and may extend over a horizontal area of hundreds of square miles, as it is estimated some do

FIG. 13. Near view of one of the dikes in the Highwood Mountains, Montana. (*Photograph by W. A. Tarr.*)

FIG. 14. Granite dikes (light) intruded into schists (dark), Big Horn Canyon, Wyoming. (*Photograph by E. B. Branson.*)

in South Africa. Opposite New York City, the Hudson River exposes a thick sill, known as the Palisades of the Hudson.

Laccoliths. Laccoliths, though somewhat similar to sills (see Fig. 17), differ from them in that the overlying beds are arched. The horizontal area occupied by a laccolith is usually smaller than that occupied by a sill.   This is because the magma forming a laccolith was too viscous to flow far between the beds of the rock and so pushed them up to form a dome.   Laccoliths may merge into sills and they are also commonly associated with dikes.   Several laccoliths may occur in the same area. They form numerous buttes and mountains in western United States. Bear Butte in the northern part of the Black Hills and the Henry Moun-

FIG. 15. Map showing some of the dikes (straight lines) and sills (irregular lines) around the Spanish Peaks, Colorado.   Black dots indicate East and West Spanish Peaks.

tains of southeastern Utah are such examples.   The laccoliths forming the Henry Mountains were the first of the type to be recognized and described.

Necks or Plugs.   Necks or plugs are nearly circular masses of igneous rock having a vertical position.   They occupy the conduit through which magma moved upward to form a volcano, laccolith, or batholith.   When movement ceased, the material still in the conduit became solid; and, after erosion had cut away the overlying mass of rock, this rock was exposed.   This method of origin explains the name "neck" or "plug." These forms are numerous in some areas where volcanoes and laccoliths were formerly abundant. A striking example of such a feature occurs in northeastern Wyoming, where a high column of rock, known as the Devils Tower, rears itself 600 feet above the surrounding country (Fig. 18).

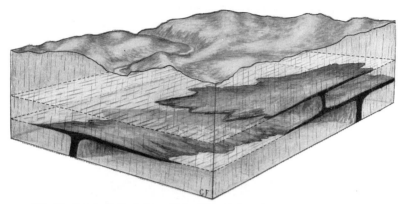

FIG. 16. Sketch of sills fed by dikes. Note that a sill is thickest over the dike.

FIG. 17. Sketch of an ideal laccolith and associated dikes and sills.

Batholiths. Batholiths are very large (at least 40 square miles in area), irregular masses of igneous rock (see Fig. 10). They have their origin in the melting and solution of rock in place or in the displacement of rock by magma. An example of the latter method is the immense

magma that is believed to have worked its way upward into the crust
to form the Sierra Nevada. Pikes Peak, which has been carved from
a batholith of granite, is an example that may be viewed by many.
The world-famous copper deposits of Butte, Montana, occur in a batholith covering about 2,000 square miles. Many other valuable metal

FIG. 18. A volcanic neck (called Devils Tower) showing columnar structure. (*Darton, U.S. Geological Survey.*)

deposits are associated with batholiths. Batholiths are of common
occurrence in many parts of the world.

EXTRUSIVE FORMS OF IGNEOUS ROCKS

If a magma in working its way upward has sufficient heat and pressure, it reaches the surface and becomes an extrusive igneous rock. The
two common modes of occurrence of extrusive igneous rocks are *lava flows*
and *volcanoes*. Lava flows generally rise through fissures and usually
cover wide areas; volcanoes are fed through conduits and are much more
restricted in extent. Volcanoes are the spectacular manifestations of
volcanism and are the only form man has been permitted to witness. At
that, he is often an unwilling spectator. Through studies of active and
recent volcanoes, we have learned much about the characteristics and
composition of lavas, and by witnessing volcanic eruptions, we are permitted a startling view of the effect of the tremendous forces within the
earth.

Lava Flows. In many regions the only rock in evidence over vast
areas is that of lava flows. Some flows, like those of Idaho and Iceland,
are so recent as to have no vegetation upon them; others are very ancient
and are covered with soil and vegetation. In forming large flows, the
lava breaks through the crust along fissures miles in length, and enormous

quantities are poured out and spread far and wide over the land.   Such eruptions are relatively very quiet.   In northwestern United States (in Washington, Oregon, Idaho, and northern California), approximately 200,000 square miles of surface are covered by lava flows (Fig. 19) which, in places, are 3,000 feet thick.   This lava poured out upon and buried a region of hills and mountains.   The solidified lava occupying the fissures through which eruption took place is now visible, as dikes, where rivers have cut down through the lava flows.   Other great lava flows are found in Iceland and on the Deccan plateau in western India.   Small lava flows may accompany volcanic action.

Features of Lava Flows.   Lava caves, which are of common occurrence in recent lava flows, have an interesting origin.   As the surface of a lava flow was the first part to cool and solidify, a crust was formed under which the still-liquid lava below continued to move forward.   All of the flow gradually became cool and con-
sequently solid; but, as more lava con-
tinued to well up from below, it fol-
lowed the old channel the lava had maintained under the crust; and, when the supply from below was exhausted, the lava in these channels drained out (like water from a hose), leaving an underground passage or cave (Fig. 20).   Small stalactites (Figs. 21 and 22) of lava occur in the interior of some of these caves.

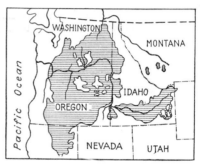

FIG. 19. Map showing areas of lava flows in northwestern United States. (*Based on data from various sources.*)

On the surface of some lava flows, small features called *spatter cones* (Fig. 23) were built up where the lava broke through the crust and piled up about the opening.   Otherwise smooth surfaces of lava flows may be broken by *ridges,* which consist of blocks of lava that resulted from the buckling up and breaking of the crust as the lava beneath it continued to move forward.   The lava of very rough, jagged surfaces is known as *clinkery lava.*   Some surfaces consist of twisted, ropelike masses (Fig. 24) called *ropy lava.*   The twisting was caused by the forward movement of an already-viscous crust.   Lava also assumes a *pillowy* surface (Fig. 24).   Fine examples of these various types of lava, lava flows, and small volcanoes are to be seen in the Craters of the Moon, a national monument in Idaho (Fig. 25), and in numerous other places in western United States.

Volcanoes.   Volcanoes have long been a source of trouble to man because he has persistently sought to live upon or near them, an act that simply invites trouble.   There is no natural phenomenon that is more

FIG. 20. Entrance to lava cave south of Bend, Oregon, on Highway 97.   (*Photograph by W. A. Tarr.*)

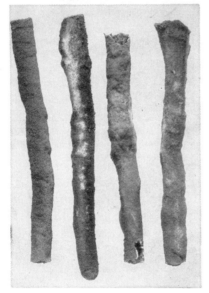

FIG. 21. Stalactites of lava from lava cave near Bend, Oregon.   One-half natural size.

FIG. 22. Another type of lava stalactite from lava cave near Bend, Oregon.   One-half natural size.

awe-inspiring than a volcano in vigorous eruption.   The earth movements, explosions, dust and ashes, and fiery lava are sufficient to satisfy the most avaricious thrill seeker.   Detailed descriptions of eruptions cannot be given here, but accounts of Pelée in the West Indies (1902),[1]

[1] E. O. Hovey, "The Eruptions of 1902 of La Soufrière, St. Vincent, and Mt. Pelée, Martinique," *American Journal of Science,* vol. 14, pp. 323–328, 342–349, 1902.

FIG. 23. Spatter cones in the Craters of the Moon National Monument, Idaho. Hills in background are cinder cones. (*Photograph by W. D. Keller.*)

FIG. 24. Ropy lava in the crater of Vesuvius, Italy. Pillowy lava in background. (*Photograph by W. A. Tarr.*)

Vesuvius in Italy (1906),[2] Katmai in Alaska (1912),[3] and Parícutin in Mexico (1943)[4,5] are readily available in libraries and are fascinating reading.

[2] FRANK A. PERRET, "The Vesuvius Eruption of 1906," *Carnegie Institution of Washington, Pub.* 339, 1924.

[3] ROBERT F. GRIGGS, "The Valley of Ten Thousand Smokes," 1922 (National Geographic Society, Washington). (Contains 340 pp., 9 maps, and 233 illustrations.)

[4] F. M. BULLARD, "The Story of El Parícutin," *Scientific Monthly*, vol. 65, pp. 357–371, 1947.

[5] T. A. JAGGAR, "Volcanoes Declare War," 1945, pp. 124–126 (Paradise of the Pacific, Honolulu, T.H.).

Character and Source of Volcanic Phenomena.   A volcano is the opening of a circular conduit about which have been or are being piled the lava and volcanic dust ejected through the conduit.   The ejected material forms a conically shaped hill or mountain (Figs. 23 and 26), and the

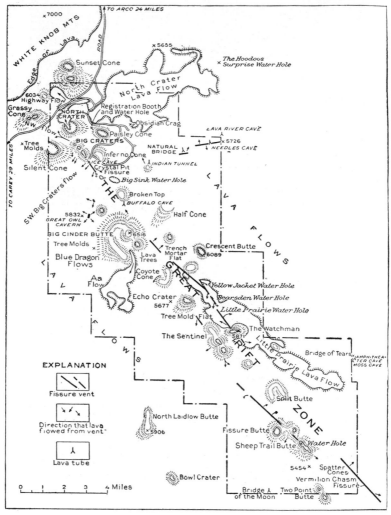

FIG. 25. Sketch map of the Craters of the Moon National Monument, Idaho, showing location of the fissure (the Great Rift Zone) through which the lava was extruded.   (*Idaho Bureau of Mines and Geology*, Bull. 13, pl. 1, 1928.)

depression in the top of the cone is known as the *crater* (Figs. 26 and 27) of the volcano.   The range in size of volcanic cones is great; many are only a few hundred feet high; others tower more than 20,000 feet above sea level.   Some have steep sides (the slope near the top of Mt. Vesuvius is nearly 50°), and others have gentle slopes. For the most part, the structure of volcanic cones is similar. They are formed of successive lava flows and dust beds (Figs. 27, 28, and 29). These layers may be

FIG. 26. Air view of an Alaskan volcano. Crater well shown. (*Courtesy of U.S. Navy Air Service.*)

FIG. 27. Interior of crater of Vesuvius, February, 1925. Shows lava floor and small active cone. Note edges of sills in crater walls.

cut by dikes which formed where the lava broke through fissures in the sides of the cone.

Volcanic cones represent a final form of lava that has reached the surface from a magma below. The magma that feeds a volcano may be large or small; it may be within two or three miles of the surface or at a considerable depth below it. A study of volcanic eruptions has shown

that adjacent volcanoes may or may not be fed by the same magma.   The
two great Hawaiian volcanoes, Mauna Loa and Kilauea, are only 22
miles apart; and the crater of Kilauea is about 10,000 feet lower than that
of Mauna Loa, yet sometimes the two volcanoes erupt independently.

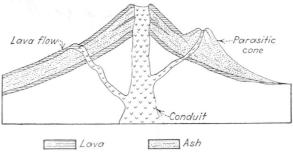

FIG. 28. Diagram showing structure of a volcano and method of forming parasitic cones and lava flows.

FIG. 29. View of Parícutin in eruption, showing lava flow which issued from side of cone (at back). (*Photograph by Tad Nichols.*)

Sometimes, however, they erupt simultaneously, and a careful study of
the character of their lava and other features has not made it possible
to decide whether they are fed by one magma or two, as all their features
and characteristics may be explained by either mode of origin.

FIG. 30. Enormous cloud (about 4 miles high) hanging over Mt. Lassen, California, during the eruption of May 22, 1915. Picture taken at Anderson, California, 50 miles away. (*Photograph furnished by B. F. Loomis.*)

The temperature of volcanic lavas is high: from 900 to 1200°C. or higher. Some volcanic lavas are very viscous, but many are quite fluid and may be able to flow for miles. Some are accompanied by large quantities of steam and other gases, and some are not. The presence of water (as steam) in the lava has a marked effect upon the eruption of a volcano; if the quantities are large, the volcano is usually of the explosive type, as the rapid escape of the steam causes explosions. If small quantities of steam are present, the lava usually wells up quietly to the crater and flows down the sides while the steam escapes and condenses, forming the enormous cauliflower-like clouds (Fig. 30) that hang over such a volcano. Numerous gradations exist, of course, between these two types of volcanoes. If the lava is quite viscous, a volcano may remain quiet for long periods of time during which the gases accumulate at

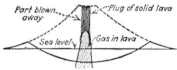

Probable outline of the ancient volcano (dotted) and its shape (solid) after an unknown explosion

Outline due to the filling up of the ancient crater before the eruption of 1883

Outline today, showing the effects of the explosion of August, 1883

FIG. 31. Sketches illustrating probable history of Krakatoa, a volcano in the East Indies. (*Figures from "The Eruption of Krakatoa," The Royal Society, London, pp. 7–23, 1888.*)

some point below the crater; and, when their pressure has become sufficient, the top of the volcano is blown off (Fig. 31). This is what happened at Vesuvius, in A.D. 79, when Pompeii and Herculaneum were buried under many feet of volcanic dust and mud.

It has been possible to study the gases that are associated with lavas by collecting and analyzing those that escape from volcanoes. Water (steam) is by far the most abundant, but carbon dioxide (CO_2), carbon monoxide (CO), sulfur dioxide (SO_2), chlorine (Cl_2), and other gases are given off also. Considerable amounts of some of these gases make the fumes ejected from a volcano extremely poisonous. Clouds of hot, poisonous gases have swept down upon towns and cities near volcanoes and snuffed out the lives of thousands of people in a few seconds, as

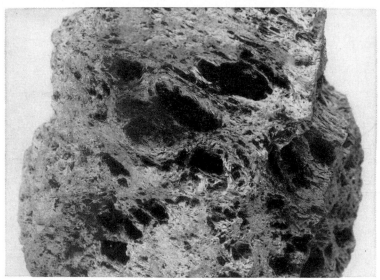

FIG. 32. Pumice from a bed of volcanic ash and pumice, near Crater Lake, Oregon. Note large holes and thread-like fibers of glass. About $\frac{1}{2}$ natural size.

happened at St. Pierre at the foot of Mt. Pelée on the island of Martinique, in 1902 (see Fig. 44, page 41).

Features Produced by the Escape of Gases from Volcanic Lavas. The gases of volcanic lavas produce several interesting features in connection with their escape. They expand in the lava of a flow and thus cause the formation of *scoriaceous and pumiceous* rocks; by their explosion they blow the hardened lava above them in the conduit into bits and thus produce *pyroclastic material;* they form clouds above volcanoes, the rain from which assists in the production of *mud flows;* and, finally, when the volcano has become inactive, they escape, aiding in the formation of *fumaroles, geysers,* and lastly *hot springs.*

Scoriaceous rocks are extremely porous. They were formed by the expansion of the steam and other gases beneath the hardened crust of a lava. The final escape of the gases from the hardening lava left large, rounded holes in the rock.

Pumice is a rock also formed by the expansion and escape of gases (Fig. 32). In it, many of the holes are in the form of long, minute closed tubes, which make the rock so light that it will float on water. These tubes were formed by the expansive force of large amounts of gases in an extremely viscous lava that cooled very rapidly, forming a glassy rock. Pumice is the rock that is usually formed from the lava ejected from explosive volcanoes. It has been blown miles by explosions. Pine forests in the vicinity of Crater Lake Mountain in Oregon are growing

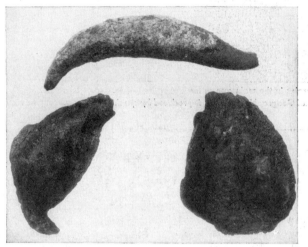

FIG. 33. Volcanic bombs. One-fourth natural size.

over beds of volcanic dust and pumice that are still powdery beneath the thin layer of soil that has formed over them.

Explosive volcanoes eject great quantities of broken and pulverized lava (*pyroclastic material*). These fragments range in size from great *blocks* weighing tons down to the finest *dust*. Two of these products of intermediate sizes that have special names may be noted. Particles like coarse gravel are called *lapilli*, and more or less rounded masses that are liquid when thrown into the air but cooled before falling to the surface are called *bombs* (Fig. 33).

The steam accompanying an eruption forms clouds from which rain may fall. If much volcanic dust has been ejected, the rain and dust cause great *mud flows* that rush down the sides of the volcano, burying all before them.

Long after the eruption of a volcano has ceased, the escape of gas, steam, and hot water gives evidence of the former activity. The gases and steam may be escaping from hot magma that is still cooling below the

FIG. 34. Fumaroles in the main arm of the Valley of Ten Thousand Smokes, Katmai, Alaska. (Copyright by National Geographic Society. Reproduced by special permission from the National Geographic Magazine.)

FIG. 35. Roaring Mountain, Yellowstone National Park. Escaping steam and other gases have killed off all the trees. The fumaroles first developed in 1902, in an area 30 feet square near the top of the mountain. (Photograph taken in 1928 by W. A. Tarr.)

surface, or they may be produced when surface water, having percolated downward, comes in contact with hot magma or even solid hot rock. The cracks and fissures in the rocks through which the steam and gases issue are called *fumaroles*. The vast number of these fumaroles in a valley near the Alaskan volcano Katmai has given it its name, the Valley of Ten Thousand Smokes (Fig. 34). Vegetation is destroyed by the gases, as on Roaring Mountain (Fig. 35), Yellowstone National Park. This area of fumaroles is increasing in size.   At Lardarello, Tuscany Province, Italy, steam issuing from fumaroles (Fig. 36) is used to generate power. In this region, high-pressure steam in large quantities is obtained, also, from wells drilled for that purpose.

FIG. 36. View of the main natural-steam plant at Lardarello, Tuscany, Italy.   After electric power is generated, the steam is processed to remove from it boric acid and other chemicals it has brought from the earth.   (Photograph by W. D. Keller.)

FIG. 37. Riverside Geyser, Yellowstone National Park.   (Photograph by W. A. Tarr.)

A *geyser* (Fig. 37) ejects both steam and hot water and thus represents an intermediate stage between a fumarole and a hot spring.   Geysers originate as follows.   Surface water containing dissolved gases in descending along a fissure comes in contact with steam rising from some hot rock (solid or liquid) below and is heated.   The pressure of the accumulating

steam and heated gases finally becomes great enough to eject violently
the water above it in the fissure. The eruption lasts until the pressure is
relieved. Water then finds its way back into the fissure and the process
is repeated, commonly at regular intervals. Thus the action of a geyser
is dependent upon surface water from above and steam from a magma
below. The magma or rock furnishing the steam is gradually cooling, of
course, so the time interval between eruptions becomes longer and longer.
Old Faithful Geyser in Yellowstone Park formerly had an interval of 60
minutes; at present it is 63 minutes.

Three areas, Yellowstone National Park, Iceland, and New Zealand,
are notable in having the conditions needed to produce geysers. Some
of the New Zealand geysers throw water and steam to a height of 1,500
°eet, which is the greatest height attained by geysers anywhere in the
world.

Finally, when the quantities of steam coming from the lava are no
longer sufficient to cause eruptions, water from their condensation,
together with the heated surface waters, will be present as *hot springs*.
Water from hot springs is used extensively as a source of domestic heat
at Reykjavik, Iceland, and in other places. Eventually even the springs
cool down, signifying that the igneous activity is over, at least temporarily.

Cones and Other Features of Volcanoes. A beautiful symmetry is
exhibited by most volcanic cones, the classic example of which is the
Fuji in Japan. The symmetry of some cones is broken, however, by
the presence of small *parasitic cones* upon the sides of the major peak
(see Fig. 28, page 28). These small cones are formed where volcanic
action took place on the sides of the large cone and produced miniature
eruptions. A type of cone built most commonly during the closing
stages of an eruption (either fissure or volcanic) is a *cinder cone* (Fig. 38),
as the final gases in escaping break up the lava which had solidified and
blow it out of the crater. Cinder cones are composed largely of lapilli
with more or less fine and coarse fragmental material. These cones are
usually very symmetrical and have perfectly circular craters. Cinder
cones are very abundant near Flagstaff, Arizona; Lassen Peak, California; and in the volcanic regions of Oregon and Idaho.

Lava caves occur in volcanic lavas, also, and the surfaces of volcanic
lavas show the same *smooth, ropy* (see Fig. 24, page 25), and *clinkery
structures* as do the surfaces of the lava from fissure eruptions.

Location of Volcanoes. Volcanoes are widely distributed over the
earth (Fig. 39), but they are more abundant in certain belts. One such
belt encircles the Pacific Ocean and includes many of the islands in it.
Other volcanic areas are the islands of the West Indies, those off the west
coast of Africa, the Mediterranean region, and Iceland. Most volcanoes
occur around or near the margins of the continents, so these areas are

regarded as weak zones in the earth's crust where lavas can readily work their way upward.   There are more than 400 active volcanoes, at present (1951), and many more inactive ones.   Very probably, numerous submarine volcanoes exist, also, of which we have no knowledge.   Of the many known volcanoes we shall describe a few briefly.

Parícutin.   We shall describe, first, the recent (1943) eruption of Parícutin because we can thus begin with an eye-witness account of the birth of a volcano.   Because of its accessibility to Mexico City (about 200 miles west), detailed scientific observations were begun shortly after the first eruption and have been continued ever since.

FIG. 38. Sunset Crater Cone, Arizona.   A cinder cone showing crater depression in top.   (*Photograph by Tad Nichols.*)

The first evidence of volcanic action is strikingly related in the simple language of a Tarascan Indian who witnessed the outbreak, February 20, 1943, in his corn field.   Dr. T. A. Jaggar[6] quotes him as follows:

That Saturday I was in the field with my wife Pabla and our ten-year old son Cresencio who were shepherding our little lambs while I was plowing the field to plant corn.

Suddenly I heard the ground in front of me snort and there the smoke came out of the earth and I thought the world had caught fire.   The ground thundered for ten minutes and water seemed to be running down below.   Then the ground hissed and I saw smoke and I remembered that an engineer had said a volcano might come as we had been having earthquakes every day for eighteen days.

The intensity of the eruption increased rapidly during the first day and continued for several months, as shown in the following quotations from descriptions by Professor F. M. Bullard:[7]

[6] *Ibid.*
[7] *Op. cit.*

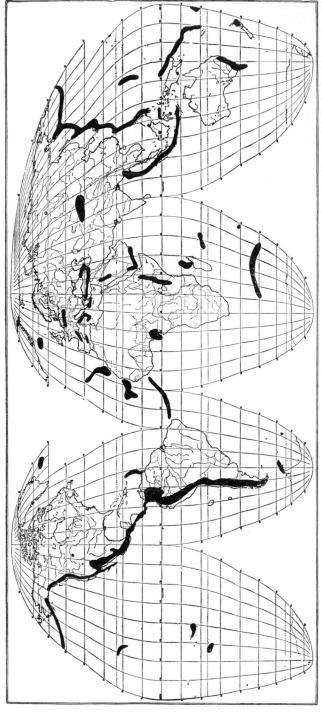

FIG. 39. Map showing the distribution of volcanic areas in the world. (Map used by permission of University of Chicago Press.)

. . . By four o'clock the small columns of gas had changed to thick black clouds, accompanied by violent explosions, dust, rocks, and red-hot fragments.   Terrified, the Indians hurriedly abandoned the scene. . . . During the night the roar of the explosions and the glare from the red-hot material kept the panicky population of Parícutin and San Juan de Parangaricutiro awake.   Groups of frightened men and women gathered in the churchyard to witness the magnificent spectacle and to ponder its meaning. . . . Early next morning . . . they found a black cone, already 120 feet high, with an opening in the top through which hot gases, ash and cinders, solid fragments, and molten bombs were being ejected in violent explosions at intervals of one to two seconds. . . . At night the volcano presents a magnificent spectacle.   During the early months, when the explosions were frequent and continuous, the night spectacle was at its best.   With each explosion literally thousands of red-hot fragments were thrown to a height of 2,000–3,000 feet above the crater rim, and, as they reached their zenith, they seemed to stop before beginning to fall, showering the cone like a giant skyrocket and leaving a trail of fire as they cascaded down the sides.   So abundant were these fragments that frequently the entire cone was covered with interlacing fiery trails, which outlined it against the blackness of the night. . . .

The first lava began to flow at Parícutin on the second day.   It came from a fissure 1,000 feet north of the explosive vent (see Fig. 29, page 28).   Fragmental material, however, continued to be ejected in major quantity until the cone was about 1,100 feet high, at the end of 3 months; whereupon the decline in activity began, and after 4 years the cone was only about 1,700 feet high.   Lava flows were the chief form of later activity (Fig. 40).   In the second year (1944), a large flow buried San Juan de Parangaricutiro (4 or 5 miles distant) under 30 feet of lava (Fig. 41).

Parícutin is now (1951) still less active, which causes volcanologists to think that it will follow the pattern of the many other nearby, relatively short-lived volcanoes.   Likewise, the composition of its lava, its gaseous emanations, temperature (1000 to 1200°C.), and other features conform to conventional volcanic characteristics.   It is the scientific observations and accounts of its birth that make it unique.

Vesuvius.   The very famous volcano Vesuvius had been dormant for an unknown period of time when, in A.D. 79, it suddenly became very active.   Its eruption consisted of a series of great explosions by which enormous quantities of rock were pulverized and blown high into the air, obscuring the light of the sun.   The fragments fell as dust and mud, burying cities and towns.   Pompeii, a city of 20,000, located on the shore of the Bay of Naples at the foot of Vesuvius, was buried under 25 or 30 feet of volcanic dust.   This city has now been excavated (Fig. 42), and thus many incidents of the eruption have come to light.   Although most of the inhabitants of Pompeii escaped, we know that some were suddenly overwhelmed and killed by hot gases, for they are found in

FIG. 40. Lava flow from Parícutin advancing through forest, burning or burying the trees.   Volcanic dust fell first.   (*Photograph by Fred M. Bullard, September, 1944.*)

FIG. 41. Towers of the cathedral at San Juan de Parangaricutiro projecting above the lava flow from Parícutin which buried the rest of the town 30 feet deep.   (*Photograph by Tad Nichols.*)

positions that show what they were doing at the time of the explosion. Facial expressions of the plaster casts made of bodies found standing, sitting, and lying down show that death in many cases must have been instantaneous. Foods were found in cooking vessels on stoves and in dishes on tables, people were found sitting about the tables, and thus many facts relating to people of that time and their habits have been learned. About 2,000 people perished in Pompeii, and an unknown number in Herculaneum, which is also being excavated. As Herculaneum was buried under 50 feet or more of mud, the work of excavation has not progressed so far as at Pompeii.

FIG. 42. Paved street in Pompeii, Italy, after excavation. Note steppingstones, and tracks worn by Roman carts. (*Photograph by W. A. Tarr.*)

Since this first eruption of which we have knowledge, Vesuvius has had several dormant periods followed by eruptions, of which some have been violent, destroying many lives. The last great eruption, in 1906, although not so destructive of life as some of the earlier ones, destroyed much property. Figure 43 illustrates the character of activity prevalent in recent years.

Krakatoa. Krakatoa, a volcano of the East Indies, is of interest because of the violence of the explosion that destroyed the cone. This eruption occurred on August 27, 1883, and was probably the greatest volcanic eruption of historical times. The steam in the volcano had accumulated in enormous amounts, and after some minor explosions and earthquakes it suddenly blew away the upper two-thirds of the mountain which comprised the island (see Fig. 31). Krakatoa was 2,623 feet high, but after the explosion the ocean was 1,000 feet deep over most of the area.   Only small parts of the outer edges of the cone now remain as islands.   The explosion was heard in southern Australia, 2,200 miles away, and at other points at distances of about 3,000 miles.   The air waves produced by the concussion traveled around the globe several times.   Dust from the explosion was shot to a height of 20 miles or more and, in 15 days, was carried around the world by the upper currents of air.   Pieces of rock were spread over the ocean floor for miles around. For months afterward the sunrises and sunsets all over the world were of exceptionally brilliant colors due to the dust particles in the air, some of which are estimated to have reached a height of 70 miles.   These particles

FIG. 43. Clouds of steam issuing from inner cone in crater of Vesuvius, and numerous fumaroles a little farther down the cone.   Black spots in cloud are blobs of lava being ejected.   (*From the Illustrated London News, June 22, 1929.*)

finally settled down over all parts of the earth.   A great sea wave, which was created by the explosion, rushed upon neighboring shores, destroying hundreds of towns and about 30,000 people.   Had this eruption occurred in a densely populated part of the earth, the loss of life would have been tremendous.   Since this eruption, Krakatoa has been fairly quiet, only occasionally showing signs of activity.

Mt. Pelée.   Mt. Pelée, on the island of Martinique in the West Indies, was also an explosive volcano, but its last eruption was of a different type.   The city of St. Pierre, located on a flat plain on the sea shore, lay at the foot of the volcano.   Pelée became activated late in April, 1902. Explosions of gases and dust accompanied by earthquake shocks were the first evidence of what was to come.   It is worth noting that the gases ejected during these preliminary explosions were so poisonous that horses in the streets of St. Pierre were killed.   The explosions steadily increased in violence until, on May 8, a terrific eruption of dust and hot poisonous gases occurred.   This great cloud of dust and gas swept out of the crater through a notch in its south side and rolled down the cone and across the plain to St. Pierre and its harbor (Fig. 44).   It traveled with such tremendous force that in two minutes it had destroyed all in its path: buildings, people, trees, even the boats in the harbor.   Fire finished the destruction of the city, and then rain from the condensed steam carried the dust down as mud and buried it.   Very few of the 30,000 inhabitants escaped; one survivor, a prisoner in a dungeon, was found many days

FIG. 44. Cloud of poisonous gases from Mt. Pelée rolling down on the city of St. Pierre, Martinique.

later.   As the activity of the volcano grew less, a great column of lava slowly rose through the crater to a height of 1,200 feet.   This column, which is known as Pelée's Spine, has since gradually disintegrated and decreased in height.

Mt. Katmai.   Mt. Katmai is on Alaska Peninsula in southwestern Alaska, about 750 miles due west of Juneau.   As it is located in a very sparsely settled country, we have no record of any action previous to the eruption of 1912.   This eruption occurred about 1 P.M. on June 6, and was witnessed only by a few natives.   The noise of the explosion was heard at Juneau.   The eruption was followed by another at 11 o'clock that night and by a third at 10:40 the next night.   During the first explosion, an enormous quantity of gray volcanic dust was ejected, which began to fall in Kodiak, 100 miles away (Fig. 45), about 5 o'clock that afternoon.   By 6:30, the dust was so thick that the darkness of night prevailed (at that time of the year daylight at Kodiak lasted nearly 24 hours). The fall ceased at 9:10 the next morning (the dust was then 5 inches deep), but ashes from the second explosion began falling at 12:30 P.M., and in an hour and a half it was again dark. The darkness continued until 2:30 P.M. on June 8. Dust from the explosions fell 1,500 miles from the volcano. The extent of the area covered by 0.02 foot or more of dust is shown in Fig. 45. It is estimated by Griggs that 4.75 cubic miles of dust were blown out of the volcano; that a cubic mile of coarse ash was ejected in the sand flow in the Valley of Ten Thousand

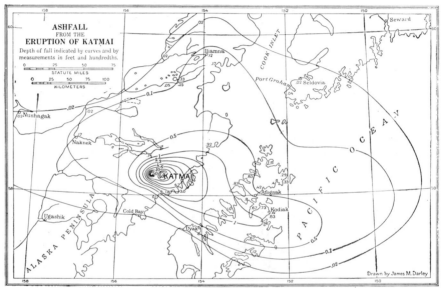

FIG. 45. Map of the ashfall in vicinity of Katmai, Alaska. (Copyright by National Geographic Society. Reproduced by special permission from the National Geographic Magazine.)

Smokes; and, in addition, that enough material from smaller craters was ejected to bring the total amount to 6.25 cubic miles. It would take all the stone crushers existing at the present time in the United States about 500 years to produce this quantity of crushed material. For six months after the dust was thrown into the air at Katmai, a decrease in the amount of heat received from the sun was noticeable throughout the world. The amount of water ejected as steam was enormous also. A study of the pumice resulting from the explosion indicates that the quantity of gas it contained was about 12 times greater than its own volume. This was water newly added to that at the surface of the earth.

The Valley of Ten Thousand Smokes, lying several miles northwest of Katmai, covers about 53 square miles. Before the eruption of Katmai, the floor of this valley had been covered (in places to a depth of nearly

100 feet) by a white-hot mass of volcanic sand, which, together with much steam, had welled up from below through fissures in the floor of the valley. Though Katmai is now (1951) quiet, in this valley steam is still escaping from a vast number of fissures (Fig. 34). The temperature of the steam from some of the fumaroles is very high; in one it was 1200°F. Such steam is invisible and a piece of wood placed in it catches fire. During the expeditions of the National Geographic Society to this region, considerable cooking was done over these natural cookstoves.

Hawaiian Volcanoes. The Hawaiian Islands are entirely volcanic in origin. They contain many volcanoes, all of the quiet type, but only

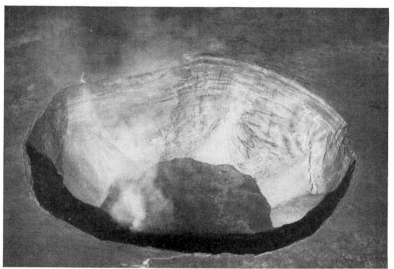

FIG. 46. Air view of Halemaumau fire pit in crater of Kilauea, Hawaii.   Fire pit is 3,000 by 3,400 by 1,400 (depth) feet. Wall of crater in background. (*Courtesy of U.S. Air Force.*)

Mauna Loa (nearly 14,000 feet high) and Kilauea (about 4,000 feet high) are widely known. The craters of these volcanoes are large; that of Mauna Loa being 2 by 3 miles in areal extent and 1,000 feet deep; and that of Kilauea, about 3 miles in diameter and over 1,000 feet deep. Within each of these craters are local fire pits (Fig. 46). The lava usually breaks through the sides of these volcanoes and flows quietly down them, and thus the volcanoes have broad, flat cones. The width of their bases, being below the ocean, is unknown; but considering their height and the fact that they are built up from the floor of the ocean, which is 16,000 feet deep around them, they must be enormous peaks (Fig. 47).

Lassen Peak. Lassen Peak in northern California is the only even moderately active volcano within the territory of the United States proper. The volcano, which is 10,453 feet high, had been dormant for

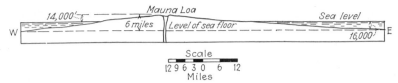

FIG. 47. Sketch of Mauna Loa volcano, Hawaii, drawn to scale (vertical and horizontal the same) to show its enormous height above the sea floor.

FIG. 48. Photographs taken at intervals of a few minutes during eruption of Mt. Lassen, June 14, 1914. *(Reproduced by permission of B. F. Loomis, the photographer.)*

200 years until 1914, when several mild eruptions occurred (Fig. 48). Two violent eruptions occurred in 1915: one on May 19 and the other on May 22 (see Fig. 30, page 29).   The early activity was mainly explosive action, which removed much material from the old crater, allowing the rising lava to fill it and overflow slightly.   This lava then solidified, forming a solid lid in the crater under which the gases accumulated until finally the lid was lifted and a horizontal explosion took place from under it.   Lava flowed down the mountain side, melting the snow and destroying everything in front of it.   The water from the snow, mixed with the volcanic dust, caused a great mud flow.   Lassen Peak, which is readily accessible, is quiet now; but there are many fumaroles, hot springs, and boiling mud pots in its vicinity, and many lava caves in the earlier lava flows about the peak.

STRUCTURAL FEATURES OF IGNEOUS ROCKS

The structural features of igneous rocks are rather large and are best seen in the field, though they may be studied also in laboratory specimens.   The following structural features are distinctive of igneous rocks and can be used to distinguish them from the other types of rocks:

> Ropy structure
> Clinkery structure
> Block structure
> Flow structure
> Columnar structure
> Massiveness

Ropy and *clinkery structures* have already been described (page 23).

Block structure is the result of the formation of a crust on a lava flow followed by movement of the still-liquid portion below.   The crust is thus broken into blocks and becomes a rough, jumbled mass as the lava moves forward.

Flow structure is the result of movement in a viscous lava.   It is seen as lines or streaks of different color in a rock (Fig. 49), or as the parallel arrangement of the phenocrysts of a porphyry (Fig. 50).   This banding is well illustrated by the lines and bands formed in taffy as it is being pulled.   Thick asphalt shows the same features.

Columnar structure results from a certain type of jointing formed in igneous rocks as the lava cools and contracts.   The joints or cracks that start on the surface of the cooling mass (a flow, dike, or sill) penetrate deeper and deeper as the interior cools and contracts.   The cracks are remarkably uniform in their spacing, the result being extraordinarily symmetrical columns (Figs. 51, 52, and 53).   A noteworthy feature of these columns is their dominantly six-sided character, although the number of sides ranges from three to nine.   The columns of the Giant's

Causeway on the north coast of Ireland are among the most perfect known (Fig. 52). In the main part of the Causeway, the columns average about 15 inches in diameter, in other parts several feet. The columns

FIG. 49. Flow structure in obsidian.

FIG. 50. Flow structure due to rudely parallel arrangement of phenocrysts. This arrangement was caused by movement of viscous lava.

FIG. 51. Columnar structure in basalt, Giant's Causeway, Ireland. Hammer is 12 inches long. Some columns are concave on ends (those containing rain water); others are convex. (*Photograph by W. A. Tarr.*)

in the Devils Tower in Wyoming are from 6 to 8 feet in diameter (see Fig. 18, page 22).

Massiveness is a term applied to igneous rocks that, over a wide extent, are uniform in texture. This feature is most typical of granites, diorites, and similar rocks and is but rarely exhibited by other types of rocks.

FIG. 52. The Giant's Causeway, Ireland. Note great number of columns—estimated at 70,000. (*Photograph by W. A. Tarr.*)

FIG. 53. Quarry in columnar basalt at Toowoomba, Queensland, Australia. (*Photograph by courtesy of Prof. W. A. Albrecht.*)

THE COMMON MINERALS OF IGNEOUS ROCKS

One of the outstanding facts about the common igneous rocks is that the majority of them consist of fewer than six major minerals (mineral families). Many other minerals occur in igneous rocks, but either they are minor constituents or, if fairly abundant, they give rise to rare types of rocks that are of interest chiefly to the petrographer. We shall ignore these rarer varieties in our study, aiming only to acquire a working acquaintance with the simpler rocks.

The minerals that form the basis of the igneous rocks are *feldspar, quartz, hornblende, pyroxene,* and *olivine.* Leith and Mead have given the following estimate as to the relative abundance of the minerals found in igneous rocks:

Minerals of Igneous Rocks	Percentage
Feldspars	50.0
Quartz	20.5
Hornblende, pyroxene, and olivine	17.0
Mica	7.5
All other minerals	5.0
Total	100.0

The description of the minerals which follows gives necessarily only their general characteristics; the student must study them in the laboratory also and, if possible, in the field.

The Feldspars. The feldspars are minerals containing potassium, sodium, calcium, aluminum, silicon, and oxygen. A very convenient

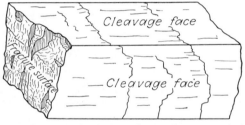

FIG. 54. Sketch of cleavage fragment of orthoclase, showing the two smooth cleavage faces at right angles to each other, and the position of the fracture face.

way of stating their composition is to say that they are silicates of potassium, sodium, calcium, and aluminum. There are two common feldspars: orthoclase, which contains potassium; and plagioclase, which contains sodium and calcium. Simple chemical formulae may be written for them as follows: orthoclase ($KAlSiO_n$) and plagioclase ($NaCaAlSiO_n$). (The subscript n signifies that the number of atoms of each element included is not specified.) The feldspars are white, pink, red, gray, and, rarely, dark gray or black. They are so hard that a fragment rubbed on glass will scratch it. Feldspars have two smooth cleavage surfaces, *i.e.,* they break readily along two surfaces. These two surfaces are at right angles (or nearly so) to each other (Fig. 54), and the break in the third direction is rough and jagged. Practically all common igneous rocks contain at least a little feldspar. The term *felsic* ("fel" for feldspar; "s" for silica or quartz; and "ic," the general ending) is coming into common use for these minerals.

Quartz. Quartz is common, not only in igneous, but in most kinds of rocks. It is composed of silica (SiO_2) and is the hardest of the common minerals found in rocks. Its hardness is generally given as 7 in a scale that runs from 1 to 10. (The diamond has a hardness of 10, being the hardest substance known.) Quartz occurs in all colors; but transparent, white, pink, red, violet, and green quartz are the most common varieties. Quartz does not show cleavage, but breaks, usually, with an uneven surface that looks like glass. Well-developed crystals of quartz are common. The crystals are six-sided and on the ends have faces arranged as six-sided pyramids. Most sand consists dominantly of quartz grains.

Hornblende and Pyroxene. Hornblende and pyroxene are similar in composition. Both are calcium-magnesium-iron-aluminum silicates ($CaMgFeAlSiO_n$), but due to variations in the constituent amounts of these elements, the two minerals possess different physical properties. Numerous varieties of each mineral occur. Both minerals are black or dark green and have a hardness of 5 to 7. Both have two cleavages, and their different cleavage angles (for hornblende 124 and 56°; for pyroxene 93 and 87°) are the most important physical means of distinguishing between them. Hornblende crystals may be longer and more slender than those of pyroxene. Where the two minerals occur as small grains in igneous rocks, it is difficult, even by their cleavage angles, to distinguish between them. These two minerals are commonly called the *ferromagnesian* ("ferro" means iron) minerals or, the newer term, *mafic* ("ma" for magnesium; "f" for iron; "ic," the general ending) minerals. Rocks rich in hornblende or pyroxene are called *ferromagnesian* or *mafic* rocks. In a great many dark-colored rocks, the beginning student will find it impossible to distinguish between these two minerals and would better simply call the rocks "mafic."

The Micas. There are two common varieties of mica: one is white or transparent, *muscovite* ($HKAlSiO_n$); the other is black, *biotite* ($HKMgFeAlSiO_n$). Micas are easily determined because they have shiny cleavage faces, split readily in one direction into extremely thin sheets, and are soft. Both biotite and muscovite are fairly common.

Olivine. A mineral of somewhat rarer occurrence in igneous rocks is *olivine*. It is a magnesium-iron silicate ($MgFeSiO_n$). It occurs in certain dark mafic rocks, notably one called *peridotite*, which, though not very abundant at the surface, is believed to be the dominant rock below the gabbroid zone. Olivine has a characteristic olive-green color, breaks unevenly, has a glassy luster, and is about as hard as feldspar.

NAMING THE IGNEOUS ROCKS

Having followed the development of igneous rocks from their source in the magma deep within the earth's body to the various forms of the solid rock, we now come to the final phase of their consideration, *i.e.*, the development of names by which we may know them. There are many different kinds of igneous rocks; hundreds, in fact. Fortunately, however, for the beginning student and layman, geologists have found it possible and convenient to group most igneous rocks under a few simple names, called *field names* because they can be applied to a rock in the field before it has been critically studied in the laboratory. These are the names that should be used by the beginning student of geology.

Three factors are involved in developing the names of the different igneous rocks: the *texture* (always important), *color*, and the *mineral composition* (if it can be determined).

Texture is the chief feature used in developing the names or classes of igneous rocks, as all of them can be placed in one of four textural groups, which are as follows:

Texture	Characteristics
Grained..............	Grains large enough to make megascopic determination of minerals possible
Dense...............	Grains so small as to make megascopic determination of minerals impossible
Glassy...............	Rock is like glass
Fragmental..........	Composed of fragments of minerals and rocks

Further subdivision of these groups will be necessary, as any rock of the first three groups may occur as an even-grained rock or as a *porphyry*.

The four textural groups of rocks we shall subdivide on a basis of *color*. For our purpose, only a division into "dark-colored" and "light-colored" rocks will be needed. As dark colored, we shall designate black, dark-gray, and dark-green rocks; as light colored, those that are light gray, light green, white, red, pink, brown, and yellow.

The third and last factor we must consider in naming the igneous rocks is their *mineral composition*. Inasmuch as it is only in the grained rocks that all the mineral grains are large enough to be determinable, it is only in naming the rocks of that group that we can make use of the mineral composition. Even in the fine-grained varieties of the grained rocks, it may be difficult or impossible to determine all the constituent minerals.

Combining now the different kinds of texture, varieties of color, and known mineral composition, we are able to produce the following table (next page) for determining igneous rock names.

A sample determination will illustrate the ease with which the name of an igneous rock may be determined by the use of this table. Suppose the specimen of rock is light colored; it is assigned to the left-hand section of the table. Closer inspection shows that the mineral grains of the rock are recognizable; hence it comes under the section of the grained rocks. The determination of the minerals in the specimen shows that it consists dominantly of feldspar and quartz, and so we decide that the name of the rock is "granite." By a similar use of the table the name of any common igneous rock can be determined.

IGNEOUS ROCK TABLE

		Light colored		Dark colored
		Felsic minerals predominate		Mafic minerals predominate. Some feldspar
		Feldspar and quartz	Feldspar and some mafic minerals	
Grained	Even textured	Granite	Diorite	Gabbro
	Porphyritic	Granite porphyry	Diorite porphyry	Gabbro porphyry (rare)
Dense	Even textured	Felsite		Basalt
	Porphyritic	Felsite porphyry		Basalt porphyry
Glassy	Even textured	Pumice, Obsidian		
	Porphyritic	Obsidian porphyry		
Fragmental		Tuff, Volcanic ash, Volcanic breccia		

As seen by the table, grained, dense, or glassy rocks may be porphyritic, but porphyries are most common in dense rocks. The name of the phenocrysts may be used as a part of the rock name: thus, if the phenocrysts in a felsite are quartz, the rock may be called a "quartz-felsite porphyry"; or, as is commonly done, the term "felsite" may be dropped and the rock called a "quartz porphyry." If two kinds of phenocrysts are present, as quartz and feldspar, the name of the rock would be (if quartz were the smaller in amount) "quartz-feldspar porphyry." The phenocrysts of porphyries may be any of the minerals that occur in igneous rocks.

Tuff is a name used for accumulations of volcanic dust; and *volcanic breccia* ("breccia" means "broken") is the name for volcanic deposits of larger angular fragments.

MODE OF OCCURRENCE OF THE DIFFERENT KINDS OF IGNEOUS ROCKS

There is more or less of an association between the type of igneous rock and its mode of occurrence, as would be expected when it is recalled that the texture of the rock is dependent upon the rate of cooling of the parent mass.

The Grained Rocks.   The grained rocks solidified, of course, under conditions that favored the growth of large grains.   For the most part, these rocks were formed at considerable depths below the surface.   They are the dominant rocks in batholiths, laccoliths, and large sills and dikes. All of the grained rocks are found at the surface, owing to erosion, but *granites* are by far the most abundant there, as the name "granitic" for the outer 10 or 12 miles of the earth's crust indicates.   Though most granites show strong evidence of having resulted from the slow solidification of a magma, others show as convincing evidence of being the result of the interaction of hot solutions and vapors with preexisting rocks— usually those rocks which are rich in silica.

Diorites, though common at the surface, are considerably less abundant than the granites.   The *gabbroid rocks* are fairly widespread at the surface but become increasingly abundant downward.   Below the zone in which they are found is a zone rich in olivine (the peridotitic zone). The grained rocks are not commonly porphyritic.   Some granites and diorites are porphyritic, however, especially those occurring in dikes and sills; but the magmas which gave rise to the mafic rocks were so fluid even at low temperatures that most of these rocks are wholly crystalline. Cooling and crystal growth may occur in two stages, however; hence even gabbro porphyries are known.

The Dense Rocks.   The dense rocks occur commonly in lava flows. The silica content of the *felsites* is about the same as that of the granites and diorites; in fact, had the lava forming the felsites cooled slowly, it would have become granite or diorite.   As this felsite lava was usually viscous, it could not flow far from the opening but solidified rapidly; hence felsites are common in volcanic lava flows.   *Basalts* were formed from magnesium-iron-rich lavas that, being quite fluid, were able to flow for long distances.   In the vast area of lava flows of northwestern United States, the rock is dominantly basalt.   In addition to these extrusive occurrences, both felsites and basalts occur as dikes, sills, and necks. The dense rocks are very commonly porphyritic because most magmas that finally reach the surface are halted for a time on their way up. During this time various minerals start to crystallize, and these crystals are the phenocrysts of the rock that is formed after further movement toward the surface has taken place.

The Glassy Rocks.   The glassy rocks are always formed at the earth's surface, where the lava cools very rapidly.   As they are formed from lavas rich in silica, they, like the felsites, would have been granite or diorite had the magma cooled far below the surface.   Such silica-rich (felsic) lavas are very viscous at the surface, and it is the expansion of gases in them that gives rise to *pumice*. *Obsidian* Cliff in Yellowstone Park is a good example of a thick mass of glassy rock. Basaltic lavas rarely form glassy rocks because, on account of their extreme fluidity, crystals can grow in them rapidly. Rarely, a thin layer of black glass is formed around the outside of a mass of solidifying basaltic lava. The formation of porphyries is possible in glassy rocks, but it is not common.

The Fragmental Rocks. The fragmental rocks are formed from the material ejected from the explosive type of volcano. The coarse fragments and lapilli, which form the *volcanic breccia*, settle near the volcano, but the volcanic dust and pumice may be carried long distances by the wind. Dust from volcanoes that formerly were active in the

FIG. 55. Tuff beds containing fossil plants and animals, near Florissant, Colorado. (*Photograph by W. A. Tarr.*)

Rocky Mountains is now found as *tuff* beds as far east as central Kansas and Nebraska. Beds of tuff thousands of feet in thickness occur in the San Juan Mountains in southwestern Colorado. Volcanic dust becomes somewhat stratified, as dust particles of the same size settle together to the earth. In this respect, tuffs resemble sedimentary rocks. Tuffs have been found that were deposited in water (Fig. 55) and contain fossils of various kinds. Much care is required in the determination of such deposits, for it is readily seen that the presence of fossils in a rock is not sufficient evidence to prove that a rock is wholly of sedimentary origin.

ORE DEPOSITS RESULTING FROM IGNEOUS ACTIVITY

Having discussed the formation of igneous rocks from magmas, it will be of interest to note also the formation, from these same magmas, of deposits of the valuable metals and minerals used by man. Such deposits are called *ore deposits* or *mineral deposits*. Thus, we read of a "gold ore" or a "platinum ore." Some magmas contained, in addition to the elements that went into the formation of the igneous rocks, small amounts of various rare metals or other elements, which under the proper conditions were concentrated into deposits sufficiently valuable to pay man to go to the expense of mining them. It was only the occasional magma, however, that contained sufficient amounts of such elements; and, even then, only occasionally that a concentration of those elements into an ore deposit took place. This is shown by the fact that platinum, or nickel, or diamonds, for example, have been found in only a very few localities over the entire earth. The earth is thus shown to be heterogeneous in composition. We shall consider briefly the separation, in the magma, of these valuable substances from the igneous rocks, and the forms they assumed upon being deposited.

We have already seen that, as a magma cooled and the igneous rocks solidified from it, the gases (largely steam) were eliminated. It is in these gaseous, and later liquid, solutions (*magmatic solutions*) forced out of the solidifying rock that the valuable elements were contained. The gaseous solutions are called *mineralizers*, for a double reason: (1) because they aid in keeping a lava in a liquid state and thus allow minerals to grow to large sizes, and (2) because they are very strong solvents, dissolving the most insoluble of elements (such as gold and lead), which are subsequently deposited as minerals. This solvent action of the solutions is due to the contained gases, *viz.*, steam, carbon dioxide, chlorine, sulfur, and, more rarely, stronger gases such as fluorine and boric acid.

It should be noted that the majority of ore deposits are connected with large igneous masses, such as batholiths and, less commonly, thick dikes, sills, and laccoliths. As these large masses cooled, the rock-forming minerals solidified and the gaseous solutions were thus forcibly eliminated. A small part of them passed outward into the surrounding rocks during the early stages of cooling; but, as soon as the outer part of the igneous mass was solid (the outer part, of course, cooled first), the gases were steadily forced inward as the solidification progressed and thus accumulated in the still-liquid interior of the cooling mass (Fig. 56A). These gaseous solutions, having penetrated all parts of the magma, had acquired by their powerful solvent action whatever rare elements or metals (if any) the magma contained. Some of the magmas were rich in one or two metals, such as gold, gold and silver, copper, iron, lead and zinc, or a rarer metal. Some magmas were rich in several metals: commonly, such an association as copper, iron, lead, zinc, gold, and silver.

After the magma had become solid, it contracted with continued cooling, and thus cracks and fissures were developed in the solid outer part (Fig. 56B). The magmatic solutions on the interior were under great pressure (largely due to the expansive force of the gases), and, therefore, they took advantage of these openings and passed outward into them (Fig. 56B). They were able to force their way into even very tiny fissures and to move outward through them to areas of less pressure, carrying with them, we must remember, the valuable metals and minerals they had collected from the magma.

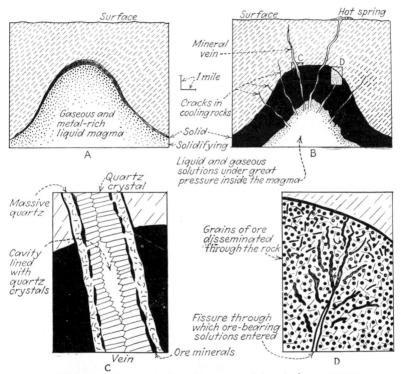

FIG. 56. Sketch showing the formation of mineral deposits from a magma.

As time passed, the temperature of the solutions grew less, of course, and especially because they found their way into cooler areas near the surface and probably mingled with the cooler solutions there. As a result, many changes took place in the solutions and these changes caused the deposition of the metals and minerals being carried (Fig. 56C). The deposition took place not only near the surface, but also, under favorable conditions, deep within the earth. Erosion later cut away the overlying rock and exposed some of the deposits at the surface, where man discovered and made use of them.

The deposits made by magmatic solutions are of innumerable forms, the most common of which is a vein-like deposit (Fig. 56B and C, and Fig. 130, page 138) filling fissures and cracks in the rocks. These *veins*

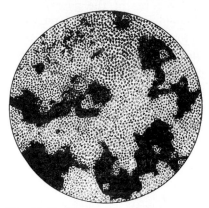

are of all sizes and shapes. Some are many miles long and about 100 feet wide; others are no thicker than a sheet of paper. They are found in all kinds of rocks and at all depths. Some mines in which copper and gold veins are being worked are over a mile deep. Another common form of deposit is a *disseminated deposit*, in which the valuable mineral is scattered throughout the rock (Fig. 56D and Fig. 57). These deposits may be hundreds of feet thick. One at Bingham Canyon, Utah (Fig. 58), is being mined on the surface with steam shovels, and the whole side of a mountain has been cut away.

FIG. 57. Sketch of a disseminated deposit (a black lead mineral in limestone) as seen through a microscope. (*Buckley, Missouri Geol. Survey, vol. 9, p. 213.*)

Inasmuch as these deposits whose origin we have been considering are formed directly from cooling magmas, they are called *primary deposits.*

FIG. 58. Open-cut copper mine, Bingham Canyon, Utah. (*Photograph by W. D. Keller.*)

They include the world's largest *copper, gold, silver, lead, zinc,* and certain, but not all, *iron* deposits. Other valuable but less common metals, like *chromium* (used for plating), *nickel, tin,* and *tungsten* (used in electric lights), are also formed by magmatic solutions, and so are, likewise, primary deposits.

As the igneous rocks are the primary rocks, they are the source of all the substances found at the surface of the earth. Not all of the products at the earth's surface are primary, however, as certain valuable deposits there, as well as certain kinds of rocks, were formed by secondary processes. These *secondary deposits* are all found on or near the surface and are the result of the alteration of the igneous rocks, or primary mineral deposits, by water, aided by various agents (as will be discussed in the next chapter). Deposits of the metals *aluminum* and *platinum* are examples of the many valuable mineral deposits due to secondary processes, and *salt* is an example of a useful rock derived by secondary processes.

Most aluminum ore deposits are the result of ground water's attacking a feldspar-rich rock, leaching out the potassium, sodium, calcium, and silica, and leaving the aluminum to accumulate into a valuable deposit of insoluble aluminum oxide. The largest deposit of aluminum ore in the United States is just south of Little Rock, Arkansas.

Platinum is a very insoluble, heavy mineral occurring in the original primary rock (usually a rock rich in the mafic minerals) as the metal, but in small grains scattered through the rock (thus a disseminated deposit). Valuable as the metal is, such a deposit could not be mined profitably, but various geologic processes may bring about a concentration of the grains. If the rock containing the platinum is exposed at the surface, it will break down or disintegrate into soil and the grains of platinum will thus be loosened. Streams may wash away the soil and leave the very heavy platinum grains in the stream bed along with sand and gravel. Thus the platinum grains slowly accumulate until a deposit known as a *placer deposit* is formed. It is a very simple matter, then, to wash away the sand and gravel and obtain the platinum. The world's largest deposit of platinum is in Russia, on the east slope of the Ural Mountains.

The two elements sodium and chlorine composing salt (NaCl) were present in the original magma: the sodium in the part that formed the igneous rocks, and the chlorine in the gaseous solutions. Ages later, at the surface of the earth, the sodium was freed by the decay of the feldspar of the igneous rocks, and the chlorine escaped to the surface during volcanic eruptions. Then the two elements, having a great affinity for each other, combined whenever they came in contact. As the salt formed was readily soluble, it was carried to the sea, where an enormous quantity still exists in the sea water. Beds of salt that were deposited from the sea water are found on the land.

Summary. Most of the valuable ore deposits of the earth were formed by the gaseous solutions given off from a magma as it cooled and became an igneous rock. The solutions entered openings in the rocks and deposited the valuable metals they carried as veins and many other types of deposits. Such deposits are said to be of magmatic origin. Later processes formed secondary deposits from these primary ones.

SUMMARY OF VOLCANISM AND IGNEOUS ROCKS

Magmas move outward from interior parts of the earth and give rise to intrusive and extrusive forms of igneous rocks and to associated ore deposits. The minerals, feldspar, quartz, hornblende, pyroxene, and olivine, unite in different combinations to form the primary igneous rocks. These rocks are named with reference to their mineral composition, texture, and color.

CHAPTER 4

WEATHERING OF IGNEOUS ROCKS

Most rocks when exposed at the earth's surface soon show the effects of attack by the agents of the weather. No rocks can endure long. Some soften and crumble; others dissolve and are carried away by water. In the weathering process, new secondary materials are produced that enter into the formation of sedimentary rocks. In this chapter, we shall study the source and production of these new substances.

Our study will begin with the fresh, unaltered igneous rock at the earth's surface and will follow the changes it undergoes in producing the final products. Figure 59 shows this alteration, from the solid rock below, containing fine cracks and fissures, to the much altered layer over it, called the "mantle rock." The lower part of the mantle rock consists of a much cracked and jointed rock which merges into an area containing a mixture of rock fragments and decomposed rock, known as the "subsoil." This also merges into the layer at the surface, called the "soil," which is one of the final products of the alteration of the rock. This process of breaking up a rock at the surface is called "weathering" because the chief factors in the alteration are the me-

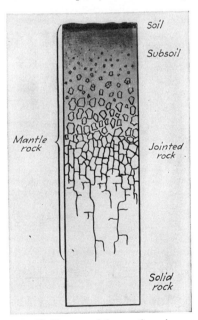

FIG. 59. Diagram of the mantle rock over an igneous rock.

chanical and chemical agents that are associated with the weather. "Weathering," as we shall use the term, includes the mechanical breaking up (disintegration) and the chemical alteration (decomposition) of the rocks. The *agents of weathering* may be classified, therefore, as *mechanical* and *chemical* agents. These agents differ widely in their ability to break up rocks, and individual agents are most effective under

59

different conditions. In some regions, mechanical agents are the more effective; in others, the chemical agents. Factors, such as the character of the vegetation, topography, and climate, are important in influencing the rate at which the agents accomplish their work.

MECHANICAL WEATHERING

The agents of mechanical weathering are *temperature changes and freezing water, growth of vegetation, work of animals,* and the *abrasive action*

FIG. 60. Slab of limestone split off face of bluff on Missouri River, Boone County, Missouri. (*Photograph by W. A. Tarr.*)

of wind, water, and ice. Of great importance in the work of the mechanical agents are the openings that already exist in the rocks: both those, such as cracks, fissures, and joints, that are due to earth movements; and any original openings, such as the holes caused by the expansion of gases and the minute openings between mineral grains. With these openings in the rock as a beginning or a starting point, the mechanical agents break up the solid rock into fragments ranging in size from enormous boulders to the finest dust. These fragments are as like the original rock in composition as they would be had the rock been put through a crusher. It will be readily seen how this production of rock fragments prepares the way for effective work by the agents of chemical weathering. Mechanical weathering is not finished, of course, before chemical weathering begins, the two processes usually going on simultaneously.

The Effects of Temperature and the Freezing of Water. Exposed rock surfaces expand when heated by the sun and contract when chilled by rain or cool night air. These slight volume changes are not effective in rock destruction unless wide expanses of rock are involved, whereupon the effect may be somewhat similar to the buckling or gaping which develops in a long section of pavement or sidewalk that is subjected to wide variations of temperature. However, even though the exposed rock surfaces are small, continued alternate expansion and contraction will widen the tiny cracks that already exist between the mineral grains of the rock.

If surface water enters the cracks or joints in a rock and freezing takes place subsequently, the pressure exerted by the ice on the walls of the cracks will aid materially in widening the cracks and so in finally disrupting the rock.   This pressure (150 to 200 pounds per square inch) exerted by the ice is due to the expansion (a one-tenth increase in volume) during the freezing process.   Figure 60 is a picture of a slab of rock (limestone) being split off a southwest-facing bluff along the Missouri River.   This disruption is due to a combination of causes, *i.e.*, jointing in the rock, effects of the freezing of water in the joint, and possibly some aid from

FIG. 61. (A) Angular boulders due to mechanical weathering, top of Pikes Peak, Colorado.   (B) Rounded boulders due to chemical weathering, at base of Pikes Peak.   (*Photograph by W. A. Tarr.*)

gravity.   On the tops of high mountains where freezing occurs frequently, great quantities of the angular fragments it helps to produce accumulate, as seen (Fig. 61A) on the top of Pikes Peak.

Effects of Other Mechanical Agents.   The *growth of roots* in cracks of rocks gradually splits them open and thus aids in their disintegration. *Burrowing of animals and the various activities of man* also aid in the disintegration of rocks.

By the ceaseless *abrasive action of the wind* (see Fig. 277, page 273), *water* (Fig. 62), *and ice* (Fig. 63), particles of rock are ground off.   These pieces are of various sizes but are, largely, fine material that may be readily attacked by the chemical agents of weathering.   The milky color of the streams flowing away from the end of a glacier is due to the large amount of ice-ground rock powder they contain.

Talus Deposits. At the foot of cliffs or other steep slopes where the bare rock is exposed, the fragments of rock that have been produced by the work of the various agents of mechanical weathering accumulate

FIG. 62. Abrasive action of running water on granite boulders, St. Francis River, Madison County, Missouri. (*Photograph by W. A. Tarr.*)

FIG. 63. Ice-abraded surface of a hard igneous rock, Gananoque, Ontario. (*Photograph by W. A. Tarr.*)

into what are known as *talus deposits* (Fig. 64) and *rock slides* (Fig. 65). The slope of the talus deposit is usually steep, and it is not only difficult but dangerous to ascend or walk across it. Freezing of water in cracks of the rocks is probably the most important single force in the creation of this talus material, because by the wedging action of the ice the fragments produced are loosened and pushed outward until gravity pulls them down. Not uncommonly, a large talus deposit or rock slide moves outward from the base of a cliff and may even flow down a valley, whereupon it is called a *rock stream* (see Fig. 149, page 149).

FIG. 64. Talus slope at foot of cliff which is part of a laccolith, Highwood Mountains, Montana. (*Photograph by W. A. Tarr.*)

FIG. 65. Rock slide in mountains above Ouray, Colorado. (*Photograph by W. A. Tarr.*)

CHEMICAL WEATHERING

The chief agents of chemical weathering are *water* and *air*. These agents attack the minerals of the original rock and change them into other minerals, and thus the composition of the rock is entirely changed. The chemical agents may attack and completely alter a rock before it is exposed at the surface, as water penetrates the crust to varying distances, sometimes hundreds of feet. The chief means of entrance to the rocks is furnished by the cracks and fissures that earth movements have developed.

Water is present in the air, from which it falls upon the earth's surface as rain (meteoric water). This water then drains off the surface into rivers or other bodies of water, or soaks into the soil and passes on downward into the rocks, or evaporates and goes back into the air. Though pure water is a solvent for many substances (for example, sugar and salt), the water as it falls through the air takes up small amounts of oxygen, carbon dioxide, and other gases, thereby increasing its solvent power. The air consists dominantly (four-fifths) of inert nitrogen; but it contains also nearly 21 per cent of oxygen, considerable amounts of certain inert gases, water vapor (in greatly varying quantities), carbon dioxide (3 parts in 10,000 by volume), and smaller quantities of sulfur dioxide, chlorine, ammonia, and even nitric acid. The air penetrates the openings and pores in the rocks at the surface and thus brings all its constituent substances into contact with the minerals of the rock. Also, after bringing these substances down to the surface, the rain water carries them underground, where they aid the water in its work. While it is bringing about alterations in the minerals of the rocks, the water acquires still other substances that increase its solvent power. It is especially apt to acquire sulfuric acid from the breaking up of minerals that contain sulfur, and it acquires organic acids from decaying organic matter on the surface. Water, however, is not dependent upon acids for its solvent power, as it is possible for pure water to effect the complete alteration of a rock.

The chemical effects of the air consist of the union of oxygen, carbon dioxide, and other gases with the substances in the rocks. The oxygen, especially in the presence of water, readily unites with the iron of iron-bearing minerals to form iron oxides. Iron rust is a familiar example of this change. Both oxygen and water are required in its formation, which takes place so rapidly that a clean piece of iron may become rust-covered in an hour or less. This change can be expressed as follows: 2 parts iron (Fe) unite with 3 parts oxygen (O) to form Fe_2O_3, which is hematite, red iron oxide. If the reaction takes place in the presence of water, limonite[1] ($Fe_2O_3.nH_2O$), yellowish-brown iron rust, is commonly formed. The conditions determining which one of the iron oxides will be formed are not fully understood. The union of oxygen with another substance is called *oxidation*, and its union with iron is the only such alteration of common occurrence in rocks. The carbon dioxide of the

---

[1] "Limonite" is the common name for the brown iron oxides, which are made up of the hydrated iron oxide minerals, goethite and lepidocrocite, which cannot be differentiated megascopically.

air does not readily unite with substances, but that contained in water (in carbonic acid, H_2CO_3) can combine with several elements. The process is called *carbonation.*

The most effective agent in rock decomposition is water, which may split apart the combination of elements in minerals (such as the feldspars and other silicates) and form entirely new compounds with the products of division. This process is called *hydrolysis.* It will be illustrated later in the discussion of clays. The union of water with a substance is called *hydration,* an example of which is the formation of limonite, given above. Water attacks the rocks upon the surface, of course, and also beneath it, as a part of the rainfall or *meteoric water* seeps downward and becomes ground water.

The water (whether pure or containing various solvents), upon moving downward and coming in contact with the minerals or particles of rocks, may alter them into new substances. The alteration may be slight or nonexistent, as in such minerals as quartz and muscovite; or it may be complete, as in feldspar and the mafic minerals. The finer the particles that were formed by the mechanical weathering of the rocks, the easier it is for the water and other chemical agents to alter them. Near the surface, therefore, where the fragments produced by mechanical weathering are finest, the chemical alteration is most rapid. The result of the attack by water is the formation of a group of more or less soluble compounds that are removed in solution and of a group of insoluble products that are left behind to form the dominant constituent of the soil and subsoil. Any insoluble impurities in a soluble mineral or rock are also left behind.

Character of the Changes Produced during Chemical Weathering

A very fundamental law, called the *law of stability,* controls the changes that occur in minerals at the surface. Simply stated, the law is as follows: *a mineral is stable* (*i.e.,* remains unchanged) *as long as it is surrounded by the same conditions as those under which it was formed.* Thus, feldspar is formed during the solidification of magma under conditions of high temperature and, if solidification takes place deep within the crust, of great pressure. Under the conditions of low temperature and pressure at the surface, the feldspar is no longer stable and so is readily attacked and altered by water and air. A corollary of the law of stability as applied to weathered products is that *the new minerals formed are stable at the surface.* This, we shall see, is true, and the new products that arise go into the formation of the dominant types of the secondary (sedimentary) rocks. We shall follow the changes that meteoric water produces in a rock as it works its way down through it.

The outermost zone of the earth is composed dominantly of granite, which was undoubtedly one of the most abundant rocks of the surface during the earth's early history and is at present one of the most common of the igneous rocks found there. We shall, therefore, choose it as the grained rock whose weathering we shall discuss first and in the most detail.

FIG. 66. Closely spaced joints in porphyry, Hogan, Missouri. (*Photograph by W. A. Tarr.*)

FIG. 67. Widely spaced joints in granite, Graniteville, Missouri. Ladders are 10 feet long. (*Photograph by W. A. Tarr.*)

Weathering of a Granite. An exposed granite surface is attacked by both water and air, and the alteration proceeds slowly downward. This downward progress is accelerated by the cracks and joints that have been developed in the rock by earth movements, as these openings permit the chemical agents to penetrate deep into the rock. Such cracks and joints may be small and closely spaced (Fig. 66) or large and widely spaced (Fig. 67). Figures 68 and 61B show the weathered forms produced in a granite that contained a system of closely spaced joints, and Fig. 69 shows a huge boulder weathered from a granite in which the joints

FIG. 68. Boulders developed by weathering along closely spaced joints, Graniteville, Missouri. (*Photograph by W. A. Tarr.*)

were widely spaced. These cracks and joints (supplemented by the further disintegration due to mechanical weathering) are essential in the process of chemical weathering, as granites (and most other igneous rocks) are impervious; and the penetration of water and air would be a

FIG. 69. Boulder (34 feet long) formed by weathering along widely spaced joints, Graniteville, Missouri. (*Photograph by W. A. Tarr.*)

slow process if confined to the openings inherent in the granite itself, *i.e.*, the minute openings between the grains of feldspar and quartz and those along the cleavage planes of the feldspar.

The Alteration of Orthoclase to Clay Minerals, Soluble Silica, and Potas-

sium. The first mineral attacked in granite is feldspar, because of the openings along its well-developed cleavage planes and its susceptibility to chemical reaction. The microscope has revealed the fact that the alteration of feldspar occurs along these cleavage planes on the interior of the mineral, the change to other substances being shown by a cloudy whiteness in the feldspar. It will be recalled that the feldspars (as a group) are potassium, sodium, calcium, and aluminum silicates. Orthoclase is the potassium feldspar and plagioclase the sodium-calcium feldspar. Orthoclase is altered chemically by water to some clay mineral (a hydrous aluminum silicate), soluble silica, and potassium compounds (Fig. 70).

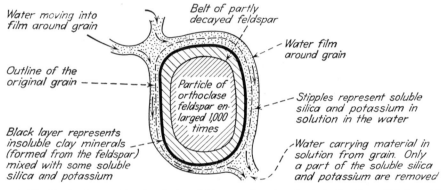

FIG. 70. Sketch of a particle of orthoclase feldspar undergoing chemical alteration. What would the water carry away if the mineral were plagioclase feldspar?

All the *clay minerals* are relatively insoluble and thus accumulate where they are formed. We have already noted that feldspar is the most abundant mineral in the outer part of the earth, and, since all the aluminum in the feldspar eventually passes into the clay minerals, these minerals are probably the most abundant and widespread minerals on the earth's surface. They are the dominant constituents of our soils and of most rocks called *clays* and *shales*. A pure white clay mineral, kaolinite, is the material used in making porcelain, chinaware, and pottery. It should be noted that the aluminum in any mineral, during weathering, usually goes into the formation of these clay minerals.

The silica freed from the feldspar during its decomposition is a soluble compound, and is thus very different from quartz (SiO_2), which is a crystalline mineral and very insoluble. *Soluble silica* is set free whenever any silicate breaks up chemically. It is liberated as minute, invisible particles that readily unite with water, and this ease of union aids the water in removing the silica particles from the mineral that is being altered. With the elimination of some of the water, this silica forms a gel. Although soluble, much of the silica remains behind in an intimate mixture with the clay minerals; therefore, owing to the water in the silica, the mantle rock and soils (as well as clays and shales) are rendered plastic or sticky.

The *potassium* upon release is usually sorbed by the other weathered products and so remains among the residual materials over a decaying rock. Thus, as potassium was always present in the soils, plants became adapted to its use, until it is now an essential plant food. The potassium could unite with carbon dioxide, but that it rarely does so is shown not only by its presence in the soils but also by the fact that streams contain only about one-fourth as much potassium as sodium, though the quantity of the two elements in the crust is nearly the same. Only about one-thirtieth as much potassium as sodium is found in the sea water. On the other hand, clays and shales contain more potassium than sodium.

The Alteration of Plagioclase into Clay Minerals, Soluble Silica, and Sodium and Calcium Compounds. If the granite contained plagioclase instead of orthoclase, the clay minerals and soluble silica would again be formed during the alteration; but, instead of potassium's being liberated, sodium and calcium would be set free through their reaction with water. The reaction (an example of hydrolysis) may be represented as follows:

Na-Ca aluminum silicate (plagioclase) $+$ HOH (water)
$\rightarrow$ H aluminum silicate (clay mineral)
$+$ Na and Ca compounds and silica in solution.

It is seen that the plagioclase undergoing weathering reacts with the water, whereby the aluminum silicate unites with the hydrogen (H) of the water to form an insoluble clay mineral. The sodium and calcium react with OH of the water and go into solution, as does part of the silica. The specific compounds formed by the sodium and calcium in solution are not designated in the above equation because they vary according to the other substances that are dissolved from the rocks and obtained from the air. For example, sodium chloride (table salt) and calcium sulfate (gypsum) are formed in the semiarid western United States, whereas the carbonates of calcium and sodium are more probable compounds in humid regions.

Students who have had chemistry will recognize that the sodium and calcium acquire electric charges upon going into solution and thus become ions that are stabilized by the hydroxyl (OH) of water, or by carbonate, sulfate, or chloride ions present in ground water. For students having little knowledge of chemistry, the end results may be summarized satisfactorily by saying that the calcium released during weathering is usually deposited as calcium carbonate ($CaCO_3$) in the ocean, where the sodium also accumulates—as sodium chloride ($NaCl$). The fact to remember is that calcium and sodium are set free in solution by the chemical weathering of any mineral containing them.

The Insolubility of Quartz. Quartz is relatively insoluble under all ordinary conditions; hence the main change it undergoes during the weathering of the granite is disintegration, the larger quartz grains becoming smaller particles. Quartz is the dominant mineral in sands and gravels.

The Alteration of Other Minerals in a Granite. Besides the essential constituents feldspar and quartz, granites not uncommonly contain *biotite, muscovite,* or *pyrite. Muscovite,* in the form of very fine scales, is a very stable mineral; it ranks next to quartz in that quality. As a result, it is an important constituent of some clays and shales, for the thin, flat muscovite flakes are easily carried away by streams or wind.

On the other hand, *biotite,* containing iron and magnesium, is even more readily altered than the feldspar. As a rule, any iron-bearing mineral is apt to alter easily, the iron uniting with oxygen to form the iron oxide, as shown on pages 64 and 74. Adding water to biotite causes it to change easily into brown biotite, then into a green, scaly mineral called *chlorite,* which finally alters to *iron oxides, clay minerals,* and *silica.* Biotite contains magnesium, which unites with water and carbon dioxide as readily as calcium does and goes away in solution, usually in association with carbonate. From biotite we get, therefore, two new alteration products in the decomposition of granite: the iron oxides, which are insoluble and remain in the soil, and magnesium carbonate ($MgCO_3$), which is removed.

Pyrite (FeS_2), a hard brass-yellow mineral (called "fool's gold"), is very common in small amounts in granites and many other rocks. This mineral alters to the *iron oxides,* freeing dilute sulfuric acid (H_2SO_4). The latter readily reacts with calcium, magnesium, potassium, or sodium to form soluble compounds that are easily removed in solution. These sulfate compounds, especially *magnesium sulfate* ($MgSO_4$) and *calcium sulfate* ($CaSO_4$), are in solution in the sea in large quantities.

Substances Added during the Alteration of Granite. It should be noted that in the alteration of the feldspar of the granite only *water* and *carbon dioxide* were added to form the new minerals. In the weathering of the iron-bearing minerals biotite and pyrite, *oxygen* was added to unite with the iron. The quantity of these three substances needed to alter a granite is well illustrated by the following example of the weathering of a granite (Fig. 71). This granite contained about 70 per cent of feldspar, 23 per cent of quartz, 5.7 per cent of biotite, and some clay minerals that had resulted from a minor amount of previous weathering. A study of the altered product of this granite by Leith and Mead[2] showed that there had been added to 100 grams of the original granite 6.03 grams of water, 2.74 grams of carbon dioxide, and 0.14 gram of oxygen, a total of 8.91 grams. As water furnished more than two-thirds of the new substances added, hydration was the dominant chemical change in the process.

The volume of the altered product resulting from the weathering of the granite greatly exceeded the volume of the original granite, and the quantity (8.91 grams or about 9 per cent of the volume of the unaltered granite) of the materials added does not account for all of this increase, which is 51 per cent (including the percentage increase due to the pore space produced). This unaccounted-for increase in volume is due to the

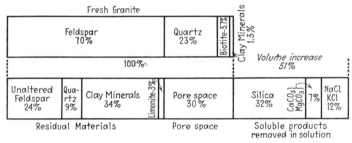

FIG. 71. Diagram showing the original mineral composition of a biotite granite from Georgia, and the alteration products due to weathering. Note presence of unaltered feldspar in residual (insoluble) materials, and pore space developed by leaching out soluble products. Note also volume increase due to formation of soluble products. (*Data from Leith and Mead, "Metamorphic Geology."*)

fact that the new minerals formed are greater in volume for the same weight of material than the original minerals of the granite. This expansion greatly aids in the disruption of the rock.

Altered Zone Produced in the Granite. The various changes we have been considering produce an altered zone on the surface of the granite (if exposed at the earth's surface) and extending inward from the cracks and joints. The thickness of this zone depends upon the depth to which the water and air can penetrate the granite, and this depth varies not only with the size and number of the cracks and fissures in the granite but also with the size of its grains, its porosity, and the accessory minerals it contains. The chemical changes taking place in this zone, aided mechanically by the freezing of water in openings, form a layer of altered rock that may disintegrate grain by grain, producing a roughened surface (Fig. 72). If the granite (or other grained rock or a dense rock) is exposed at the earth's surface, a shell may split off as a unit at the depth

[2] C. K. LEITH and W. J. MEAD, "Metamorphic Geology," 1915, p. 14 (Henry Holt and Company, New York).

of maximum alteration (A-B, Fig. 73). This process is called *exfoliation* (Figs. 73 and 74).

Summary. The alteration of a granite by chemical weathering proceeds as follows: (1) water (with or without carbon dioxide and oxygen) enters the rock along the crack and fissures produced by earth move-

FIG. 72. Granite mass showing roughened surface and widened joints, Independence Rock, Wyoming (*Courtesy of U.S. Geological Survey.*)

ments (and further developed by mechanical weathering) and penetrates, also, the minute spaces between and within the grains; and (2) the water reacts with the feldspar (and other minerals, except quartz) to form new alteration products, of which some are stable and insoluble (as the clay minerals) and some are soluble and are removed partially (as potassium and soluble silica) or entirely (as calcium and sodium carbonates). The

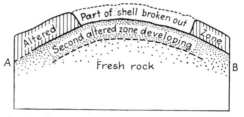

FIG. 73. Diagram showing development of chemically altered zone in outer part of a rock and formation of a shell that finally splits off (exfoliation).

new minerals formed have a larger volume per unit weight than the original ones had, and this fact is largely instrumental in causing the granite, before complete decomposition, to crumble into grains or scale off in shells (exfoliation).

Weathering of Diorite and Gabbro. Diorite and gabbro are the two most common grained igneous rocks next to granite. These rocks contain feldspar, but also one or both of the mafic minerals hornblende and pyroxene. The feldspars alter, of course, to the same minerals they produce in the weathering of granite, so we need only discuss now the weathering of the mafic minerals.

Hornblende and *pyroxene* are calcium, magnesium, iron, and aluminum silicates. The aluminum silicate goes into the formation of *clay minerals;* the iron unites with oxygen and water to form the two *iron oxides,* *hematite* and *limonite;* the *calcium* and *magnesium* are soluble, usually as *carbonates* or *sulfates;* and some *soluble silica* is liberated. The soluble

FIG. 74. Exfoliation of granite, near Virginia Dale, Wyoming. (*Photograph by W. D. Keller.*)

compounds, silica and the calcium and magnesium compounds, are removed in solution; and the clay minerals, stained red, yellow, or brown by the iron oxides, are left behind.

The soil over either a diorite or a gabbro consists dominantly of clay minerals, and hematite and limonite which give it various colors. It does not contain quartz, of course, and is a heavy soil. If much organic matter is present in these soils, it will mask the color of the iron oxides, and the soil will be gray or black, depending upon the amount of the iron oxides present. The topsoil, which contains the greater part of the organic matter, may be black, though the subsoil below is a deep red.

Response of the Common Elements of Igneous Rocks to Chemical Weathering. From the preceding examples of rock weathering, it is apparent that a particular chemical element responds in the same general way to chemical weathering regardless of the rock in which it occurs.[3] Therefore, we may clarify our study by grouping these responses in chart form. The generalizations given hold satisfactorily for weathering in a temperate climate in the presence of ordinary ground water containing oxygen and carbon dioxide. Under these conditions, the usual responses of the chemical elements are as follows:

RESPONSES OF CHEMICAL ELEMENTS DURING ROCK WEATHERING

Elements	Reacts with	Products	Properties of products
Iron (Fe)	Oxygen and water	Limonite	Yellow to brown hydrated iron oxide ($Fe_2O_3.nH_2O$). Insoluble
	Oxygen	Hematite	Red iron oxide (Fe_2O_3). Insoluble
$AlSiO_n$ group	Water	Clay mineral	White, $HAlSiO_n$. Insoluble
		Soluble silica	Silica in solution
SiO_2 (quartz)	Almost no reaction	Quartz	Quartz (SiO_2). Insoluble
Calcium (Ca)	Water and carbon dioxide	Calcium carbonate	Soluble in ground water (imparts hardness to water)
Magnesium (Mg)	Water and carbon dioxide	Magnesium carbonate	Soluble in ground water (imparts hardness to water)
Sodium (Na)	Water	Sodium compounds	Soluble in ground water
Potassium (K)	Water	Potassium compounds	Mostly sorbed by clay; some soluble ions
Sulfur (S)	Oxygen and water	Dilute sulfuric acid	Soluble in ground water

The insoluble products of weathering remain behind to form the soil (or some may be carried away in suspension), and the soluble materials go away in solution in spring and stream waters.

The application of the chart, just presented, may now be made in our consideration of the weathering of the dense and glassy rocks.

Weathering of Basalt, Felsite, and Obsidian. The texture of the dense and glassy rocks is too fine to permit a field identification of their

[3] This is true not only during the weathering of igneous rocks, but also during the weathering of the igneous-rock derivatives, *i.e.*, the sedimentary and metamorphic rocks, which we have not yet studied.

mineral constituents. It is known, however, from chemical analysis that these rocks contain the same elements (iron, magnesium, calcium, sodium, potassium, aluminum, silicon, and oxygen) that go into the composition of the grained rocks. By referring these elements to the above chart, it is readily seen that they produce during weathering the insoluble iron oxides and clay and soluble silica, magnesium, calcium, sodium, and potassium, which we have already seen are the weathered products of the grained rocks.

It has been shown by chemical analysis (and indicated in the igneous-rock table, page 51) that *basalt* is most nearly equal in composition to gabbro, so the products of its weathering will be the same as those of weathered gabbro. These may be any or all of the products given in the chart, with the exception of the insoluble quartz particles, as quartz is not present in these mafic rocks.

It has also been determined that *felsite* and *obsidian* are the chemical equivalents of a granite, so the weathered products of all three rocks would be the same. We have considered at great length the weathering of granite (the products of which may be any or all of those shown in the chart), so it will be sufficient here to point out the only way in which the products of weathered felsite and obsidian can differ from those of granite. This difference is that no quartz grains can result from the weathering of felsite and obsidian unless those rocks were porphyries containing quartz phenocrysts.

Summary. Igneous rocks weather chemically to a common group of a few relatively insoluble minerals and to other substances which are soluble in ground water. The soil-forming insoluble minerals are the clay minerals (which absorb potassium and soluble silica), iron oxides, and resistant quartz particles.[4]

Intermediate Alteration Products of Weathering. During the weathering of any igneous rock, several minerals or compounds, intermediate between the original and the final product, may form. The process of their formation is too complicated to be discussed here, but one or two of the commonest products may be mentioned.

There is good evidence for believing that a *fine-grained muscovite* may form during the alteration of orthoclase feldspar. As it is a very light, scaly mineral, it is easily removed from the soil by wind or running water. Both biotite and the mafic minerals may alter to *chlorite*, and this green mineral may be so abundant as to give the rock of which it is a constituent a green color.

---

[4] Since the soil-forming weathered products of the primary igneous rocks (and the sedimentary and metamorphic rocks derived from them) are so few in number, the same kind of grass, trees, or grain can, if climatic conditions are similar, grow without special adaptation anywhere on the earth—Colorado, the Ukraine, or Timbuktu!

The Stable and End Products of Weathering. As we have seen, clay minerals, quartz, and the iron oxides are the insoluble and relatively *stable products* of weathering formed under conditions of average rainfall and temperate climate. If the conditions of weathering are modified significantly, the stable products formed, especially the clay substances, will likewise be different. *Kaolinite* is the most commonly known clay mineral. It is formed under weathering conditions that ensure efficient removal of the soluble elements, such as Mg, Ca, and Na, by well-aerated (oxidizing) ground water. Kaolinite is the characteristic clay mineral of the soils occurring across the humid southern part of the United States.

FIG. 75. Bauxite from Arkansas.

Apparently, kaolinite is a stable product of weathering under those conditions.

In the drier, cooler climate of central and northern United States, a clay mineral of the *montmorillonite* family is commonly formed. Incomplete removal of magnesium during weathering favors the formation of montmorillonite, as do also poor oxidizing conditions. The chemical composition of montmorillonite is more complex and variable than that of kaolinite. Moreover, the montmorillonite clay minerals have a pronounced capacity for absorbing and releasing, *i.e.*, exchanging (ionic exchange) Ca, Mg, Na, K, and H, while kaolinite possesses this capacity in a much lower degree. By the exchange, montmorillonite acts as a medium of transfer for the plant nutrients (Ca, Mg, Na, K) from their rock sources to the growing plants. This property of ionic exchange is very important in agriculture.

In contrast to the conditions of montmorillonite formation, *bauxite* (Fig. 75) is formed in a humid, tropical climate and under a well-aerated drainage. Bauxite (an ore of aluminum) is hydrated aluminum oxide ($Al_2O_3.nH_2O$), which developed under conditions of such severe weathering that all the silica was removed from the original aluminum silicate. *Iron oxides* also persist under these conditions of weathering and give a red color to the residue. This reddish mixture of hydrated iron and aluminum oxides, together with variable amounts of silica, is called *laterite* and characterizes the soils of tropical, wet regions. Laterite has very low ion-exchange capacity (lower even than that of kaolinite). These oxides are stable under the weathering conditions just described and have long been called the *end products* of weathering. However, their designation as "end products" may prove to be misleading because recent evidence has indicated that silica may recombine with bauxite (hydrous aluminum oxide) to form kaolinite. Therefore, it is better to regard each of the different clay minerals and the iron and aluminum oxides as relatively stable indicators of the particular environment of their formation.

The Influence of the Products of Weathering on Mankind. Aside from the geologic significance of the processes of weathering which we have described, it is of interest to consider also the agricultural, nutritional, and even sociological implications. As we have previously pointed out, the processes of weathering in a region of cool temperature and moderate rainfall produce the clay minerals of the montmorillonite group, which possess relatively high ability (through ionic exchange) to transfer to plants inorganic nutrients (such as calcium and magnesium) that are needed in the production of protein foods. High-protein foods are necessary to people for full growth, endurance, vigor, and virility, and the possession of these characteristics by the inhabitants of temperate regions is traceable in a marked degree to their adequate diet.

As we have previously noted also, in regions where high temperatures and abundant rainfall combine to promote drastic weathering (commonly in the tropics), lateritic materials with their low ion-exchange ability predominate. Therefore, the inorganic nutrients needed for the production of protein foods are supplied in such small amounts that a dearth of protein results.[5] The characteristic and well-known "lush" vegetation of the tropics furnishes chiefly sugar, starches, oils, and fiber (such as cotton and timber). Therefore, the diet of the inhabitant who subsists chiefly upon the native foods of such a region is typically low, and may be

[5] Means of augmenting the scanty delivery of plant nutrients by the soil clays are being tested by agriculturists. The use of organic matter grown, *in situ*, and plowed under and the carefully controlled application of inorganic fertilizers are proving successful.

deficient, in protein.   The strength, productivity, and stamina of such a person are at once retarded by inadequate nutrition, in comparison with the experience of his better fed neighbors of cooler, drier regions.   However, in warm but more arid regions, weathering will not be so drastic and the food nutrients may, therefore, be salvaged from the rocks and go

into the production of protein foods. We know that great civilizations have developed in such areas.   Moreover, a high production of protein foods is possible even under conditions of high temperature and heavy rainfall if the region is underlaid by a rock that is notably rich in food-producing nutrients.   Such a region, at present, is Java, which is covered by a geologically recent volcanic ash, rich in inorganic plant nutrients.   Java is densely populated by a vigorous people, in contrast to adjacent areas where the rocks contain the food nutrients in lesser amounts.

FIG. 76. Channel of stream produced by the rapid weathering of a basalt dike, Madison County, Missouri. (*Photograph by W. A. Tarr.*)

We certainly do not mean to imply that man is a product only of what he eats, yet a careful consideration of the above facts and generalizations will surely show that the chemical weathering of rocks has import far beyond an exercise in introductory geology.

Rate of Weathering.   The decomposition of a rock is a slow, complex, and variable process, and depends upon many factors, such as mineral and chemical composition, texture, mode of occurrence, and the climate of the region in which the rock is exposed.   Some portions of a rock may be more readily attacked by the agents of weathering than other portions a few inches or a few feet away.   This might be due to a greater solubility of that portion, to the presence of minerals that decompose easily (like iron-bearing minerals), or to the presence of a mineral (like pyrite) whose decomposition would liberate a strong acid (sulfuric) that would dissolve the other minerals.

The igneous rocks weather very slowly; a lava flow, hundreds of years old, may show very little change on the surface.   Many hard igneous rocks that were worn smooth by glaciers show little evidence of weathering since the retreat of the ice, which was many thousands of years ago. As igneous rocks are also very resistant to cracking and jointing, this scarcity of openings helps to make their weathering slow.   In general, dark-colored rocks weather faster than light-colored rocks. Dikes of basalt may weather faster than the rocks around them and when the materials are carried away, form depressions (Fig. 76); though this is usually not the case, for they commonly weather more slowly and so stand out as ridges or walls (see Figs. 12, page 18, and 13, page 19).

No time value can be assigned to the rate of weathering; observations made on rocks used in buildings show a wide range. A rock that undergoes a rapid change in a moist climate will last many times as long in a dry climate. The Egyptian obelisk in Central Park, New York City, had stood unaltered in Egypt for 33 centuries, but began to show signs of decay within a few years after being brought to this country in 1881. Monumental stones in cemeteries also furnish clues to the rate of weathering.

ECONOMIC IMPORTANCE OF WEATHERING

It can be safely stated that the process of weathering is of more importance to man than any other of the geologic processes, for it produces the *soil*, upon the products of which man is absolutely dependent for his existence. The story of weathering in relation to soil has been developed above. This process is slow, but it is continuous. All rocks eventually break down and contribute material to the soil. However, the rate of erosion in a given area may be so rapid as to remove the weathered materials as fast as they form and thus leave the unaltered rock bare.

Because soil formation is a slow process and erosion a much faster one, man must conserve the soil and endeavor to stop its erosion. As long as a field has a covering of grass or trees, soil erosion is slow; but cultivated fields are exposed to excessive wash after heavy rains, and thus it is necessary to terrace sloping fields and otherwise to use care in farming. The gullies, widely prevalent in fields in this country, testify to a lack of such care and the consequent great damage being done to farm land. Muddy and overloaded streams and rivers tell the same story.

Weathering processes are of further economic benefit to man, as they aid in bringing about a concentration of valuable minerals, such as *gold*, *platinum*, and *gems*, by breaking up the rocks enclosing them. These minerals are insoluble and are heavier than the minerals associated with them. As a result, they can easily be concentrated by the removal of the other substances. Rarely, the wind may do this, whereupon the concentrated product is known as a *wind placer*. The only wind placers of importance are found in Australia. Streams readily sort the materials that find their way into them and concentrate the heavy minerals along the bottom of the channels. Thus a stream in crossing a gold-quartz vein collects the freed gold in the channel, forming a gold placer. Sands and gravels have been found that contained $200 or $300 worth of gold in one quart of sand, but such placers are rare.

Another result of weathering of economic value is the formation of *enriched copper deposits*. If a rock containing a small amount of copper is exposed at the surface, water may dissolve the copper, carry it downward, and redeposit it in a much smaller space. For example, small amounts of copper contained in a thickness of 100 feet of rock form a much richer deposit when redeposited below in a thickness of 10 feet.

SUMMARY

Weathering is the process by which rocks are altered through mechanical and chemical means. Any igneous rock may break down and, in so doing, form both soluble and insoluble compounds. The soluble compounds are removed by ground water, and the insoluble compounds are left behind to form the soil. If the weathering of the rock keeps pace with the removal of the soil, a soil is maintained; if not, the bare rock is exposed.

The composition of the mantle rock and soil is dependent upon the character of the underlying rock, but essentially all soils contain, in different proportions, the insoluble products of weathering: clay minerals, quartz, and the iron oxides, together with soluble silica and potassium. If intense chemical weathering can continue uninterrupted by erosion, the most insoluble products formed from rocks, *i.e.*, iron and aluminum oxides, are the result.

We are next to consider the removal of the products of weathering by the different agents and then their deposition as the sedimentary rocks.

CHAPTER 5

INTRODUCTION TO THE PHYSICAL AGENTS

Our study of the earth thus far has dealt only with its composition. We have seen that the outer part is composed dominantly of igneous rocks, and that as soon as these rocks are exposed to the climatic conditions existing at the surface they undergo an alteration by which they are converted into a group of materials that are stable at the surface. We have seen, also, that these alteration products formed by weathering consist of both soluble and insoluble materials, and that the insoluble materials form the mantle rock, which is a loose, porous aggregate of minerals and rocks easily removed by any agent.

The next subject in our study is these agents of removal. They are called *physical agents* because their work is accomplished by mechanical and chemical means, which are physical processes. If it were not for these agents, the surface of the earth would become covered with a mantle of loose rock. But variations in the temperature and composition of the atmosphere, coupled with the distribution of land and water and of mountains and plains, produce winds and rainfall, which are the source of all the physical agents.

In order to accomplish work, the physical agents must be in motion, and the greater their velocity the greater their ability to do work. Motionless air would not move the finest particle of dust, and motionless water would not carry the finest particle of mud. Quiet water might take material into solution, but it would soon become saturated and unable to dissolve more material, and so even its chemical action would cease. But, as we have said, variations in temperature of the air cause winds, and, given a sufficient velocity, wind will sweep a land surface bare. A stream of water having great velocity will also sweep away man-made structures and boulders of enormous size. If water that is dissolving substances in the rocks keeps moving, immense caverns will in time be formed.

The *wind* not only accomplishes much work (*i.e.*, removes much material) itself but it is the indirect agent in accomplishing much more, as it carries moisture-laden air everywhere. The rain formed from this moisture is the source of two great modifying agents: part of the rain runs off over the surface and becomes the *streams*, which are the most important physical agents in shaping the surface features of the land; another part passes beneath the surface to become the *ground water*, which also accomplishes a tremendous amount of work.   The streams do their work dominantly by mechanical means, and the ground water dominantly by chemical means.   Another of the great physical agents is the *ocean*, which is the accumulation of the water of the earth's surface in the low places.   Although not so effective an agent in shifting material as the streams, the ocean performs a share of the physical work of shaping the earth's surface.   Lastly, rain water in the form of ice, *i.e.*, as *glaciers*, may also become a great eroding agent.

These physical agents, wind, streams, ground water, the ocean, and glaciers, we have said, perform *work*, which we understand to be the removal of the material of the earth.   We may well ask what the end or object of all this work is, and the answer is that it is *to reduce the land to the level of the sea*.   When these agents have accomplished this end (they never have and probably never will, because of factors operating on the interior of the earth), and water thus covers the surface of the earth, the rainfall, snowfall, ground water, waves, and wind will be useless. The wind might create waves, but they would roll ceaselessly and uselessly around the world.   The work of the physical agents would be over.

The common objective of all these agents, however, as long as there is land, is to attack it and cut it down.   In the accomplishment of this purpose, there are three steps which all of the agents follow: (1) removing the material, (2) carrying it elsewhere, and (3) depositing it.   Removal of material the agents accomplish in two ways, *i.e.*, *mechanically* and *chemically*.   Bits of rock are loosened mechanically by abrasion, or wearing away, just as a metal is worn away by passing a file over it. Chemically, the rock is attacked by being dissolved by the agent of removal.   Streams, waves, wind, and ice, *i.e.*, all the surface agents, are constantly abrading the rocks; and, below the surface, ground water is just as steadily dissolving them.   Each of these agents is a moving agent; and thus the second step in the process is accomplished, for, as the agent moves on, it carries with it the material that has been loosened from the rocks.   The transportation by the surface agents is usually downward toward the lowest points of the surface.   These two phases of the work of any of the agents, *i.e.*, the removal and transportation of material, are commonly called *erosion*.   Finally, on account of a decrease in the velocity, the load of solid material is deposited; and the materials carried in solution are deposited by chemical means in the oceans and lakes and, from ground water, in openings in the rocks and soil.

These agents are forever at work.   They vary in effectiveness from time to time, and they differ from one another.   The deposits formed are temporary, until deposition finally takes place in the ocean.   The quantity of earth materials emptied into the sea is enormous.   Clarke has estimated that the amount of material annually carried to the sea in solution by the streams is 2,491,585,000 tons, or an average of 62.3 tons from each square mile of the 40,000,000 square miles on the earth's land surface. The quantity of material carried mechanically each year by the streams he has estimated at 16,000,000,000 tons, or 400 tons per square mile of the earth's land surface.   Other agents besides the streams are also contributing material to the sea, though in minor quantities.

With this brief introduction to the study of the physical agents that are engaged in a ceaseless struggle to reduce the land surface to the level of the sea, we shall turn to the detailed study of each.   We shall study first the streams and next the ground water, as these two agents furnish most of the materials for deposition in the ocean.   We shall then study the ocean, as the place of deposition, and the deposits formed there, i.e., the sedimentary rocks.   As the features formed by wind and ice are transitory forms that may be produced on any land surface, we shall study them after we have finished our study of the rocks.

CHAPTER 6

RUNNING WATER

Running water is the most important agent in shaping the land surfaces of the earth and in carrying and depositing materials. This fact is not readily apparent, because the changes are slow and unspectacular. The principal factors which govern the speed of geologic work are the quantity of water and the rate of its flow.

The primary source of running water is rainfall. Rainfall is unequally distributed in the various zones of climate of the earth. The Atacama Desert in Chile receives a shower once in several years, while at the other extreme, places in India have an average annual rainfall of nearly 500

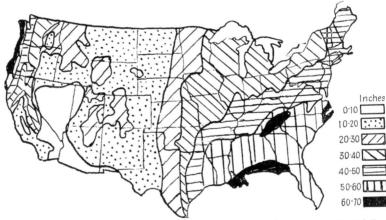

FIG. 77. Outline map of the United States, showing distribution of mean annual rainfall. (*After Fuller. Courtesy of U.S. Geological Survey.*)

inches. Within the United States the range in average annual rainfall is from under 10 to over 70 inches (Fig. 77). Rain water on the surface evaporates, sinks into the soil, or runs off on the land surface.

Run-off and Factors upon Which It Depends. The water which runs off is the most readily observed part of the rainfall, and the proportion which becomes run-off depends upon several factors. The most important of these is the *slope of the land* on which the water falls. If the slope is steep, nearly all the water runs off.   In steep mountain regions, 80 per cent of the rainfall may run off, whereas in relatively level regions, the run-off may be less than 1 per cent, with the amount of rainfall the same in both cases.

The *rate of rainfall* is of great importance in determining the amount of run-off.   Farmers call the heavy, dashing rains "gully washers," as the run-off is so great that gullies are created in the fields.   From a rainfall of 2 inches in an hour on wet land most of the water will run off, whereas if 2 inches fall in a day on dry land, most of the water will sink in.   Some regions have insufficient moisture for crop growing because the rain comes in heavy downpours of a few minutes' duration and the run-off is proportionately great.

The *condition of the mantle rock* influences run-off.   If it is loose and deep, a great deal more water will sink in than if it is compact.   If the mantle rock is clay, most of the water will run off, but if it is sand and gravel, most of the water will sink in.

Vegetation is another factor on which the run-off depends.   Run-off is much greater in regions of sparse vegetation than in forested or heavily grassed regions.   Detimbered regions, overgrazed areas, and steep cultivated fields are readily gullied.

Annual distribution of rainfall is also important in determining run-off. In some regions the rainfall comes well distributed through the year, about as much one month as another, but other regions have dry seasons and wet seasons.   The western part of Central America has about 5 months with no rainfall and 3 or 4 months with heavy rainfall, and the run-off is much greater than it is in areas where the rainfall is evenly distributed throughout the year.   In dry regions rain may evaporate almost as fast as it falls.

Water that runs off the land collects into streamlets, and the streamlets join to form larger and larger streams.   The most important and constant source of stream water is rainfall that sinks into the ground and returns to the surface as springs or seeps along valley courses.

Streams Form Their Valleys.   People who have no knowledge of geology frequently raise the question of how valleys and hills were formed. Some take it for granted that they have always existed where they are at present, and others think the earth must have cracked open to form the valleys.

Everyone has observed that stream waters are muddy in times of flood and that they are likely to be clear at times of low water.   One can readily find out what makes the water muddy by dipping up some of it and letting it stand.   Sand and clay settle to the bottom, and the water becomes clear.   One-third of the volume of very turbid streams may be made up of sand and clay.   Streams carry away large amounts of sediment during their flood times. Every average year the Mississippi River carries enough sand and clay to cover a square mile of land surface to a depth of 268 feet. If the Mississippi River worked 100,000 years at the same rate and confined its work to an area 5 miles wide and 5,280 miles long, it would excavate a valley 200 feet deep. If the amount of sediment carried by the river were taken in equal amounts from all parts of the Mississippi basin, the land would be lowered about one foot every 5,000 years.

Farmers are troubled by gullies that form in their fields during heavy rainfall. They know that these gullies get wider, deeper, and longer, and that in time they will cut the fields into separate units and become so deep that they cannot be crossed with teams or tractors.

It has been observed that a stream breaking loose from its channel and flowing across a valleyless region very quickly forms a trench big enough to contain its waters, *i.e.*, it digs itself a new channel. A conspicuous example of this was the work of the Colorado River in southern California when it broke away from its bed and flowed westward to the Salton Sea. It formed a new valley several hundred feet wide and several feet deep within a few days.

Such examples as those mentioned above indicate that streams form the valleys in which they flow, and geologists accept that as a general principle.

Streams Fit Their Valleys. In many ways streams fit the valleys in which they flow, but valleys vary greatly in their relationships to their streams and to their surroundings. Streams of the same size may have deep narrow valleys, shallow narrow valleys, deep wide valleys, shallow wide valleys, or any intermediate grades. That the size and shape of valleys do not depend entirely on the size of the streams that made them is as obvious as that the size of an excavation does not depend entirely on the size of the group of men that digs it. Following out the analogy between the digging of an excavation and the making of a valley, the next controlling factor is the length of time consumed in the work. Obviously the longer a stream works in a valley, the larger the valley will become. If a stream is given opportunity to start a valley on a new land surface, it will first excavate a trench just large enough to contain the normal flow. This would be the case, for example, if the Atlantic Ocean retreated so that the Hudson River had to cross the emergent ocean bottom.

How Streams Attain Their Courses. *Extended Consequent Streams.* When one becomes convinced that streams make their valleys, the question arises as to how they happen to take their courses. If the Atlantic Ocean margin should move eastward 100 miles from the east coast of the United States, a rather uniform plain—the old sea bottom—would become land, and every stream now flowing into the Atlantic would have to develop a valley across this land (see Fig. 78 as an example of such a sea withdrawal). Many streams emptying into the Atlantic along this coast are of large volume; and, if the sea should retreat 100 feet or 1 mile or more per day, the streams would not be left behind, but each would follow down the steepest slope of the new land and dig for itself a new valley. (This assumes that the newly formed land would be made of unconsolidated sand and clay, an almost universal condition.)

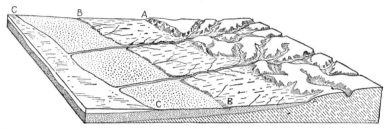

FIG. 78. Extended consequent streams. The sea cliffs and a beach were formed when the sea margin was at A-A. The sea withdrew to B-B and the streams extended their courses across the newly emerged sea bottom. A second withdrawal of the sea margin to C-C caused the streams to extend their courses again.

If you can picture for yourself the emerging sea bottom of mud flats, the edge of the sea moving away from the land about 100 feet per day, and a large river flowing into the sea and keeping its channel across the newly emergent land, you will get an idea of how the courses of most large rivers were attained. In 10 years the sea margin would have retreated about 70 miles and laid bare 70 miles of mud flats. The river would have taken a nearly straight course across this 70 miles; and if the gradient were low the valley across the mud flat would be just big enough to contain the normal stream water. Flood waters would probably overflow and spread out over the surrounding flats. Every big stream would have such a valley across the newly emergent land.

The Red River of the North took its course in the wake of a retreating margin of a lake, and other streams emptying into the lake from the south took their courses nearly parallel to the Red River. Figure 79 shows the course of the Red River, as well as the margin of the old lake. Within relatively recent times, Lake Erie has withdrawn several miles from its old southern shore; and the streams entering it from the south are examples, on a small scale, of *extended consequents*. Maps of the region show the nearly parallel streams flowing across the old lake bottom.

Consequent Valleys. Many streams, but not the large ones, take their courses in consequence of the topography rather than as extended consequents. Picture again the newly emergent mud flats of the old ocean bottom between the large extended consequents. These flats

would slope gently seaward, in the main, but would have no drainage
channels.   When rain fell on them, the water would run off through the
lowest places and soon form gullies that would end in the main valleys
or in the sea margin.   The course that the water would take would
depend upon the slopes, and the result would be *consequent valleys*.   If
the rainfall were heavy, the gullies would form rapidly and furnish drainage channels for the entire area, but if the rainfall were light, it would

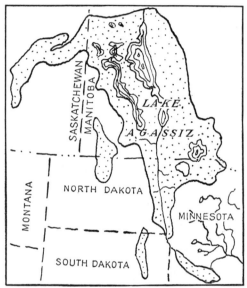

FIG. 79. Map of a lake which existed about 20,000 years ago.   As it shrank to the present smaller
lakes, the Red River of the North formed an extended consequent valley.   (*After Upham.   Courtesy
of U.S. Geological Survey.*)

take a long time to form gullies for all of the area.   There would be many
little streams, but they would join to form larger streams in their lower
courses.

The two main ways in which streams attain their courses are, therefore, "extended consequents" for big streams, and ordinary "consequents" for the smaller streams; but other ways of valley development
deserve mention.   At some places the earth has warped down so as to
create depressions, and these have become stream valleys.   The Great
Valley of California, through which the Sacramento River runs, had such
an origin.   Along large fissures in the earth, movement has taken place,
one side going up relative to the other, and this has created stream
courses.   Long blocks of the earth have settled down between two
fissures and created valleys; the Red Sea is in a depression of this type.
Man has acquired the habit of making valleys: the smaller ones as irri-

gation ditches, the larger as canals. In some cases an irrigation ditch has drained the stream from which the water came and has become the main stream.

VALLEY DEVELOPMENT

The Infant Valley. Imagine a nearly smooth area of gentle slope. At the upper edge a large hydrant is opened and the water allowed to take

FIG. 80. Consequent gullies on a newly graded slope. (*Courtesy of Agricultural Experiment Station, University of Missouri.*)

its own course. The course would be determined by the shape of the land surface, *i.e.*, the direction of flow would be a *consequence* of the original slopes (Fig. 80). Over a surface with only slight irregularities the course would be in a nearly straight line down the steepest slope. If the surface rocks were sand and clay, the water would soon remove enough material to form a channel or valley large enough to accommodate it. The valley would be very steep sided and narrow, only a little wider than the stream (Fig. 81).

Meanders Develop. Though the valley had a nearly straight course, it would be impossible for the stream to maintain a straight current.

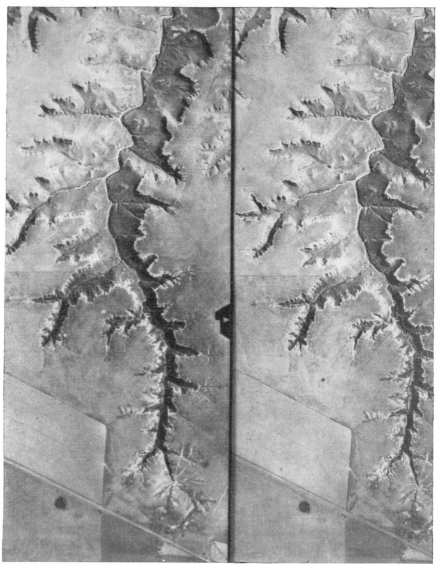

FIG. 81. Young stream in the Great Plains developing by headward erosion. (This is a stereoscopic pair. Look between the two pictures and stare through them into the distance. When the line of sight of your two eyes is parallel, the picture will be seen in three dimensions.) (*Courtesy of U.S. Department of Commerce, Civil Aeronautics Administration.*)

Winds would create crosscurrents, materials would slump in from the sides and divert the current, and various other things would tend to make the current irregular. A current once diverted would strike one of the banks and be deflected from that bank to the other, and thus would begin a zigzag movement down the valley. Where the water struck the bank, it would remove some of the materials and take them as part of its load. Between such points, the velocity of the water would be reduced,

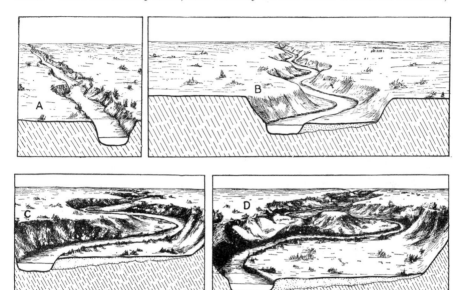

FIG. 82. Development of a valley from a gully to the stage at which it has a distinct stream flat. Figure D shows a later stage in which there are unusual conditions leading to the formation of an isolated hill. All stages are young.

and some deposition would take place. The stream would begin to cut into the bank on one side and deposit on the other, and would finally create subsymmetrical curves called *meanders*. Where it cut into the bank, it would widen the valley, but as it deposited on the other side it would tend to keep the original width of its channel.

Flats Form in the Valley. The top of the deposits made by a stream on the inside of meanders reaches about the level of the top of the stream water and is, therefore, below the general level of the region. By building on the inside of meanders, the stream creates flats within the valley that it forms (Figs. 82 and 83). As it continues to cut on the outer side of the meander and to build on the inner, the flat within the valley widens as fast as the valley itself does.

Streams Straighten and Then Develop New Meanders. Gradually, as the stream course changes from straight to gently curving to large

curves, the valley changes from narrow to wide. But all widening does
not take place with the development of one series of meanders. When
the meanders reach the stage in which the loop of one nearly touches the
loop of another, the stream straightens itself by cutting away the land
between the loops (see Fig. 85, page 94). During floods the entire width
of the valley may be occupied by water, and the current may take a rather
direct course across the neck of one of the meanders, where it may cut a
channel. During low water the stream would follow the course through
the short channel rather than around the long bend and for some distance
would resume its original condition of straightness.

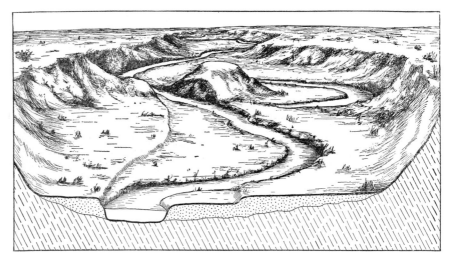

FIG. 83. Development of flats and an isolated hill at a later stage than Fig. 82D.

In its straight new course the stream again begins to meander and
first cuts into its own flood-plain deposits, *i.e.*, the deposits that it formed
as it created the earlier meanders. The outer part of a meander may
finally reach the valley wall and again begin the process of widening the
entire valley (Fig. 84 at B).

The Meander Cycle. It is not likely that the completion of a cycle
of meanders[1] would lower the bottoms of large valleys by as much as
an inch, and the deepening of a valley like that of the Mississippi to some
400 feet below the original level would take, at that rate, 4,800 cycles of
meanders. The greater the velocity of a stream, the greater the amount
of downcutting during each meander cycle.

The completion of the cycle of meanders is much more complex than
would appear from the above discussion. Actually, the stream is likely

---

[1] A cycle of meanders is the development from a straight course, through a complete
series of meanders, to a straight course again.

to cut off not more than 1 meander in 1,000 at the time of any one flood, and the cycle is completed for one meander long before it is completed for others. In one area three or four cycles of meander development may have been completed before one is completed in another.

Meanders Move Downstream. Meanders move slowly downstream and in course of time one (Fig. 84A) may reach the position that the adjacent downstream meander formerly occupied (Fig. 84B). While the stream is cutting against the outer wall of the valley, it keeps the side vertical or nearly so; but as soon as it moves away, weathering processes and slope wash reduce the slope. However, the next bend upstream keeps moving down and finally comes to occupy the place of the next

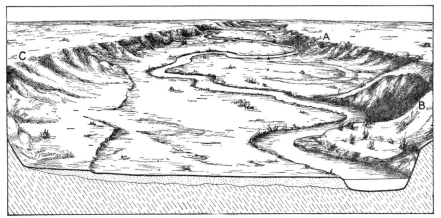

FIG. 84. A valley in early maturity, a later stage than that shown in Fig. 83.

lower bend, the stream again begins to cut at the place where the gentle slope had been created and may cut far enough to make that side of the valley vertical again. In this stage of valley development there are alternate vertical and gentle slopes at the same location in the valley and one side of the valley may be steep while the other is gentle (Fig. 84 at C and B). As the valley becomes wider and wider, a time comes when the outer parts of some bends do not touch the valley sides. The meander, in moving downstream, does not come against the valley side of the next lower meander; and the slope that has had time to be reduced to gentleness since the meander left it is not touched by the next meander that moves downstream and therefore goes on becoming gentler and gentler during another cycle of meander movement. As the valley widens still more, fewer meanders touch the outer side and more of the sides acquire gentle slopes. The valley bottom finally reaches about the maximum width of the meander belt, a stage illustrated in Fig. 84.

Shifting of Meander Belt. The meander belt is the area between imaginary lines drawn on either side of a valley connecting the extreme outer parts of a series of meanders. The shifting of the entire meander belt now enters into the valley-widening process. As the meander belt shifts in the valley, it widens on one side by the outer sides of some meanders touching the extreme outer part of the valley. The belt may later shift to the other side of the valley and by changing back and forth many times makes the valley much wider than the belt. The widening would be checked only by the meanders' cutting away the divide between their valley and an adjoining valley (Fig. 85).

FIG. 85. Two streams with wide valleys which have nearly removed the divide between them. The dashed lines indicate the width of the meander belt.

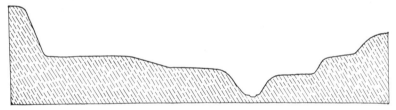

FIG. 86. A cross-section of the Grand Canyon of the Colorado River in Arizona where it is 9 miles wide and 5,000 feet deep.

In Fig. 109, page 116, the stream occupies the left side of the valley, and the entire valley is three or four times as wide as the meander belt. The widening taking place by meander-belt shifting is much slower than in the earlier stages. The valley of the Mississippi River south of Cairo, Illinois, is more than 60 miles wide, and the meander belt is less than 10 miles wide. Many of the larger rivers of the world have reached this stage, but many others have not. The Amazon is an example of this stage of valley development, the Colorado of a stage preceding meander-belt shifting.

Examples of Valley Development. The Colorado River is a swift stream, and such streams deepen their valleys much more rapidly in proportion to widening than do slow streams. In the Grand Canyon part of the Colorado, the valley is 8 to 10 miles wide and about 1 mile deep (Fig. 86). The Missouri River Valley east of Kansas City is 8 to 10 miles wide and about 250 feet deep (Fig. 87). The downcutting compared with side cutting in the one case has been ten times as rapid as in the other. This has not been due in any sense to difference in hardness of the bedrock, as the Colorado has cut through harder rock than the Missouri. One may wonder about the future development of the Colorado Valley. The river is swift and will continue to deepen its valley rapidly in proportion to widening it for a long period, but gradually the lateral cutting will increase in importance and downcutting will be slow enough to allow large flats to form. The later history of the valley should differ from that of other valleys only in the great depth that the valley will retain for a length of time long enough to cover the entire history of most rivers. In order to attain the lowest possible grade to sea level, the river must loosen and carry away some 10 times the volume of material

FIG. 87. A cross-section of the valley of the Mississippi River near Cairo where it is 9 miles wide and 400 feet deep.

that the Missouri must carry away to attain that grade. On account of aridity the rate of weathering is much slower than in the Missouri Valley, and most of the loosening of the rock materials will be done by the stream itself. It will require tens of millions of years to bring the Colorado Valley to the stage of the Missouri Valley.

Widening of Stream Valleys. The widening of the valley depends on the size of the stream, in some degree, but a small stream may create a wide valley. Increase in width of a valley may not mean that the stream is growing in size. Streams may increase in size by capturing other drainage, but they may become smaller by having their own drainage captured and from various other causes. A common misconception is that the streams that formerly occupied valleys must have been much larger than they are now, as the valleys are so much larger than the streams.

Valleys Widen at the Top. In discussing the widening of valleys at the bottom by lateral cutting, widening at the top has been mentioned only incidentally. The steep sides of valleys produced by side cutting of streams gradually become gentle after the stream stops cutting against the sides. Weathering along the top of the valley sides loosens the more prominent parts; they fall to the bottom; gradually the slope is reduced and the angle at the base of the cliff is filled up. Water falling near the valley margin runs over the edge as slope wash and carries with it loose materials that lie on or near the edge. These materials are in turn dropped at the base of the cliff and help to reduce the slope. Gradually the slope decreases, and if the stream does not return to its base, reduction continues until the velocity of the water can no longer carry materials down the slope. The reduction of the slopes of the valley sides is slow, but nearly every valley furnishes numerous examples of steep slopes where the stream is cutting against the bank and gentler slopes where no lateral cutting has taken place for a long time (Fig. 84). Along the Mississippi River one may go directly down the valley slope

FIG. 88. A meandering stream with meander belt widening the valley. (*Photograph by the Royal Canadian Air Force.*)

without encountering a perceptible grade on one side, cross 5 miles of flat, and on the other side find almost vertical bluffs more than 100 feet high. By the time a valley reaches a width three or four times that of the meander belt, nearly all side slopes are gentle and finally there is no perceptible change in slope between upland and valley bottom.

Tributaries Make Flats. Tributaries work in the same way as the main streams and cut flats continuous with the flats of the main valley. The slopes between the tributaries will have become very gentle by the time the valleys are wide, and the entire region may become reduced to stream flats with low divides between them and all of the slopes toward streams.

Other Factors Influencing Valley Development. The development of valleys depends upon several factors not mentioned in the preceding discussion. The rate at which a stream corrades or removes materials

FIG. 89. Big Thompson Canyon, Colorado. A steep-walled canyon cut through steeply inclined sedimentary and metamorphic rocks. (*From Emmons, Thiel, Stauffer, and Allison, "Geology," courtesy of Denver Tourist Bureau.*)

from its bottom and sides varies as the square of the *velocity*. (To corrade is to loosen by friction.) If one stream has twice the velocity of another, it will corrade four times as fast. A given object will be struck twice as hard by a unit amount of water, doubling the wear; but twice as much water will strike it in a given time, again doubling the amount of wear. In swift streams the currents are diverted less easily than in slow streams, and on that account meanders are likely to develop less rapidly and to be smaller. As the widening of the bottoms of valleys is accomplished almost entirely by meanders, swift streams have narrower valleys than slow ones of the same size. Figure 88 illustrates valley development by a slow stream, and the Big Thompson River (Fig. 89) illustrates valley development by a rapid stream.

The rate of corrasion by streams depends, in part, upon the *amount of material carried* by them. Waters that carry no sediment do little or no wearing. The Niagara River, with great volume and velocity, does little corrading above the falls. The greater the load of sediment carried

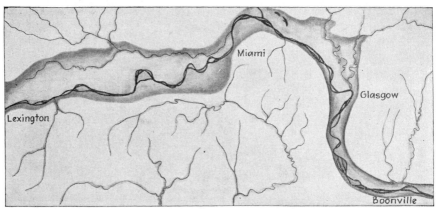

FIG. 90. Missouri River Valley in central Missouri. Note the abrupt narrowing of the valley near Glasgow.

by a stream, the greater its efficiency in wearing rock, until the stage is reached in which the size of the load reduces the stream velocity.

The rate of wear depends partly upon the *kinds of rock over which the stream flows.* Along all streams parts of the valley are much wider than other parts, and, if one investigates the rocks which make up the sides and bottom of the valley, he may find that the rocks where the valley is narrow are hard and those where it is wide are soft. A good example of this may be noted along the Missouri River, about the central part of Missouri. Maps of the Missouri River Valley show that it narrows abruptly about 75 miles east of Kansas City, near the town of Glasgow (Fig. 90). Between Kansas City and Glasgow the river flows on shales; south and east of Glasgow it flows on limestone.

The *character of the load* is also a large factor in determining the rate of wear. Angular grains wear other rocks much faster than rounded grains, and hard particles are more effective than soft particles.

Engineering Control of Valley Development. In attempting to control the cutting by rivers, many serious mistakes have been made by engineers. An example in Central America will illustrate this (Fig. 91). A railroad was built along a rapid stream in a narrow valley. At one place a meander started cutting against the solid rock on which the railroad was built, and, as the rock was not resistant, the stream undermined the railroad. The construction engineer attempted to stop this by filling in quantities of material and building concrete walls at the place where the stream was cutting, but the stream cut out the concrete walls as rapidly as it had the other rocks. By filling in a relatively small amount of material in a bend of the meander a few hundred feet upstream, where the water was not swift, the direction of the current could have been changed so that it would have cut across the neck of a meander and left the railroad safe.

FIG. 91. A stream undercutting a railroad in Central America.

Sources of Stream Load. During the entire time of valley development, streams get more of their load through *slope wash* than through any other means; and the materials are prepared mainly by weathering processes other than friction. We have found that most of the earth is covered by mantle rock from a depth of a few inches to several feet. During every rain some of this mantle rock is washed into the gullies and small streams, and these carry the material to the main streams. The material that has been produced by weathering is mainly clay and sand, regardless of the kinds of rock from which it originated.

Streams loosen some fragments from the solid rock by their own work. After they have cut through the mantle rock, they encounter solid rock, and as little chemical weathering takes place in the bottoms of streams, they must deepen their valleys by *actual wear*. They do this by rolling sand and gravel over the solid rock.

Character of Stream Load. The materials that streams actually wear off the solid rocks are different from the materials produced by chemical weathering that enter the streams by means of slope wash. If a stream flows over a granite, the little pieces of material that are worn off consist of granite, or of the minerals that make up granite: feldspar and quartz, or some of the accessory minerals, if present. Slope wash brings mainly the materials resulting from chemical weathering, *i.e.*, clay minerals and quartz sand.

AGES OF VALLEYS AND TOPOGRAPHIES

In a preceding paragraph the valley of a very young stream was called "the infant valley." As streams develop, their valleys go through stages of youth, maturity, and old age, and each has its peculiarities. Ages are not considered in years but in terms of stage of development.

Young Valleys. The narrow, steep-sided, beginning valley is called "young," as it is in an early stage of valley development. In the gully stage the young valley has no flats, or only small ones. The young valleys having swift streams that carry away deposits soon after they form have only temporary flats. Most young valleys have narrow, discontinuous flats, and the deeper the valley the wider the flats may be before a mature stage is reached.

Mature Valleys. At the stage where flats become continuous from one meander to another, as shown in Fig. 84, the valley is entering the stage of early maturity. The mature stage continues until the valley is several times as wide as the meander belt, and most of the side slopes are gentle. Steep slopes exist along the sides, here and there, where the meander belt has shifted to the side of the valley; and the outer sides of the meanders again eat into the higher land, as shown at B in Fig. 84.

Old Valleys. The old-age stage of valleys begins with wide flood plains and few steep side slopes and passes to the stage where the valley is so wide and slopes of the sides are so gentle that it is indistinguishable as a valley. Most of the divides between valleys have become so low that they do not appear as features of the landscape.

The shape of the land surface is called "topography." Topographies are developed by various agents. Man levels an area to make a tennis court or a landing field, or he roughens an area by digging ditches in it; but he has had little to do with the surface features of most of the earth. Streams have been the most important agents in shaping earth topographies. We have considered the development of stream valleys, and stream-developed topographies consist of stream valleys and the intervening divides.

Young Topography. A newly uplifted sea bottom would form an ideal *young topography*—a flat or gently sloping surface. However, the newly uplifted sea bottom would be likely to have valleys of large streams crossing it, and the areas between the streams would be the most ideally young. As no large area exists without some sort of valley in it, most young topographies consist of broad flat or gently sloping uplands between

streams (Fig. 82 B).   Young topography grades into mature topography
where only small remnants of the original upland remain.

Mature Topography.   With the progress of time, more and more
stream tributaries establish themselves, form valleys, and change all
the land into slopes toward the streams.   This is the stage of full maturity, and the region is all slopes except the wide valleys.   Mountain and
badland regions are mature, but many regions of plains and plateaus
have reached this stage also.   Figure 92 shows an ideally mature region.

FIG. 92. Mature topography in southwestern Colorado.   (*Photograph by E. B. Branson.*)

Old Topography.   The mature stage continues to early old age, when
most of the slopes become gentle.   The region has passed from a nearly
level stage (youth), through a stage where it is nearly all in slopes and the
slopes are steep (maturity), to the stage where it is all gentle slopes and
flats (old age).   The streams have cut laterally until the divides between
them are inconspicuous.   Two phases of old-age topography are designated by special names: "peneplain" and "base level."

Peneplain.   A peneplain is a region that has been eroded to very
gentle slopes by streams.   It may still have isolated hills owing to their
being composed of harder rock than that of the surrounding region or to
their being the result of accidental stream erosion.   Peneplains are made
up of valley flats and the gently sloping uplands between them.   Part
of the work of leveling the region has been accomplished by wearing and
part by filling.

Base Level.   A peneplain that has been eroded nearly to sea level is
called a "base level."   Streams cannot erode a region to sea level, but

only to such gentle slopes that the water runs off without doing further work of cutting or carrying. A true base level, then, is an ideal never attained; but geologists speak of a low, almost level region produced by stream erosion as a "base level." Base level is not created by just one stream, but by a number of streams. One stream valley in a topography might be as low as the base level, but by definition the term "base level" applies only to regions and not to single stream valleys.

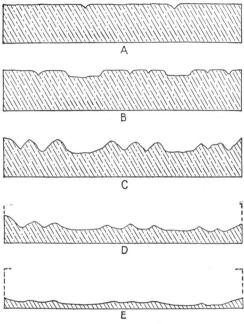

FIG. 93. Cross-sections of (A) very young topography, (B) topography in middle youth, (C) mature topography, (D) topography in late maturity, (E) topography in old age. Vertical scale greatly exaggerated in all cross-sections.

Relation of Valley Age to Topographic Age. The age of stream valleys does not necessarily have anything to do with the age of topographies. Most of the stream valleys in mature topography are young, and young topographies may have mature valleys. Mature and old topographies always have some young valleys. Old topographies have streams with wide flats; and one of the main streams, shifting its course, may cause a tributary stream to cut across a wide flat, creating a young valley in that flat. The age of the valleys and topographies may not be related more definitely than the age of a house with that of its newly shingled roof.

It should be clear that no sharper gradation separates young, mature, and old topographies than divides the youth, maturity, and old age of persons. The age of topography discussed is strictly in terms of stream erosion, and other types of topographic development may change the surface so completely as to destroy the evidence of the age; for instance, a glacier passing over a region may change it from a mature, back to a youthful stage.

Cycle of Erosion. Where a peneplain or base-leveled region has been uplifted and the streams rejuvenated, the narrow, steep-sided valleys that result give the topography the appearance of youth; and the region is said to have entered a second cycle of erosion. By "cycle of erosion" the geologist means the things that take place from the starting of erosion on a newly emergent surface to the old age of the region and the uplift that starts a new cycle. A complete cycle consists of the emergence of a sea bottom; its erosion by streams through youth and maturity to base level; and, then, the uplift. If uplift comes before the base-leveling of the region, the cycle is said to be incomplete. In the Appalachian Mountain region, three periods of rejuvenation or uplift and four cycles of erosion may be recognized by erosion features. Figure 93 shows five stages in a cycle of erosion.

FEATURES DEVELOPED BY STREAM EROSION

In the making of valleys, streams develop many features of the landscape that are familiar to everyone and other features that are unusual. Rapids and falls, terraces, oxbow lakes, and isolated hills belong in the first group; and, in the second, are canyons, buttes and mesas, badlands, hogbacks, pinnacles and pedestal rocks, natural bridges, and intrenched meanders.

Rapids and Falls. Rapids and falls are both due to stream erosion of alternating hard and soft layers of rock or to rapidly constructed dams. Where a stream flows from hard rock to soft, it lowers the soft faster than the hard and produces a steep grade from the hard to the soft, resulting in rapids (Fig. 94). The rapids increase in grade until the greater velocity of the water over the hard rock causes a rate of erosion equal to that of the slow water over the soft rocks. This balance may be maintained for long periods of time, and the rapids may be lowered without altering their grade. When downcutting has produced such a low grade on the soft rock that erosion is exceedingly slow, the hard rock is reduced faster than the soft, the rapids gradually decrease in speed, and, finally, completely disappear. If the difference in rate of erosion of the two beds is so great that the face of the hard rock becomes nearly vertical, falls are formed (Fig. 94). Rapids are common along streams in young or mature valleys, but falls are not.

Many different conditions exist under which soft rocks may alternate with hard ones to produce falls. Beds of rocks of different hardness may be horizontal, dip upstream, be vertical, or dip steeply downstream.

Igneous rocks may alternate with sandstones, shales, or limestones by intrusions into them or lava flows over them. In every case the soft rocks must be downstream from the hard rocks to cause falls to develop. Under most conditions falls change their location as the rocks forming them are cut down by erosion.

Falls and rapids are hindrances to navigation. Many rivers are navigable to some particular falls or rapids, though the latter may not completely stop navigation on a stream if there is deep water through them. Engineering plans have been completed for canals around the rapids of the St. Lawrence River large enough to allow ocean steamers to reach the Great Lakes.

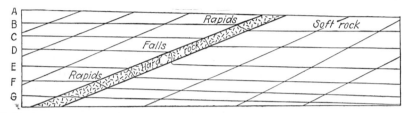

FIG. 94. A diagram showing development of rapids and falls, upstream migration of falls, and disappearance of falls and rapids. (A) Stream has even grade; (B and C) rapids develop; (D) falls have formed; (E and F) falls have become rapids; (G) the stream is near sea level and is at low grade.

Migration of Falls. At Niagara Falls the rocks dip slightly upstream; hard limestone beds overlie shales. Water running over the falls and striking at the bottom takes on a sort of whirling motion, strikes against the shales and wears or plucks them out so that the limestone overhangs. When the undermining reaches a vertical crack in the limestone, part of the rock slumps off and the falls recede by the width of the slumped block. Undermining causes the Canadian Falls to retreat upstream at a rate of about 3 feet per year. The American Falls, having much less water to work with, moves back only about 8 inches per year. Niagara Falls has migrated upstream from Lewiston, a distance of about 7 miles, and at the rate of 3 feet per year the migration has taken more than 12,000 years. This geological clock, however, is not perfect, since it has been found that in its earlier stages the river was only about half as large as it is at present. If Niagara Falls continues to move upstream, it will finally reach Lake Erie, lower the lake about 160 feet, and cease to exist as falls. The rapids, however, will exist until the grade between Lake Erie and Lake Ontario becomes low and uniform.

In many regions soft sedimentary rocks overlie hard sedimentary or igneous rocks. If the hard beds are strongly tilted downstream, steep rapids or falls form where the water flows from hard to soft rocks, even though the slope downstream is much less than vertical (Fig. 95). In this case, as the river lowers its bed, the falls migrate downstream. If the hard layer that forms the falls meets the soft rocks in a vertical plane, the falls remain stationary as the river cuts down (Figs. 94 and 95).

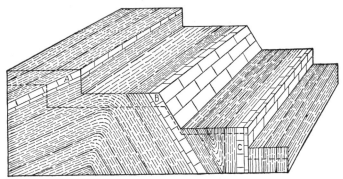

FIG. 95. A diagram showing conditions under which falls move upstream (A) as the stream cuts downward; move downstream (B); remain stationary (C). The broken line shows the location of the falls after the stream has lowered its channel.

Terraces. In all river valleys there are numerous flats terminated on one side by steep slopes that descend to lower flats. Such features are called "terraces" and are developed where a stream cuts across a meander and starts meandering again. Terraces are shown in Fig. 96,

FIG. 96. Terraces and symmetrical meanders. (*Photograph by E. B. Branson.*)

and the starting of terraces in Fig. 83, page 92. We have found that in cutting a valley the stream meanders back and forth across it hundreds and even thousands of times, and, as each shift creates terraces, their number is very large. However, as the stream cuts on the outer side of the meander and moves across the valley, it destroys all former terraces as far as it goes. It may not cut to the extreme side of the valley and therefore may leave some of the terraces.

In some valleys there are very wide flats, a few feet to possibly hundreds of feet higher than the next flats below, and these make striking features. Such terraces develop in mature or old valleys where the stream velocity increases and cuts a deeper, narrower valley within the old one. The higher terraces become the sites of cities and are much desired as farm lands where the climate is humid; in a semiarid climate they are not so good farm land as the lower terraces, as the ground-water level is much farther below the surface in them than it is in the lower lands. Wide terraces are well developed along the Rio Grande in New Mexico, the Missouri in its course from Montana to Missouri, the Connecticut, the Nile, and many other streams.

Oxbow Lakes. Where streams straighten their courses by cutting across meanders, the old curves are deserted by the stream but remain filled with stagnant water and are known, in some regions, as "bayous." The ends that join the streams are soon filled with deposits and the bayous become "oxbow lakes," named from their shape. Such lakes are numerous in old valleys and common in mature ones (Fig. 83, page 92).

Isolated Hills. Figures 82 D and 83 illustrate the development of an isolated hill by stream meandering. Hills of such origin are common. If the cap rock is hard and the lower rock soft, buttes may form. Isolated hills form also where tributaries develop secondary tributaries that cut back, connect with one another, and leave a hill unconnected with the adjacent ridges. These are buttes in arid or semiarid regions, and probably hills of gentle slope in humid regions. The hills are not due in any sense to harder rocks, but to the accident of the stream's failure to cut this particular area to flood-plain level. Goat Island in the Niagara River between the American Falls and the Canadian Falls will become an isolated hill when the falls recede above the island.

Canyons. Canyons have become sites of national parks and objects of excursions to millions of people. They are present, in the main, in the regions where buttes and mesas occur. The Grand Canyon of the Colorado (the most famous canyon in the world) is bounded on both sides by mesas, and buttes are numerous on its margins. Canyons may be defined as unusually deep, narrow, steep-sided valleys (Figs. 97 and 98). Again, as with the terms "butte" and "mesa," the term "canyon" is somewhat colloquial. In western United States most valleys are canyons to the inhabitants; in eastern United States the term is not used. Niagara Gorge is as truly a canyon as the canyon of the Yellowstone in Yellowstone Park. It is neither so deep nor so narrow, but it is steep sided and fits our definition of a canyon.

In the main, canyons are developed in nearly horizontal sedimentary rocks, are steep sided because of slow weathering and slope wash, are narrow because their streams are very swift, and are deep because the regions in which they are cut are high. One might raise the objection that Niagara Gorge is in a region where weathering and slope wash are important, but one condition that produces a canyon—the swift, powerful stream—is so dominating in the case of the Niagara River below the falls that it has outstripped the agents that reduce the side slopes. The gorge of the Columbia River is a real canyon not in an arid region; but

FIG. 97. Part of the Grand Canyon of the Colorado River; buttes in the foreground, a mesa in the background. (Official photograph, U.S. Air Force.)

it too has been cut by a swift, large stream, and cut through basalt, a rock that weathers rather slowly. One who visits the Grand Canyon in Arizona, Zion Canyon in Utah, the canyons of the Yellowstone in Yellowstone Park or of Snake River in Idaho and Washington will be impressed by the wearing power of the streams that have produced them and by the steepness of the walls bounding them. Short canyons are striking features of the flanks of mountains, and many of the scenic highways of western United States pass through them. Some canyons cut clear through mountain ranges, so that one may traverse the entire range without going either up or down to any great degree.

Though the Grand Canyon of the Colorado River in Arizona, as stated, is the most famous canyon in the world, it is by no means the deepest valley or canyon. By combining great depth, steep-sidedness, and length, however, the Grand Canyon excels all others. The very deep part of the canyon is about 100 miles long. Its maximum depth is about a mile, and its normal width at the top 6 to 10 miles. However, it gives the impression of much greater proportional depth because of many steep

FIG. 98. Canyon in Mesa Verde National Park, southwestern Colorado. (*Photograph by E. B. Branson.*)

faces in the walls. The horizontal rocks making up its sides are highly colored, and the colors of the beds are different, which emphasizes the steepness of the walls. For example, the Redwall formation (forming a cliff 500 feet high in places and extending for miles along the canyon) is a dull red in color, the rocks above it are buff, and those below are yellow, green, and brown. At places along the canyon there are sheer drops of 2,000 to 3,000 feet. The onlooker is impressed by the steepness, ruggedness, and harshness of the canyon.

If one listens to the comments of the visitors to the canyon, he hears the question asked: "How did the canyon form?" Only rarely does he hear an answer that is in any way adequate. Possibly the old Navaho legend that Ye, their most powerful god, dragged something along there and thus created the canyon is as adequate as the guesses of the ordinary tourist. By determining the amount of sediment carried and the amount of water that flows through the canyon, one may find that it has not taken much longer for the Colorado River to form the Grand Canyon than for the Mississippi River to form the valley in which it flows. The time required for either has been millions of years, but that is a short time in geologic history.

FIG. 99. A butte capped by a resistant layer of sandstone which appears black in the picture. (Photograph by E. B. Branson.)

FIG. 100. A flat-topped butte. Sandstone beds form the cap; shales are below. (Photograph by W. T. Lee, courtesy of U.S. Geological Survey.)

Buttes and Mesas. Numerous flat-topped, steep-sided, isolated hills that are capped by resistant horizontal beds are common features of badland topography, but are also present in many other regions. Such features are called "buttes" (Figs. 99, 100, and 101), but the term is somewhat regional in its application. It is used much more in western than in eastern United States, not only because these topographic features are much more numerous in the West, but because there it is the custom to call any steep-sided, flat-topped hill of a diameter less than a mile or two a "butte," as it is also the custom to call such a hill several miles across a *mesa*. The terms "butte" and "mesa" are not used with complete distinction either outside of geological literature or in it. Enchanted Mesa in New Mexico is only about 1,000 feet across the top. Mesas owe their existence to the same conditions as do buttes: a hard, nearly horizontal bed of rock capping softer rock in an arid or semiarid region where weathering and slope wash are slow. The butte and mesa regions of the United States extend from western Kansas, Nebraska, and Oklahoma nearly to the Sierra Nevada.

FIG. 101. Jail Rock, a butte in the semiarid West. (*Photograph by N. H. Darton, courtesy of U.S. Geological Survey.*)

Badlands. The so-called "badlands" attract the attention of everyone who crosses them. They are normal features of stream erosion under rather peculiar conditions. They constitute a type of mature topography with narrow, steep-sided valleys and narrow-crested hills, the entire region being dissected by closely spaced valleys. The rocks making up most badlands are alternating shales and sandstones with shales, predominating, as shown in Fig. 102. Badlands develop in arid or semiarid regions where the rainfall comes mainly in heavy showers. Figure 92 shows a type of badlands with slopes much gentler than those in normal badlands. The slopes are gentler because there are no hard sandstone layers to hold them up. In humid regions weathering and slope wash reduce all slopes too rapidly for typical badland development.

In some regions the rocks making up the badlands are highly colored,

FIG. 102. Badlands near Steveville, Alberta. *(From Emmons, Thiel, Stauffer, and Allison, "Geology," courtesy of Geological Survey of Canada.)*

FIG. 103. Hogback near Iron Mountain, Wyoming. *(Courtesy of U.S. Geological Survey.)*

and color attracts attention to them. In the Painted Desert of Arizona bands of red, green, yellow, and blue set off the picturesqueness of the rough topography. This is one of the most accessible and beautiful of the badland regions of the United States, and it covers an area of several thousand square miles. The Sante Fe Trail passes through it, and the road from the Sante Fe Trail to the bridge across the Colorado River at Lees Ferry runs through it for 30 or 40 miles.

FIG. 104. Erosional spires in Hell's Half Acre, central Wyoming.   (*Photograph by W. T. Lee, courtesy of U.S. Geological Survey.*)

FIG. 105. Erosional pattern in Bryce Canyon, Utah.   (*Photograph by Carl C. Branson.*)

Small areas of badlands occur in almost all of the Rocky Mountain states, not in the mountains themselves but in the plateaus adjoining the mountains.   The best-known are in South Dakota, adjoining the Black Hills region, Nebraska, Wyoming, Montana, and Arizona.

Fossils in Badlands.   Many large fossils of peculiar animals have

FIG. 106. Rainbow Natural Bridge, southern Utah. (*From Emmons, Thiel, Stauffer, and Allison,* "Geology," *courtesy of Santa Fe Railway.*)

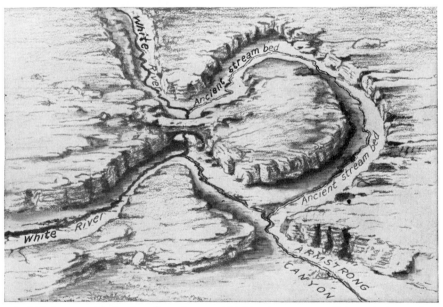

FIG. 107. Drawing showing formation of a natural bridge by a stream with intrenched meanders. (*After Gregory, courtesy of U.S. Geological Survey.*)

been found in the badlands of South Dakota, and great fossil forests occur in the Painted Desert of Arizona. Some people associate large fossils with badland topography, but in many badlands no fossils are known. The presence of fossils in an area is an accident of geographic and geologic location rather than a necessary association.

Hogbacks. The so-called *hogbacks* are features developed where rocks are tilted and hard beds alternate with soft ones. Stream erosion removes the softer rocks above the harder ones, and forms a rather sharp-crested ridge, as shown in Fig. 103. On one side of the ridge is the face of tilted rock, and on the other side a slope consisting of softer rock that is protected by the hard rock. Hogbacks are common along the flanks of all mountains formed of tilted sedimentary rocks. They develop in moist as well as in arid climates, but are somewhat sharper and more clear-cut in arid regions, owing to slower weathering, and to the lack of forests in such regions.

Pinnacles and Pedestal Rocks. In arid and semiarid regions slender spires and masses of rock perched on slender pedestals are not uncommon erosion remnants (Fig. 104). Bryce Canyon (Fig. 105) in southern Utah has more pinnacles than any other area of equal size in North America. One can see thousands of them at one glance. As they are varicolored, with some bright shades, they make a striking and picturesque landscape. They were not formed by stream erosion alone, but by stream erosion and ground water seeping out from near the bottom of the valleys and undermining the overlying rocks. The materials forming the pinnacles are soft sandstones and shales.

Natural Bridges. Natural bridges originating in any way are rare, and those developed by streams are much rarer than those developed by the work of ground water. The largest natural bridges in the United States are in southern Utah (Fig. 106), and they were developed in part by stream erosion. Two canyons were very close together, and the stream of one, undercutting at the bottom of a 200- or 300-foot cliff, undermined it and cut through into the other canyon, leaving a rock arch above (Fig. 107). This is a simple way but exceedingly rare, because two canyons seldom approach each other close enough to allow the undercutting from one to reach the other. The natural-bridge region of Utah extends into adjoining parts of Arizona and New Mexico, but the bridges of these two states are little known because the region is accessible with difficulty. The bridges are cut in red sandstone and make striking topographic features.

UNUSUAL DRAINAGE PATTERNS

Rejuvenation. In many areas which had reached maturity or old age, the velocity of streams was increased by uplift of the land or by lowering the outlet of the valley. Such streams are said to be "rejuvenated" (made young again), and they cut downward much more rapidly than they cut sideward. An individual stream may then develop a deep valley with the slopes and features of youth in the meandering pattern of late maturity.

The valley of the San Juan River in southeastern Utah is a striking example of the effects of rejuvenation (Fig. 108). The valley is a narrow canyon more than 1,000 feet deep in a pattern of closely spaced, sharp meanders. Such meanders develop only on a wide flood plain, and the deep, narrow valley could be formed only by a swift stream. The explanation of these inconsistent qualities lies in the history of the region. The stream had developed a broad valley, and its channel was a series of meander loops (Fig. 109). The gradient was increased as the Colorado

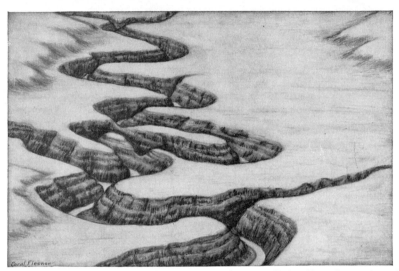

FIG. 108. Intrenched meanders of the San Juan River of southern Utah. The valley is about 1,000 feet deep.

River, into which the San Juan empties, cut downward rapidly about 1,000 feet. The meanders of the San Juan River were deepened by downward cutting and became the present intrenched meanders.

It should not be understood that rejuvenated streams cut straight down. Even in the most pronounced of the intrenched meanders the stream has cut laterally more than it has cut downward. The San Juan Valley is several times as wide as it is deep, although to the eye the depth seems greater than the width.

Most instances of rejuvenation are caused by uplift of the area, with resulting increase in the gradient of the streams. Many large streams cross mountains or ridges even where an easy way around exists. In most such instances the stream developed its course at a higher level in softer, more uniform, horizontal materials. As the region was uplifted, the stream cut downward onto a different pattern of rocks, and in many cases it was forced to cut its channel across resistant layers or masses. The Yampa River, in northwestern Colorado, has a canyon through a mountain of hard rock. A change of course of less than a mile would have avoided the necessity for any real cutting. The river maintained its earlier course, and its valley was superimposed upon a resistant mass.

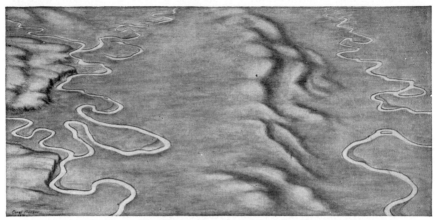

FIG. 109. Drawing representing the author's conception of the valley of the San Juan before intrenchment. The valley at the left becomes the valley of Fig. 108.

In time stream valleys become adjusted to the pattern of rocks of varying hardness by shifting onto the soft rocks and flowing around the hard rocks. In areas of dipping beds a rectangular drainage pattern results.

Stream Deposition

It is common knowledge that waters in flood carry enough sediment to make the water distinctly muddy. As the amount of material that running water can move is directly dependent upon its *velocity* and *volume*, a decrease in either means deposition of part of the stream load.

Checking of Velocity. If a loaded stream (one carrying all the sand and clay that it can) has its velocity checked abruptly, the materials it is carrying are deposited rapidly. The carrying power of a stream, as far as size of particles is concerned, varies as the sixth power of the velocity. A stream that has been carrying a pebble that weighs 1 ounce, upon having its velocity reduced one-half, can carry a pebble that weighs only $\frac{1}{64}$ ounce. It is not strange, then, that most stream deposits are formed where the velocity of the water is reduced.

Decrease in Volume. Deposits made on account of decrease in volume of water are conspicuous where streams flow from moist to dry regions and evaporation and soak-in take up much of the volume of the stream. The Platte River in Nebraska is an example. Many of its tributaries, as they come from the Rocky Mountains, carry more water during dry seasons than the Platte itself after it reaches the plains. The volume of water has been so reduced that the river actually fills much of its channel with deposits, causing the water to flow in small streams within the main channel. The small streams join together and divide frequently, producing what is known as a "braided stream."

Many streams of the Rocky Mountain region have part of their waters diverted for irrigation purposes and on that account are unable to carry the same amount of sediment that was carried before the water went into the ditches. The same volume of water is present, but the water

FIG. 110. A steep alluvial fan on North Fork of Popo Agie River, Wyoming. (*Photograph by E. B. Branson.*)

comes in contact with much more surface than while it was all in the main stream. The carrying power of a stream depends, in part, on its volume; but a deep, narrow stream can carry much more than a wide, shallow one of the same volume, as it comes in contact with much less rock surface.

Alluvial Fans. Where a stream comes from a relatively high grade to a much gentler slope, as from mountains to plains, its velocity is checked quickly and for that reason it builds up alluvial deposits. These deposits are formed so rapidly that there is little sorting of the materials; and, as they are deposited on land, no later sorting takes place. The deposit, therefore, consists of all the stream-borne materials, boulders, pebbles, gravel, sand, silt, and clay, piled up in a heterogeneous mass.

Such a deposit spreads out fanlike from the steep slope, and is known as an *alluvial fan* (Figs. 110 and 111). As the fan grows outward by additions at the outer margins, the gradient ceases to be steep, the materials are deposited less rapidly and are finer and better sorted.

The stream builds the fan by overflowing its channel. The largest deposits form where the water first overflows the channel, and thus the margins of the stream channels are the highest part. When the stream channel has been built up to a considerable height, an unusually high

FIG. 111. An alluvial fan built against the side of a valley. The main stream has shifted and has cut off the base of the fan. (*Photograph by E. B. Branson.*)

flood may cause the stream to break through the marginal deposits. It then would take the lowest course available over the fan; and this process of filling and escaping from the channel would be repeated many times.

Fans at the base of high mountains may grow until they extend hundreds of miles from the mountains. They grow laterally to join other fans, forming compound alluvial fans. East of the Andes in Argentina, the entire slope nearly to the sea is made up of alluvial fans; east of the Rockies in Colorado, fans spread far out into Kansas. In California many of the orange groves are on alluvial fans.

Flood-plain Deposits. Flood-plain deposits are formed by streams (Fig. 83, page 92) and are present in all valleys that have developed flats. In the main, they form from deposits on the inside of meanders; but, in part, are direct deposits from floods that spread from the river channel over the flood plain. Normally, the deposits range in thickness from a few inches to 50 feet but at some places are much thicker, and they occupy the entire width of valley bottoms, save where the stream has cut through them to the solid rock.

In old topography, flood-plain deposits may form nearly half of the surface of a region, although in early old age they probably constitute less than one-tenth, and in young topography they are of small area. Flood-plain deposits are, in the main, composed of clay and sand; but, as the river gets rocks of various kinds and sizes from the valley sides, granules are by no means uncommon, and boulders occur in some places. One might follow up the course of the Mississippi-Missouri River and its tributaries nearly to the top of the Rocky Mountains and find flood-plain deposits everywhere. The deposits in the flood plains of the Missouri's

FIG. 112. Deposits in the flood plain of a swift stream in Costa Rica. (*Photograph by E. B. Branson.*)

branches, coming from the Rockies, are different in composition from those of the flood plains near its mouth. The deposits of the mountain streams consist of larger fragments than those that are deposited by streams far away from mountains (Fig. 112).

Flood-plain deposits are among the richest of soils and are the most intensively tilled of all soils, particularly in semiarid regions where they have the advantage of getting more moisture than the upland soils. In Kansas, Nebraska, and other states of similar climate, the bottom lands (flood plains) may produce large crops while the uplands produce little. In some regions farmers are finding greatest profit in cropping the flood plains and grazing the uplands, and farms with both upland and valley parts prove most profitable.

Natural Levees. All large rivers in mature and old valleys overflow their main channels at times of great floods and deposit and cut away materials from their flood plains. As flood water fills the main channel and overflows laterally, it makes deposits on the immediate banks of the river course where the velocity of the water is checked by shallowing. In course of time the deposits on the bank build up above the rest of the flood plain and form a distinct topographic feature known as a "natural levee" (Fig. 113A). Along large rivers natural levees may be several feet above the general level of the flood plain of the river, but they are inconspicuous on account of their very low slope away from the river, and they are most easily observed in flood time when the flood

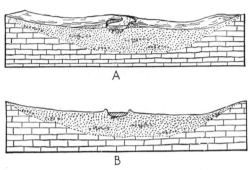

FIG. 113. (A) Natural levee; (B) artificial levee.

plain of the valley is covered with water save for the narrow strip along the immediate bank of the river. The river itself acts as a check on the height of the levee. If the levee builds a little too high, the river breaks through in flood time and does not return to its old channel. In the main, the levees help the river to keep its channel in times of high water; but the materials of the levee are loose clay and sand, and thus, as the river overflows, it easily cuts through the levee and spreads over the flood plains beyond. Nearly all streams with large natural levees are subject to disastrous floods.

A river with high natural levees and great plains in its lower course may change that course greatly in flood time. The Hwang Ho (River) flowed into the Yellow Sea previous to 1853, when it broke through its levee, took a new course, and emptied into the Gulf of Pohai, 200 miles north of its former mouth. All efforts to turn it back were unsuccessful, and it started at once to build a delta at its new mouth.

Control of River Building. The Mississippi River had many mouths which opened into the Gulf, and these filled up with sand and clay so as to make navigation uncertain. An engineer, James Eads, planned jetties that should be just wide and deep enough to enable the river current to sweep them clear of sediment. They were finished in 1879, and no trouble has been experienced with navigation of the lower delta since that time. This is an example of the application of science to the control of natural forces.   Dredging out a channel would have been easier and faster, but the dredging would have had to be kept up all the time, would have cost more than the jetties finally, and would have been less satisfactory.

The danger of floods on some flood plains constitutes a hazard in farming them.   Scientific planning of the handling of side streams may entirely eliminate flood-plain dangers from some areas.   Near Kinderhook, Illinois, a farmer purchased a rather large farm, most of which was flooded every year and part of which consisted of oxbow lakes and swamps.   The land was worth about $30 an acre.   The custom in this region was to build levees to keep water off the farms.   This farmer found that the water got into the fields in spite of the levees, and he evolved a new plan for his farm improvement.   He built a levee around one field to hold the flood water in and retained it until all the clay and sand had settled.   With water two feet deep over the field, clay and sand might settle out from one flood to a depth of 3 or 4 inches.   By treating the land in this way for 16 or 17 years, he built his entire farm up some 3 or 4 feet, and the old oxbows and swamps were filled to the level of the rest of the farm.   With his farm 3 or 4 feet above the surrounding land he was in no danger from floods, and some of his neighbors actually bought a right of way through his property to let the flood waters come through and build up their farms.   The value of the land increased from $30 to $250 an acre.

Artificial Levees.   As natural levees are made of materials that form rich soils and are densely inhabited along some rivers in spite of the danger of floods, the inhabitants, desiring to escape damage, build artificial levees (Fig. 113B) upon the natural ones.   Such levees extend intermittently along both sides of the Mississippi River from New Orleans to north of St. Louis.   As artificial levees are thin, they are weaker than natural levees, are more easily broken by floods, and the resulting floods are much more destructive.   Along the Hwang Ho (River) in China, some of the artificial levees are nearly 100 feet high and in places there are three sets of levees.   When the river breaks through all the levees, it means disaster to the inhabitants of the valley.   The river is known as "China's sorrow," owing to the number of people it has destroyed. Great floods of the Mississippi River result in breaching of the levees, and one of the big problems of the national government is flood control of the Mississippi and its tributaries.

Deltas.   It has been determined that the Mississippi River carries enough sand and clay in suspension every year to make a deposit 268 feet deep over 1 square mile.   That amount is actually carried through the mouth of the Mississippi into the Gulf, and most of it is deposited in the *delta* (Fig. 114) near the mouth.   (The volume was determined by sampling the waters of the Mississippi every day of the year for many years and ascertaining from the samples the amount of sediments carried.) Where the water of the Mississippi enters the relatively stationary ocean water, it deposits most of the load it has been carrying.   Material as coarse as fine sand goes to the bottom within a mile or two of shore. Clays will stay in suspension for several days and may be carried hundreds of miles into the Gulf before settling to the bottom.

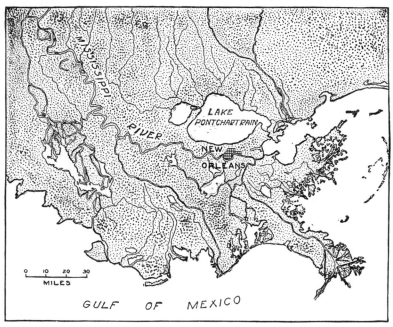

FIG. 114. Map of the delta of the Mississippi River. (After Emmons, Thiel, Stauffer, and Allison, "Geology.")

The sands that are deposited at the immediate mouth of the river gradually encroach on the sea, by filling up the shallow parts, and cause the delta to grow seaward.   They grade imperceptibly into finer sediments farther out.   At times of flood, muddy waters stand over the part of the delta that has been built to sea level, and sediments deposited from these waters gradually build the delta above sea level.   The amount of material in a delta will depend upon the amount carried by the stream and the length of time the stream has been working.   In 100,000 years, the Mississippi would carry enough materials to make deposits 268 feet deep over 100,000 square miles or 26.8 feet deep over 1,000,000 square miles.   Such deposits would be almost entirely made up of clay and sand, and most of these materials would have resulted from an advanced stage of chemical weathering. The sand would be made up mainly of quartz grains and the clay of various clay minerals.

The building of the delta of the Mississippi probably started in the region that is now southeastern Missouri and adjoining states and progressed outward some 600 miles south. The first deposits were made in the head of a narrow bay, but the bay was filled, and the near-shore deposits grew until they extended from Louisiana almost to central Texas. More than 200,000 square miles have been filled by the Mississippi to depths ranging from something over 100 to more than 12,000 feet, and the river has probably been working several million years to make the deposits. In making such a deposit the stream must have

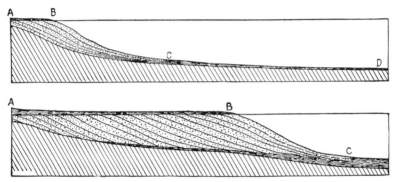

FIG. 115. Upper figure, a young delta with wide area of bottomset beds (C-D). Lower figure, a well-developed simple delta with widespread topset (A-B) and foreset (B-C) beds.

changed its course thousands of times, now flowing near the eastern margin of the delta, then near the western margin, and also occupying all intermediate places many times.

As a delta starts, no part of it is above sea level, and the submerged part continues to be very much larger than the part above sea level through the earlier stages of delta growth (Fig. 115, upper figure). If the sea is very shallow, a large stream may fill the shallow part rather rapidly, and the landward part of the delta will grow faster than the part below the sea. The 200,000 square miles of landward part of the Mississippi delta was once all suboceanic, so that, in drilling wells through the delta sediments, most of the materials encountered were deposited below the sea. This is determined by fragments of sea shells found in the well cuttings.

Seaward there is no sharp line of demarcation between delta deposits and the normal sea deposits. The very finest of the clay brought in by streams is widely diffused through the ocean waters and may settle to the bottom at places remote from the delta. Sediments direct from Amazon River waters are carried out and deposited some 700 miles from the mouth of the river, but only very large rivers with strong currents carry materials far out. All of the deposits from a distance of 20 or 30 miles out from shore are clay, unless the ocean is so shallow that storm waves strike the bottom.

We may picture a young delta with a subaqueous part made of clays, covering a large area (Fig. 115, C-D of upper figure); a very shallow water part made up mainly of sands (Fig. 115, B-C of upper figure); and a very small part above water (Fig. 115, A-B of upper figure). As the delta grows, the part above water increases and in late stages may become the main part of the delta (Fig. 115, A-B of lower figure). In drilling wells for oil or water in the Mississippi delta, the drill cuts through a few to possibly 100 feet of sand and clay deposited above the ocean level. Below this are found a few feet deposited in shallow water, and below that a few to thousands of feet of clay and fine sand deposited far from shore.

Rivers emptying into seas with strong tides or very strong wave action deposit sediments in the same way as other rivers, but the waves and currents sweep away the deposits and deltas do not form. Small deltas may form where tributary rivers empty into larger rivers with weak currents. Deltas forming in lakes may completely fill the lakes.

Deltas have been important places in human development. The Nile delta is famous for the early civilization developed upon it. The delta of the Tigris and Euphrates was also one of the early sites of man's development. The delta of the Hwang Ho has one of the densest populations in the world and one of the oldest. On the delta of the Mississippi, a few of the oldest white settlements in the United States were located, some of which are now important cities.

Streams like the Mississippi carry several times the volume of sediments that they deliver to the ocean, but the materials deposited in alluvial fans and flood plains do not actually reduce the general level of the land; the only materials lost to the continent are those carried away and deposited in the seas. Not only that, but before a region has reached base level all of the materials of its higher alluvial-fan and flood-plain deposits are removed, carried to the sea, and deposited.

Summary of Stream Deposition. Most streams carry clay and sand, and very swift streams carry and roll coarser materials. Most stream deposits are caused by checking of velocity of the water. Stream deposits are coarsest in alluvial fans and finest in deltas. Under some conditions deltas are the chief stream deposits; under others, alluvial fans; and under still others, flood plains. Alluvial deposits form some of the richest farm land. Many regions of alluvial deposit are densely populated and the inhabitants are in danger from floods.

CHAPTER 7

GROUND WATER

Ground water, as the name suggests, is water that occurs in the ground but relatively near the surface. Other names are applied to it. *Meteoric water* is a common name, which refers to the ground water that originated in the air. This term is useful as a contrast to *magmatic water*, the name applied to water originating in a magma. A type of ground water known as *connate water* occurs in some sandstones. This water was incorporated in the pores of the sandstones when the deposit was made on the sea floor and was then buried along with the sandstone. It has, therefore, a composition similar to that of sea water. Our discussion in this chapter will deal entirely with that part of the water having its source in the rain and snow that fall upon the earth's surface.

Amount of Ground Water. If the average annual rainfall for the world is regarded as 36 inches (it ranges locally from 0 to more than 500 inches), the quantity of water falling annually upon the 54,000,000 square miles of the earth's land surface is about 30,500 cubic miles. The amount of water that runs off following rains is estimated to be about 30 per cent of the total, or about 9,000 cubic miles. This is practically the volume of water that annually reaches the ocean by means of rivers, which leaves about 21,000 cubic miles of the water that falls on the land to go underground. Most of this ground water is returned to the air by evaporation from the soil and transpiration by plants. It has been estimated that for each pound of vegetable matter produced by a plant an average of 40 gallons of water must be transpired. The amount of the ground water returned to the air in these ways varies widely, depending upon differences in climate and other influencing factors. The ground water not evaporated or transpired penetrates to variable depths, but much of it eventually finds its way to the surface through springs and seeps. A small amount of ground water goes into the formation of the various secondary minerals, such as the clay minerals, limonite, and gypsum, and so remains underground indefinitely. Many estimates have been made of the total amount of ground water in the rocks. One of the estimates (probably the best) places the amount at a quantity that would cover the entire surface of a sphere the size of the earth to a depth of 100 feet. This volume of water underground is transient in character, for as some of it reaches the surface more rain water sinks down to take its place.

Factors Controlling the Amount of Ground Water. The factors controlling the amount of rain water that goes underground are (1) *rate of rainfall*, (2) *slope of the surface*, (3) *amount of vegetation*, (4) *porosity of the surface rock, and* (5) *the amount of water already in the pores of the rock*. A maximum amount of water would go underground if rain fell slowly upon a dry, porous soil of a level or gently sloping, tree-covered surface, strewn with forest litter. A ground cover of thick grass is also conducive to high soak-in. As the factors controlling the amount of water that goes underground differ widely in various parts of the earth, a similar difference is found in the amount of meteoric water beneath the surface in the different places.

The Downward Penetration of Ground Water. Water in going underground follows the joints and fissures of the rocks, and from these openings works its way into the cracks and pores. The size and number of the openings in rocks differ widely; in some rocks there are many openings; in others, such as granite, there are very few. Openings are, of course, most abundant near the surface. They may extend downward for great distances, not as single, continuous openings, but as more or less connected ones. It has been determined experimentally that the strongest rocks are unable to sustain openings below a distance of 10 or 11 miles from the surface, and weaker ones do not have openings even within a mile of the surface. The zone in which cracks, joints, and fissures can exist in the rocks is called the *zone of cavities*. However, there are good reasons for believing that the maximum distance ground water penetrates below the surface is only a few thousand feet. The vast majority of deep oil and gas wells and mines show that actually most of the ground water occurs within 2,000 or 3,000 feet of the surface. Many mines of that depth are dry and dusty; in fact, many within 1,000 feet of the surface contain very little water. Water has to be pumped into most deep oil wells during the drilling. The water occurring in these deep wells is usually salty; hence it is probably connate water. For the most part, however, the ground water is near the surface, although special positions of the rocks permit its descent to considerable depths.

Ground-water Zones. As we have just seen, the zone of the ground water, though it *may* correspond to the zone of cavities, usually lies near the surface. The top of the zone in which the rocks are mainly saturated with water is known as the *water level* or *water table*. The former name does not mean, however, that the top of this zone is level, for it follows, roughly, the surface of the land (Fig. 116); and its shifts with the seasons, being higher in a rainy season and lower during drouths. The water level tends to flatten and would become essentially flat if no more water were added from above.

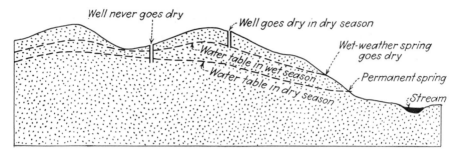

FIG. 116. Sketch showing the various positions and relationships of the ground water to the surface.

Of this zone of ground water, the unsaturated area above the water level is known as the *vadose-water zone;* and the saturated part below the water level, as the *ground-water zone* (Fig. 117).

The *vadose-water zone* is the zone of the most rapid water circulation, as the water in it is moving downward to the water level (Fig. 118). This zone has been called the *zone of aeration,* because air can be present down to the water level. As the meteoric water moves downward through this zone, it may attack the minerals and rocks along the walls of the fissures and alter them. It is aided in this

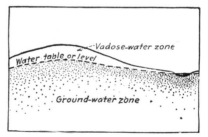

FIG. 117. Diagrammatic sketch of vadose-water zone; water level or water table; and ground-water zone. Degree of saturation is indicated by density of stippling. (*From Tarr, "Introductory Economic Geology."*)

action by the gases in the air and the acids acquired by attacking the rocks, as has been fully explained under "Weathering." In the vadose-water zone, the major part of the chemical work of ground water is carried

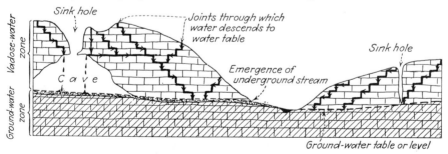

FIG. 118. Sketch showing course of ground water in vadose-water zone, and development of sink holes and caverns.

on. The greatest amount of the solvent work goes on here; for, after the water has dissolved a particle from the walls, it moves on and thus permits a fresher solution to take its place and dissolve more of the rock. In some regions the vadose-water zone contains very little water, the only amount present being that in the soil at the top, sometimes known as *soil water*. The thickness of the vadose-water zone differs with the character of the rocks and the climate.

The *ground-water zone* may extend from the surface to variable distances below it. In some regions there is no ground-water zone; in others, it may lie several hundred feet below the surface. Where the ground-water zone cuts the surface, springs and seeps are present (Fig. 116). As the water in this zone moves very slowly or is motionless, the chemical changes are largely those of cementation and hydration. The ground-water zone is the storage place from which we obtain our water supplies.

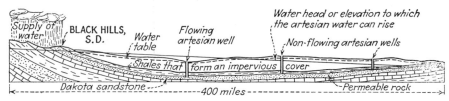

FIG. 119. Sketch showing position of water-bearing Dakota sandstone beneath the surface, and source of its water in mountains to the west. Wherever the water head is above the surface, a well drilled at that point would be a flowing well; wells drilled elsewhere would be artesian but not flowing wells. (Modified from N. H. Darton, U.S. Geological Survey, Water Supply Paper 428, p. 31, 1918.)

Rate of Movement of Underground Water. As stated, the water moves rapidly in the vadose-water zone, and very slowly, or not at all, in the ground-water zone. In some rocks, such as fissured and channeled limestones, the water flows as rapidly as it does in streams; indeed, the openings, if large, may contain underground streams (Fig. 118). In the smaller cracks and in the pores of sandstones, the increased friction greatly reduces the rate of flow of the water. As the rate of flow is so very slow in sandstones, a supply of water obtained from a sandstone whose inflow is many miles away may not equal its removal through wells, whereupon in that region the water level falls. An illustration of this is found in the Dakota sandstone (Fig. 119), which furnishes the water in the Great Plains area and has its inflow in the Rocky Mountains. Sixty years ago the deep wells to this sandstone were flowing wells. They were allowed to flow night and day, however, until the pressure was so decreased that they ceased to flow. They must now be pumped, and the water level is still falling. It is possible to determine the rate of flow of underground water by putting a substance that can easily be detected into the water of one well and watching for its appearance in adjacent wells. By this experiment the rate has been found to be a few feet per day in certain regions.

Keeping in mind these facts regarding the volume, depth, and movement of ground water, let us now turn to a consideration of the geologic work of ground water.

HOW GROUND WATER ACCOMPLISHES ITS WORK

We have already shown that the work of the eroding agents is accomplished by *mechanical* and *chemical methods* and that each agent has its dominant method. Ground water differs from all the other agents in that its work is largely chemical. This is because it is in constant contact with the minerals of the rocks and because water is able to bring about some chemical change whether it contains acids or is pure. Though the solutions move slowly, the almost unlimited time available enables them to bring about marked changes in the rocks. As the processes go on more or less continuously, a great thickness of mantle rock may be produced; enormous caverns may be formed, such as those of Mammoth Cave in Kentucky and Carlsbad Caverns in New Mexico; or poor deposits of valuable metals may be converted into rich deposits, like some of the great copper deposits of western United States (see Fig. 58, page 56) and the enormous iron deposits of the Lake Superior region. The work of ground water and the process of weathering are so nearly one process that it will be impossible to draw a sharp distinction between them in our discussion.

Chemical Work of Ground Water

As the chemical work of ground water is the more important, we shall consider it first. The material carried in solution is spoken of as the *load* of the water, and the three successive steps in the work of ground water may be outlined as follows:

1. Getting a load
   a. How?
   b. Where?
2. Transporting the load
   a. Where?
3. Depositing the load
   a. Why?
   b. Where?

Getting a Load. Water begins its attack upon the minerals of the rocks as soon as it has passed beneath the surface. It dissolves any soluble material it encounters and attacks the other materials by slowly altering them into soluble and insoluble products. The insoluble products are left behind and form the mantle rock and soil. The nature of the soluble products removed depends upon the composition of the original rock. We have shown under "Weathering" that a small group of soluble products are always being removed by ground water and it is these that we shall consider here. They are, in order of abundance:

1. Calcium carbonate and calcium sulfate
2. Silica
3. Sodium carbonate, sodium sulfate, and sodium chloride
4. Magnesium carbonate
5. Potassium compounds (in small amounts)

Carbonate waters, *i.e.*, those containing carbonic acid and carbonates, are the most abundant type of ground and spring waters. In order that the ground water may dissolve calcium carbonate ($CaCO_3$), free carbon dioxide must be available. This is furnished by the carbon dioxide gas commonly present in the water. The carbon dioxide unites with water to form carbonic acid, thus: $CO_2 + H_2O = H_2CO_3$. The carbonic acid then unites with calcium carbonate to form calcium bicarbonate (which is soluble), thus: $H_2CO_3 + CaCO_3 = CaH_2(CO_3)_2$. Magnesium carbonate is dissolved by ground water in the same way. The silica freed in a soluble form during weathering is fairly common in ground water. The sulfate type of ground water is less abundant than the carbonate, although some sulfate is nearly always present owing to the breaking up of some sulfide minerals. Waters containing chlorine are still less common, but a little chlorine may be present.

The ground water gets its load from many sources. The soil furnishes some material, but not so much as do the rocks below, because the soil consists mostly of the residual insoluble material. The surface of the rock beneath the soil, especially if the rock is limestone or dolomite, is an important source of material. In these two rocks the contact of the residual material (mantle rock) and the original rock is sharp, which is in marked contrast to the gradational contact of an igneous rock with its soil (see Fig. 59, page 59). Within a rock the material is obtained chiefly along the walls of the joints and fissures. If the rock is soluble, the openings are widened; if it is relatively insoluble, an altered zone is formed along the walls of the fissures and joints. In even the most minute openings some material may be obtained, but very slowly as the movement of the water there is practically negligible.

Results of the Solution Work of Ground Water. Since, in getting its load, ground water dissolves (or otherwise alters) some of the mineral constituents of the rocks it penetrates, let us investigate the results of this solution work upon the rocks themselves. Briefly, these results are:

1. Additional pore space in the rock   3. Stylolites
2. Roughened surface of the rock   4. Widened joints and sink holes or sinks
5. Caverns, lost rivers, natural bridges, karst topography

As material is removed from the rocks by ground water, their pore space is increased unless deposition or slumping occurs to fill it up. Some rocks become extremely porous, though as a rule the increase in the pore space weakens the rock so much that slumping takes place.

FIG. 120. Roughened surface of limestone produced by solutions, Carthage, Missouri. (*Photograph by W. A. Tarr.*)

The surface of the solid rock, whether it is exposed or in contact with the mantle rock, is the scene of the greatest amount of solvent work so a *roughened surface* is soon developed. If the soluble rock is composed of just one mineral (as is the carbonate rock limestone), the irregularities produced on the surface are due chiefly to differences in the size of the mineral grains (Fig. 120). In other rocks the roughened surface may be due, in addition, to differences in the mineral composition, as some minerals are more easily attacked and removed than others.

Stylolites (Fig. 121) are vertically striated columns, pyramids, or cones occurring usually in nearly horizontal bands in limestones, dolomites, and, rarely, in other kinds of rocks. Stylolites are developed by the solvent work of water in connection with the pressure under which the rocks exist.   The columns overlap each other and are capped by a dark, insoluble clay.   Lines of small stylolites, ½ inch or less in length, resemble "suture joints" and are so called by quarrymen.   A stylolite increases in length by the solution of more of the rock at the end of the column, the column itself being protected from solution by the cap or coating of clay. Some stylolitic columns are 8 or 10 inches long.   Stylolites are a bad feature in many limestones that otherwise would be well suited for building purposes.

FIG. 121. Stylolite in limestone, Carthage, Missouri.

It is inevitable that the walls of a joint or fissure along which water is moving will be attacked and some of the materials removed if there are soluble materials in the wall rock.   The *widened joint* may thus become an opening through which the water moves freely (see Fig. 128, page 136). Insoluble materials may accumulate in the channel of this underground stream, or material from above may be carried down into it (see Fig. 122), and thus the circulation of the water and consequently further solution work would be confined largely to the contact along the walls.   The opening would thus be more rapidly enlarged, and, if the rate of solution exceeded the rate of accumulation of insoluble materials, a depression would develop on the surface.   Such depressions are known as *sink holes* [Figs. 118 (page 127), 123, and 124] and are usually found above a cavern system into which the downward-moving water drains.   In some sink holes, surface water escapes underground; in others, the surface opening

FIG. 122. Limestone showing channels, some of which contain clay. Along highway about 100 miles north of Mexico City. (*Photograph by C. C. Branson.*)

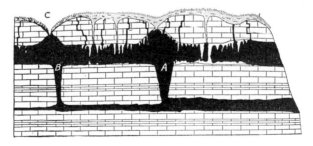

FIG. 123. Diagram showing system of solution openings in limestone. Note stalactites and stalagmites. (A and B) Pits leading from upper to lower caverns. (C) Sink hole. (*After O. E. Meinzer, U.S. Geological Survey, Water Supply Paper 489, p. 116, 1923.*)

becomes closed and the water then accumulates in the depression to form a pond or small lake (Fig. 124). Sink holes are formed, also, when the roof of a cave, which is near the surface, falls in.

Caverns are merely joints that have been exceptionally enlarged by the solution work of the ground water that flows through them. Inasmuch as the circulation must be fairly rapid to bring about much solution work, they are generally formed in the vadose-water zone. Some caverns are of great size and as scenic wonders are visited annually by thousands of

FIG. 124. A large sink hole caused by the solution of salt, Meade County, Kansas. (*Photograph by W. D. Johnson, U.S. Geological Survey.*)

people. Famous caverns in the United States are the Shenandoah and Luray Caverns in the Shenandoah Valley, Virginia; Mammoth Cave in central Kentucky; and Carlsbad Caverns (Fig. 138, page 142) in southeastern New Mexico. Large caverns are developed only in soluble rocks such as limestones, dolomites, gypsum, and salt. Caverns are most common in horizontal rocks [see Figs. 118 (page 127), and 123], but they may also be developed in inclined rocks, as were the Shenandoah Caverns.

The water in a cavern collects into a stream (many are of considerable size) in the lower part of the cave. This stream finally joins the nearest large river, reaching it either by an underground passage or after flowing out of the cavern. Many large springs are undoubtedly the outlets for underground streams (Figs. 118, 125, and 150, page 150). Surface streams that sink underground and reappear miles away are not uncommon in regions of limestone rocks.   Such streams are known as *lost rivers* (Fig. 125).   The course of these streams underground is either a cavern or a cavern in the process of formation.

A stream flowing through a cave lowers its bottom at the same rate at which the stream it enters is being lowered.   Thus in the upper part of the chambers of many caverns, the evidence of the former courses of streams may be seen.   Once a fairly large chamber is developed, the solution work of the stream is aided by blocks' falling from the roof.

FIG. 125. Drainage system of Wakulla River, Florida. Note relationship of the lost river (dashed line) to sinks and springs. (*After Meinzer, U.S. Geological Survey.*)

Some sink holes become elongated in the direction of the underground stream while a portion of the roof is left spanning the stream; these residual portions are known as *natural bridges*.   The famous Natural Bridge of Virginia (Fig. 126) is more than 200 feet above the water.   A highway passes over the top of it.   Natural bridges are also formed as follows: the water of some waterfalls, having found an outlet through joints behind and beneath the falls, emerges at a lower level and follows that channel entirely when the opening has been worn large enough.   A bridge is thus left spanning the new course of the stream.   At Double or Trick Falls (Fig. 127) in Glacier National Park, an early stage in such a development of a natural bridge may be seen.

A region containing many sink holes usually has a rough surface, and the underlying rocks are commonly exposed on the sides of the sink holes.   The name *karst topography* is applied to such an area.   Later, after ground water has removed more material from below and the sink holes become connected, a broad basin floored with good soil results.

Transporting the Load.   The material taken into solution by the ground water is carried along with the water as it moves through the rocks.   The dominant circulation is through cracks, joints, and fissures, all of which are tabular openings lying at all angles in the rocks and crossing each other at all angles.   Water moves through sandstone, channeled limestone, and tuff in any direction, but except in such a limestone (Fig. 128) the rate is slow.   Water may work its way downward along one set of joints and find its way upward again along another

FIG. 126. Natural Bridge, Virginia. It is a portion of a cavern roof left spanning a stream. (*Photograph by W. A. Tarr.*)

FIG. 127. Double or Trick Falls, which shows a stage in the development of a natural bridge, Glacier National Park. (*Photograph by W. D. Keller.*)

FIG. 128. Solution channels developed along fault plane in limestone, Monarch, Colorado. (*Photograph by W. A. Tarr.*)

set. In some mines, tunnels have been driven through hundreds of feet of rock that was dry, although jointed, and then a large fissure was found along which water was circulating in exceptionally large amounts.

Depositing the Load. The material in solution in the ground water will either be deposited in the rocks or, finally, through springs and seeps, be fed to streams and contributed to the sea. As the material which enters the sea will be discussed later under the "Work of the Ocean," we shall confine our study here to that which is deposited by the ground water.

The ground water is capable of dissolving only limited amounts of mineral matter. When it has taken up all it can hold, it is said to be *saturated*, and then slight changes will cause the deposition of some of the material.

Causes of Deposition. A full discussion of the causes of deposition will not be given here, but only a consideration of some of the simpler and more common ones.

a. The *loss of carbon dioxide* is probably one of the most common reasons for deposition, especially of the carbonate minerals. As already indicated, this carbon dioxide is a weakly combined gas and, as long as the water containing it is underground, the gas is confined and so retained, but when that water emerges at the surface the carbon dioxide escapes into the air and the carbonate is consequently deposited. Some spring waters contain so much carbon dioxide and calcium bicarbonate that deposition of calcium carbonate when they emerge is remarkably fast. Objects such as wooden images, fruits, and bird nests are often immersed in these waters and become coated with calcium carbonate. A thin layer may be deposited in 24 hours. Large deposits of calcium carbonate are formed around such springs, as will be noted later. Boiling a carbonate water drives off the carbon dioxide and a deposit is left, such as the *scale* on the inside of a teakettle or in boiler pipes.

b. The *lowering of the temperature* (except in carbonate waters) is another means of bringing about deposition, especially if the water is hot, as in the hot springs of Yellowstone Park. Hot water can hold more material in solution than cold water; hence, if the hot water is saturated and the temperature falls, some of this material must be deposited.

c. The *complete evaporation of a solution* will cause *all* the material to be deposited. Deposition by evaporation takes place in the soil near the surface during dry periods and forms a deposit known as *caliche*. Water used for irrigation purposes dissolves mineral matter from the soil and, as evaporation is rapid at the surface, redeposits it on top of the soil, often ruining it for agricultural purposes.

d. The *mingling of solutions* is a very important means of causing deposition. When waters from different sources bearing different materials in solution come together and mingle, the materials may form new compounds, some of which will undoubtedly be insoluble and thus will be deposited. This mingling may occur where two large fissures or joints cross, and the deposition of the mineral matter may finally fill up the opening at the intersection. Many different kinds of minerals, some of which are very valuable, may be formed in this way.

e. Deposition may occur as a result of *the action of the solutions upon the walls of the cavity* in which the water is moving. By this means, the wall rock is altered, *i.e.*, new minerals are formed and others are removed. These reactions involve most of the changes due to weathering.

Deposition in the Rocks. Deposition beneath the surface takes place largely in the ground-water zone, though deposits may be formed in the vadose-water zone also.

Undoubtedly the most common place in which deposition occurs beneath the surface is *the openings between the grains of the rocks.* The deposited material fills up the pores, acting as a cement to bind the grains together. In this way sands become firm sandstones. The material most commonly deposited is calcium carbonate (calcite); other common materials are soluble silica, which becomes quartz, and the iron oxides hematite and limonite. Such deposition is going on so commonly that the term *zone of cementation* is frequently applied to the ground-water zone.

FIG. 129. Quartz veins in gabbro. Note how veins intersect. Specimen from Maine coast.

The next most common place in which deposition occurs is in the *cracks, joints, and fissures of the rocks.* The deposits made in these openings are thin, tabular forms called *veins* (Fig. 129). When an

FIG. 130. Calcite crystals in vein cutting coal. Specimen from Boone County, Missouri. About ¼ natural size.

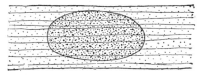

FIG. 131. Sketch of concretion formed by cementation of local area in sandstone. Note that bedding planes pass through concretion.

opening is filled up, the water must find another opening or movement must cease. These veins, unlike those formed by the cooling of an igneous rock, rarely contain deposits of valuable minerals or metals. Calcite is the most common mineral found in them. An interesting feature of these veins is the arrangement of their crystals, which started growing on the walls of the opening and grew outward at right angles to them (Fig. 130). If the crystals from the two sides have not filled the opening, a cavity lined with crystals is left (Fig. 130).

Special Deposits Formed in the Rocks. Firmly cemented, rounded masses formed locally in porous rocks are called *concretions.* They are

formed by the deposition of material at some point and the addition of more of the same material around it, the grains of the original rock being included in the concretion (Fig. 131). Such concretions are, of course, of later origin than the rocks in which they occur. Large concretions, some 10 feet or more in diameter (Fig. 132), may be formed in this manner. In shape they may be spherical, elliptical, or very irregular (Figs. 133 and 134).

Septaria are concretions in which cracks developed by shrinkage were later filled with calcite or some other mineral (Fig. 135). These cracks developed in the interior because the material there dried after that of the

FIG. 132. Concretion (about 10 feet in diameter) of sandstone cemented with iron oxides, Fergus County, Montana. (*Photograph by W. A. Tarr.*)

exterior had become hard. The ground water that furnished material to fill the cracks entered through one or more of them that had extended to the exterior of the concretion.

FIG. 133. Concretions formed by cementation of sandstone with iron oxides, Fergus County, Montana. (*Photograph by W. A. Tarr.*)

The *caliche,* already mentioned, represents another special depositional feature. It occurs just below the surface in arid or semiarid regions where evaporation is rapid. As the water evaporates at or near the sur-

FIG. 134. Calcareous concretions from varved clays along Connecticut River. (*Collected by W. A. Tarr.*)

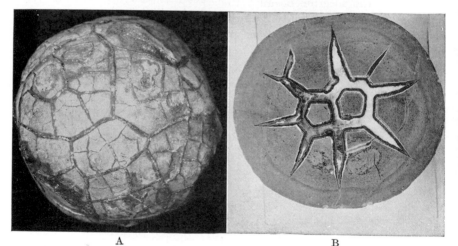

A   B

FIG. 135. (A) Septarium; (B) cross section of a septarium.

face, more water moves up from below to take its place, and it too is evaporated and so deposits the mineral matter it contains. The deposit is usually calcium carbonate and it may be a few inches or many feet in thickness. Soil may or may not be present over the caliche.

Geodes (Fig. 136) are formed by the deposition of material upon the inside of rounded or irregular cavities in the rocks. They are lined with crystals (usually of quartz, calcite, or dolomite) that point inward. The

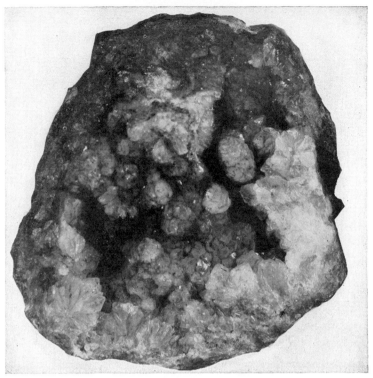

FIG. 136. Geode lined with quartz. About natural size.

way in which geodes are formed is similar to that of the formation of a vein. If a cavity is being filled with quartz introduced as soluble silica and the rate of deposition is fast, a fine-grained variety of quartz is deposited in alternating and colored bands. This variety of quartz is known as *agate* (Fig. 137). The different colors in most agates are due to the presence of varying amounts of hematite (red) and limonite (brown or yellow).

Stalactites and *stalagmites* (Figs. 138 and 139) are deposited by ground water in large openings (caverns) above the water level. The conditions that favor the formation of these features are that a water containing

FIG. 137. Agate showing channel through which the solutions entered. Brown agate inside of quartz crystals. About ¼ natural size.

calcium carbonate in solution should drip or trickle from the roof of a

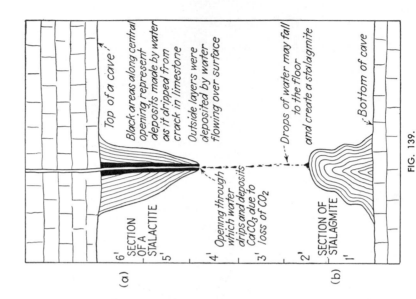

Top of cave

Black areas along central opening represent deposits made by water as it dripped from crack in limestone

Outside layers were deposited by water flowing over surface

Drops of water may fall to the floor and create a stalagmite

Bottom of cave

6'
SECTION
OF A
STALACTITE
5'

4'
Opening through which water drips and deposits $CaCO_3$ due to loss of CO_2
3'

2'
SECTION OF
STALAGMITE
1'

(a)

(b)

FIG. 139.

FIG. 138.

FIG. 138. Stalactites and stalagmites in Carlsbad Caverns, National Park, New Mexico. (Photograph by courtesy of U.S. Department of Interior.)

FIG. 139. Sketch showing development of stalactites and stalagmites.

cavern slowly enough for the water to lose its carbon dioxide and thus cause the deposition of the calcium carbonate.   If deposition occurs on the roof of the cavern, the deposit assumes a shape like an icicle (inner black area of Fig. 139a) and is called a "stalactite," if it occurs on the floor, a rounded mass called a "stalagmite" (Fig. 139b) is built up.   The two forms may join and become columns, which in the language of a guide in Mammoth Cave are "stick-tights."   During the early stages of growth, stalactites are hollow and grow dominantly at the lower end; later, the opening may be partly (Fig. 139a) or entirely closed, where-upon all or a part of the water flows down the outside and deposition occurs all over the surface.   The canopy-like masses in caverns are the

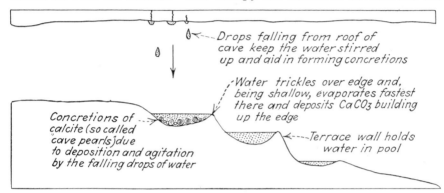

FIG. 140. Sketch showing development of terraces on stalagmites and of concretions in the depressions.

result of the union of adjacent stalactites through the deposition of material on the outside.   The surface of many stalagmites is covered with great numbers of small terraced pools in the bottom of which are rounded calcite pebbles or concretions (so-called "cave pearls").   The terraces are the result of calcium carbonate deposition as carbon dioxide escapes from the shallow water that trickles over the gently sloping surface of a stalagmite (Fig. 140).

The concretions formed in the pools are the result of the deposition of calcium carbonate about nuclei.   Their rounded form is further determined by the agitation of the pools by falling drops of water.   Stalagmites produce a banded calcareous rock known as *onyx marble*, which is cut and polished for use in interior decoration.

Replacement of minerals is an important function of ground water. The replacement of one mineral by another of entirely different composition is well illustrated when calcite (calcium carbonate) is dissolved out and another mineral, such as quartz (silica) is substituted for it.   By means of a partial replacement, one mineral may change into another of a composition not entirely different; for example, pyrite, which occurs

FIG. 141. Petrified Forest, Adamana, Arizona.   (*Photograph by W. A. Tarr.*)

FIG. 142. Polished section of petrified wood from Petrified Forest, Adamana, Arizona.   Slightly reduced.

commonly as cubes and consists of one part of iron (Fe) and two parts of sulfur (S), may be changed into limonite (an oxide of iron) by the removal of the sulfur and the addition of oxygen and water. The limonite retains perfectly the cubic form of the pyrite. A mineral that thus possesses the shape of another is called a *pseudomorph*. The name is apt, as the word "pseudomorph" means "false form."

Petrifaction is the replacement of organic material by some mineral, making it like a rock. The most common example of this change takes place when a piece of wood is buried in the ground and water bearing some silica or iron in solution soaks into it. The woody tissues are removed, particle by particle, and the mineral is deposited in their place (Fig. 141); thus the most minute details of the wood are preserved, even the exterior of it showing the cell details. Wood that has been replaced by quartz is very hard and takes a fine polish (Fig. 142). Petrifaction by iron oxides is less common, but Fig. 143 shows a piece of birchwood that was replaced by limonite while the original bark was preserved.

Surface Deposits Formed by Ground Water. The common type of surface deposits made by ground water is that formed by springs and geysers. Deposition by spring waters is due to lowering of temperature, loss of gases, and, to a less extent, evaporation. The deposited material, which

FIG. 143. Birchwood replaced by limonite. One-half natural size.

usually accumulates around the opening of the spring, is called *calcareous sinter* because of its porosity. The deposit at Mammoth Hot Springs, Yellowstone National Park, is a good example of this type, and Fig. 144 shows another such deposit in Wyoming. Some of these spring deposits spread far and wide over the surface, as do those occurring about 15 miles northeast of Rome, Italy (Fig. 145). These deposits cover an area of several square miles and have furnished *travertine* (the name applied to the more compact spring deposits of calcium carbonate) that is hard enough to be used for building purposes. This stone has been quarried and used for 2,000 years and, at present, is extensively used for interior decoration throughout the United States. A series of waterfalls caused by spring deposits of calcium carbonate occurs in a stream in the Arbuckle Mountains of Oklahoma.

FIG. 144. Hot spring deposit, Thermopolis, Wyoming. (*Photograph by C. C. Branson.*)

FIG. 145. Quarry face in travertine deposits northeast of Rome, Italy. The narrow bands represent the layers deposited by water. (*Photograph by W. A. Tarr.*)

The material deposited by geysers is largely silica, hence its name *siliceous sinter* (Fig. 146A). This material is light colored and very porous. It is deposited chiefly as a result of the loss of gases and a lowering of the temperature of the water. Small plants (algae) that live in some geysers make use of silica in their structure and thus assist in building up the siliceous deposits. A few hot springs of volcanic origin are also depositing silica.   Such springs are those at Steamboat Springs, Nevada (Fig. 146B).

Summary.   Owing to various causes, ground waters deposit their mineral matter below the surface as cements, veins, concretions, geodes, agates, stalactites and stalagmites, pseudomorphs, petrified wood, and caliche; and upon the surface as calcareous sinter, travertine, and siliceous sinter.

FIG. 146. (A) Siliceous sinter deposited about geysers in Yellowstone National Park.   (B) Siliceous sinter deposited by hot springs at Steamboat Springs, Nevada.   (*Photographs by W. A. Tarr.*)

Mechanical Work of Ground Water

We have already emphasized the point that the dominant work of ground water is chemical, but we must note also the chief results of mechanical work.   The mechanical work is accomplished by the *movement* of the water and, therefore, becomes possible whenever the underground stream attains a size that enables it to move rapidly and transport solid particles of rock.   This process is common in many caverns.   The sands, gravels, and muds in the lower part of Mammoth Cave are evidence of the ability of ground water to carry material mechanically.

Common results of the mechanical work of ground water that can be noted at the surface are *soil creep, landslides,* and *rock streams.* Downward movement of a rock mass the weight of which has been increased by water saturation begins if its position is insecure. An important contributing factor in causing creep, landslides, or rock streams is the slipperiness of clays and shales when wet. Thus the surface of a clay or shale

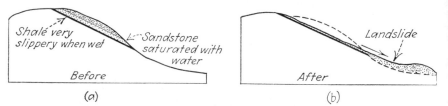

FIG. 147. Sketch illustrating how a landslide may occur.

FIG. 148. A destructive landslide in Alameda County, California. (*Photograph by Gilbert, U.S. Geological Survey.*)

that lies beneath a saturated porous rock becomes an excellent surface along which the overlying material can move (Fig. 147). For these reasons, boulders creep down a slope and great masses of rock break away on hill or mountain sides and plunge downward (Fig. 148).

In numerous places in the Rocky Mountains, rock streams consisting of great masses of broken rock are moving slowly down the valleys. Some of these streams are miles in length (Fig. 149). In the San Juan Mountains of Colorado, enormous volumes of rock are moving down the sides of the mountains and thence down the streams. The Mountains

That Walked, in China, illustrate a similar phenomenon, though on a tremendous scale, for there the area involved covers hundreds of square miles.[1]

FIG. 149. Rock stream on Mt. Etna, Colorado. Length of stream, over a mile. (*After R. D. Crawford, Colorado Geological Survey Bulletin 4, p. 34.*)

THE FATE OF GROUND WATER

We have discussed the work of ground water beneath the surface and have referred to some of its deposits at the surface. In this closing part of the chapter, we shall dwell especially on what finally becomes of the ground water.

A portion of the meteoric water that goes underground *enters into combination with mineral matter* and thus remains locked up in the minerals below the surface. Clay minerals, for example, contain about 14 per cent of water; some hydrous minerals contain less, others more, but this percentage indicates that if many such minerals were formed considerable water would remain underground. Aside from this is the water that has passed into the minute rock openings (called *capillary openings* because they are hair-like in size) and stays there.

The larger part of the ground water, however, finds its way back to

[1] See *National Geographic Magazine*, vol. 41, p. 445, 1922.

the surface and into the air by means of *evaporation*, either directly from the soil or from the leaf surfaces of plants. It is this water (that is constantly being added to the air) that falls again as rain; for, as we have seen, only one-third of the total annual rainfall on the land surface reaches the sea to be evaporated there.

A portion of the ground water reaches the surface through seeps, springs, and wells. Though the amount of ground water that reaches the surface by these means is not so great as that which reaches it by

FIG. 150. Big Spring, Carter County, Missouri.   At its emergence it is 2 or 3 feet higher than the level of the stream into which it flows.   (*Photograph by W. A. Tarr.*)

evaporation, these features form very noticeable and striking surface phenomena and so will be described.

Seeps are important in the total amount of water contributed to the surface, though they do not seem important because of the slow movement of the water.

Underground streams of water issue at the surface as *springs* of varying size, temperature, composition, and permanency. Some springs are very large, being the outlets of underground rivers. The flow of Big Spring (Fig. 150), in Carter County, Missouri, averages over 276,000,000 gallons of water every 24 hours, which is double the amount of water used daily in St. Louis and Kansas City, Missouri. This spring is one of the largest in the United States, but there are many others (Fig. 151). Silver Spring in Florida, when flowing at its maximum, could supply the daily needs of Chicago and Philadelphia. Thousand Springs, Idaho, rivals Silver Spring in size. The large springs issuing from the lava beds along the north side of the Snake River between Milner and King Hill, Idaho, yield enough water to supply all the cities in the United States of more than 100,000 inhabitants, furnishing 120 gallons a day for each person.

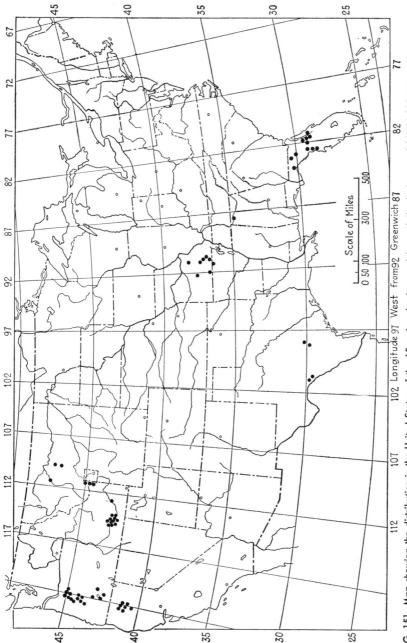

FIG. 151. Map showing the distribution in the United States of the 65 springs having a minimum daily discharge of 64,600,000 gallons. Each of these springs would supply the daily needs of a city of 650,000 people. (Meinzer, U.S. Geological Survey, Water Supply Paper 557, p. 5.)

The majority of springs are cold but a few are not. Those of Hot Springs, Arkansas (temperature of water, 125 to 135°F.), Steamboat Springs, Nevada (185°F.), and Thermopolis, Wyoming (124 to 133°F.), are well known. The most noted examples of hot springs in this country, however, are those of Yellowstone National Park in Wyoming. These springs have a temperature nearly as high as the boiling point (200°F.) of water at the elevation of the park. Many of these springs, like the Mammoth Hot Springs (temperature 162°F.) at the north entrance, are of enormous size. The flow of Mammoth Hot Springs has been decreasing, however, in recent years. Geysers are hot springs that erupt at intervals due to accumulations of steam below. As they are directly dependent upon hot igneous masses, they have been discussed under "Volcanism."

Spring waters have had short or long journeys through the rocks and, as a result, have a wide range in their content of mineral matter, but all contain some, even though it is only a few parts per million. Some springs contain unusual kinds of mineral matter, and others, unusual quantities, so special names have been given them. Some spring waters contain mineral substances of curative value and thus are called *medicinal springs*. Many such springs, however, contain no more mineral matter than do the deep wells which supply many cities. Curative powers are also ascribed to some well waters, and again many of these claims are false. A bad odor such as that due to hydrogen sulfide (the same gas that is found in bad eggs) does not signify a water of curative value.

Most spring waters are potable but it should never be taken for granted that *all* springs are pure and thus suitable for drinking purposes, as they may have become contaminated by surface waters that have found their way downward into the main underground circulation, or they may have come in contact with minerals that contain poisonous substances. Examples of ill effects due to artesian water are reported from North Dakota and Arizona, where an excessive amount of fluorine in solution causes a mottling of the enamel of children's teeth. (In slight amounts fluorine may be beneficial to teeth.)

The permanency of springs is of passing interest only. If a spring flows all the year, it is a *permanent spring;* those flowing only after rainy periods are *intermittent springs*. Since springs are dependent upon the rainfall, even supposedly permanent springs may fail to flow after a succession of dry seasons.

Wells, like springs, vary in temperature, composition, permanency, and size. As water is widespread in its occurrence within the rocks, most wells furnish some water. However, wells that are several hundred feet deep may be dry and that, too, in a vicinity of shallower, productive wells. This is due largely to the character of the rocks, some being porous and others impervious; some with many joints, and others containing

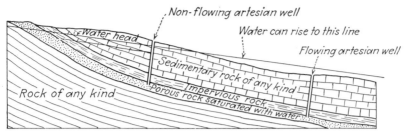

FIG. 152. Diagram showing how artesian and flowing wells are formed.

very few, or only cracks. It may also be due, however, to the other factors that control the amount of ground water. A fallacious idea

prevails among some people that it is possible by the use of the branches of certain trees to find and follow from the surface the course of underground water. The turning of the branch in the hands of these persons is due entirely to the tension developed in the stick by holding it in a certain way and thus has, of course, no connection with water below.

If the water in a well rises above the level at which it was reached, the well is an *artesian well* (Fig. 152). This rise is due to the fact that the bed containing the water crops out at a higher elevation than that at which it occurs in the well. Just so, the water from a tank is forced up to the second story of a house provided the second story is below the tank. This

FIG. 153. Flowing well, Boone County, Missouri. The water is rising from a depth of about 500 feet. (Photograph by W. A. Tarr.)

pressure of the water is called the *head* (Fig. 152). If the pressure in a well is great enough, the water may overflow, producing a *flowing artesian well* (Figs. 152 and 153).

SUMMARY

Rain water, falling upon the surface of the earth, goes underground, and there accomplishes chemical work by altering and dissolving the minerals of the rocks. The materials removed are either redeposited below or brought to the surface. Various features are formed by water below the surface and, also, by springs at the surface. The work of ground water is vital to man, as by means of it soil is developed and plant life supported.

CHAPTER 8

THE OCEAN

In the two preceding chapters we have seen that by the work of streams and ground water a vast quantity of material is removed from the surface of the land. The amount so removed in the United States every 8,000 to 10,000 years averages 1 foot of material from its entire land surface. The receiving station for such vast quantities of material is the ocean, though it is not necessarily their final resting place as the ocean

FIG. 154. Sketch comparing vertical cutting (by streams) with horizontal cutting (by ocean).

has encroached upon the land many times during the earth's history, and the materials deposited in it during such periods were left upon the land when the water retreated into the deeper parts of the ocean bed. This material was then attacked again by the eroding agents and again moved oceanward.

In addition to being the repository for eroded materials, however, the ocean is also an active eroding agent; hence its work is both depositional and erosional. The *erosive work* of the ocean is accomplished mainly along its shores. The waves, which are the chief moving agents, are always at sea level, so that the ocean may be likened to a horizontal saw that is always cutting laterally at the same level, in contrast with the other eroding agents that cut vertically (Fig. 154). The cliffs along the sea are evidence of the lateral cutting of waves. The *depositional work* of the ocean occurs from the beach to deep water; but, inasmuch as the material deposited is derived from the land, the deposits near the shore greatly exceed in amount those of midocean.   The ocean deposits are formed both mechanically and chemically, and so the sedimentary rocks that they become represent the two methods of origin.   Though we shall consider many phases of these deposits in connection with the work of the ocean, the methods of their deposition will be taken up in the chapter on sedimentary rocks.

The Extent of the Ocean.   The ocean covers about three-fourths of the surface of the globe, or about 143,000,000 square miles.   It extends beyond its true basin, overlapping about 10,000,000 square miles of the area of the continents (Fig. 155).   This part of the ocean is called the

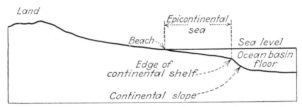

FIG. 155. Sketch showing how the sea laps up on the continents.

epicontinental sea ("epi" means "upon"), and it is this portion with which we are primarily concerned as most of the work of the ocean takes place there.   The width of the epicontinental sea ranges from almost zero to many miles, and its maximum depth is about 600 feet.   The different parts of the ocean are all connected; hence the water level, or *sea level*, is the same in all and is the datum plane from which all land elevations are measured.

The volume of water in the oceans is estimated at 323,722,150 cubic miles, yet this is only 1/4,500 of the volume of the earth.   The average depth of the ocean is about 2.5 miles (13,000 feet).   In this connection it is of interest to note that the average height of the land is about 0.5 mile (2,500 feet); hence the average height of the land above the average depth of the ocean is about 3 miles.   If all the continents were cut down and the material deposited in the depths of the ocean, the water would be about 9,000 feet deep over the entire earth.   The greatest depth known in the ocean is over 34,400 feet.   This is in the Pacific, just east of the Philippine Islands.   About 4 per cent of the ocean floor lies below 18,000 feet of water.

Composition of Ocean Water.   We ordinarily think of the ocean as "salt water," but only about three-fourths of the mineral content of ocean water is common salt.   The average content of mineral matter in solution in sea water is about 35 parts to 1,000 parts of water.   The presence of the mineral matter in sea water increases the specific gravity

of the water from 1 to 1.026.   The total quantity present is about 4,800,-
000 cubic miles, enough to cover the United States and its possessions to
a depth of slightly more than a mile.

The average composition of the soluble mineral matter in the ocean
(data from Dittmar and Clarke) is shown in the second column of the
following table:

AVERAGE SOLUBLE CONTENT OF RIVER AND SEA WATERS CONTRASTED

Constituent	Parts per thousand	
	River water	Sea water
Calcium carbonate (CaCO₃).........	0.077	0.123
Magnesium compounds.............	0.026	5.540
Silica (SiO₂).....................	0.017	0.004
Calcium sulfate (CaSO₄)...........	0.008	1.260
Potassium compounds..............	0.005	0.863
Sodium chloride (NaCl)............	0.004	27.200
Iron oxides.......................	0.003	trace
Aluminum oxides..................	0.003	trace
Total dissolved matter............	0.143	35.000

Traces of mineral substances other than those in the above list are contained in sea water, some of which are bromine, iodine, nickel, cobalt,
copper, zinc, lead, gold, and silver.

Gases are present also in sea water.   These are notably air (nitrogen
and oxygen) and carbon dioxide.   The air dissolved in sea water contains
a higher percentage of oxygen than does the atmosphere.   Cold water
holds more carbon dioxide than warm water does; a fact that has probably
had some effect upon the climates of the past.   The sea water contains
from 18 to 27 times as much carbon dioxide as occurs in the air.   The
carbon dioxide of the atmosphere absorbs heat, and because of this it has
been suggested that, if the ocean waters were cold enough to absorb large
quantities of carbon dioxide from the air, the climate would become cold—
even that a glacial epoch might result.   The most important regulator
of the temperature of the air, however, is its constituent water vapor, and
any climatic changes would be due primarily to changes in the amount of
this water vapor.

Source of Mineral Matter in Ocean Water.   The larger part of the
vast amount of mineral matter in the ocean is brought to it by streams
and ground water.   Only a small portion is taken from the solid materials
along the shores, as the amount of chemical work done by the ocean is
small.

In the first column of the preceding table (data from Russell), the amount of mineral matter in solution in river water is given. We can thus contrast the composition of average river water with that of sea water and, from the comparison, learn which elements remain in the ocean water and which ones are readily deposited. By studying the table, we see that calcium carbonate and silica, the most abundant and the third most abundant constituents, respectively, of river water, are present only sparingly in the ocean and so must have been largely deposited. The second most abundant constituent of river water, the magnesium compounds, is also second in abundance in ocean water, from which we conclude that magnesium compounds are much more soluble in sea water than calcium carbonate and silica. Of the three substances found in the smallest amounts in river water, the first, sodium chloride, constitutes the great bulk of all the soluble matter in the sea; but the other two, the iron and aluminum oxides, are present in very small amounts. The insolubility of these oxides in ocean water is thus shown by their having been deposited. The high solubility of sodium chloride in sea water is shown by its great abundance there, although it is brought in by the rivers in such small amounts. Sodium chloride must have been accumulating in the ocean over a long period of time. It may seem from the table that potassium compounds are much less soluble in sea water than those of sodium, but there is not this great difference in their solubility. The lack of an abundance of potassium compounds in ocean water is due rather, it is believed, to the affinity of potassium salts for the solid material clay. The potassium compounds cling to the clay particles and are deposited with them.

Life in the Ocean. Although living creatures are found throughout the ocean, the major part of all ocean life exists in the shallow epicontinental seas surrounding the continents. As this is also the zone of the major work of the ocean, the life in these waters plays a part in the deposits made there. A considerable part of the deposition of calcium carbonate, for example, is accomplished by organisms that use it for their shells.

MECHANICAL WORK OF THE OCEAN

The ocean accomplishes most of its work mechanically and only a very minor part chemically. The mechanical work of the ocean is of two different kinds: *erosive* and *depositional*. The depositional work is not only that which is connected with the large quantities of clastic material brought to the ocean by the rivers of the world, but a part (a minor part, of course) is concerned with the formation of deposits from the materials eroded by the waves from the rocks at the seashore. The erosional work of the ocean is concerned also with the process of reducing the size of fragments of rock brought in by the rivers.

The Mechanical Agents

Just as the ability of a stream to accomplish mechanical work is dependent upon its velocity, so the mechanical work of the ocean (a comparatively quiet body of water) depends upon the very small part of its body that is moving. The moving parts of the sea are the *waves, currents,* and *tides;* hence these are the agents that perform the mechanical work of the ocean.

Waves. Most of the mechanical work of the ocean is accomplished by the waves, which owe their origin to the wind that sweeps over the water. The stronger the wind and the longer it blows, the larger are the

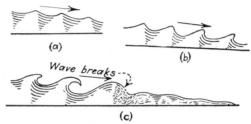

FIG. 156. Sketch of a wave breaking on a beach.

waves. Waves consist dominantly of an up-and-down movement of the water but include also a forward movement at the immediate surface. The maximum movement of the water in a wave is, therefore, at the surface. The movement dies out rapidly downward, usually within a few feet, though rarely waves reach depths of 25 or 50 feet and exceptional storm waves may extend downward 600 feet. The chief force of the wave is developed when it breaks on the shore, whether on a beach of loose materials or upon a rock surface. Waves also break in the open ocean (then called "white caps") but accomplish no work there.

Upon a beach having a wide, gently sloping surface, the waves drag upon the bottom in the shallow water. This retards their movement, deflecting it upward and therefore increasing the height of the waves (*a,* Fig. 156). At the same time, the top or crest of the wave, as it is able to move faster, rushes forward (shown in *b,* Fig. 156) until it overhangs the slower-moving trough and, lacking support, breaks (*c,* Fig. 156, and Fig. 157).

As a wave breaks on the beach (which is the place of active wave work), the water is violently agitated and the pebbles on the bottom are rubbed and ground against one another. These pebbles tend to become flatter than those made by running water because the movement of the waves is a back-and-forth sliding movement. Some beaches become covered with flattened or elliptical pebbles, 2 to 6 inches in diameter, and are then known as *shingle beaches.* The pebbles and boulders of the beach are efficient tools with which the waves accomplish much work. Waves that are driving in upon a rocky shore where the water is deep enough to prevent much retardation at the bottom will break upon the rocks. During storms the force of the blows may amount to hundreds of pounds per square foot. If these blows are rapidly repeated, immense damage may be done to piers and sea walls during a single storm. Enormous blocks of rock, weighing tons, have been shifted about by storm waves. As a matter of fact, the exceptional waves of storms, though occurring many years apart, may loosen and pry off more material than

FIG. 157. Several waves breaking diagonally on the beach at Seacroft, below Belfast, Maine. The three phases of wave motion (a, b, and c of Fig. 156) can be seen along each wave. (*Photograph by W. A. Tarr.*)

the ordinary waves can break up in the long intervals between the storms. A broad shelving shore would be less effectively attacked by the waves than a steep rocky shore.

In deep water, waves cannot use rocks as tools but must depend upon the weight of the moving water. They are aided along shore by air in the joints of the rocks. The water rushing into the joints compresses the air which, in turn, exerts a pressure upon the rocks. This process, repeated every few seconds, greatly assists the waves; in fact, in small caves along the shore, whole blocks are pried off from the roof and sides by the force of this compression and expansion.

Another point that should be noted is that the belt of active work by the waves is limited in depth to the distance between high and low tide plus the height of the highest storm waves.

Currents. Not only does the breaking of the waves accomplish work, but waves cause currents which effectively aid in the work. The drift of the water at the surface as the wind blows over it sets up currents that move in the direction of the wind. These currents occur dominantly along the shore, where the tide, also, aids in their formation. The shore currents move in any direction along the shore (Fig. 158). When the waves are breaking rapidly, shore currents are strong; at other times, they move slowly. The strongest shore currents are those formed on the floor of the beach by the backward flow of the water after a wave has broken. These are known as the *undertow* (Fig. 158), which is very important in shifting materials seaward. Currents are also produced in the open sea, but there they are unimportant in the work of the ocean as they are largely slow drifts of water. Any shore current moving offshore becomes unimportant also, save for transporting and distributing materials in suspension and solution.

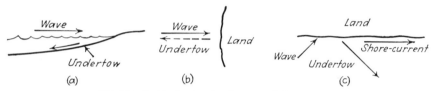

FIG. 158. Sketch showing development of shore currents.

Tides. The tide creates strong currents along a rough indented shore, and these tidal currents aid in the work of the ocean. The rise and fall of the tide, twice each day, widens the effective zone in which the waves can work. In some bays, the tide has a rise and fall of 15, 20, or even 50 feet.

How the Mechanical Agents Work and Some Results

The work of the waves, currents, and tides (like that of streams and ground water) is accomplished in three successive steps: (1) *getting a load*, (2) *transportation*, and (3) *deposition*.

Getting a Load. Though much clastic material of small sizes is contributed to the sea water by streams and very minor amounts by glaciers and the wind, considerable quantities of material are obtained directly by the ocean itself through the *work of waves* on the rocks of the shore. These loosened materials, *i.e.*, *sand*, *granules*, *pebbles*, and *boulders*, are then used as tools with which to grind or hammer off more material from the rocks. In the process, the tools themselves are ground to smaller sizes and, with the fragments worn from the rocks, furnish much clastic material of the smallest sizes, *i.e.*, silt and clay, which the ocean has thus produced by its own efforts.

Erosive Features Formed along the Shore. While the ocean is acquiring some of its load by the erosive work of its waves and currents, many interesting features are produced on its shores. Some of them are *wave-cut beaches or terraces, sea cliffs, sea caves, chimneys, and natural bridges.*

A *wave-cut beach or terrace* is produced by the waves' cutting into a land surface of moderate relief (Figs. 159, 160, and 161). The beach varies in width, depending upon the depth of the water, the force of the waves, the height of the land, and the character of the rocks. If the land is high, a *sea cliff* (Figs. 159, 160, and 161) will be developed as a result of undercutting by the waves. The height and steepness of the cliff will depend upon the height of the land above the sea and the rate of cutting by the waves. If the waves are strong and the rocks weak (as are soft shales and sandstones and the chalk cliffs of England and France), erosion will be fast and the cliff may retreat a few feet a year. Cliffs that are cut in hard, resistant rock show no change in thousands of years.

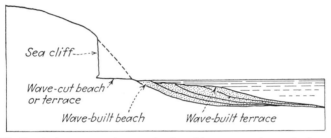

FIG. 159. Sketch showing some features developed by waves and currents along shores.

An example of rapid wave erosion in sandstone is the swift (geologically speaking) reduction in size of the island of Heligoland in the North Sea. In A.D. 800, this island had a circumference of 120 miles (Fig. 162); 500 years later, 45 miles; and, after another 500 years, in 1910 when Heligoland was transferred from English to German possession, 3 miles. Germany, in making the island a military fortress, halted the work of the waves by the construction of a sea wall, 25 feet high, of steel, granite, and concrete at a cost of $30,000,000.

During the attack of the waves on the land, many incidental features are formed, some of which are more or less striking in appearance. A *sea cave* is a fairly common feature that is formed at the level of the waves by their cutting back along weak places in the rocks. Sea caves usually develop in jointed rocks, especially if there are two sets of joints, one fairly horizontal and the other vertical. Solubility of the rocks is of some aid, but sea caves are no more abundant in limestones than in other rocks. The Blue Grotto near Naples, Italy, is a sea cave of interest because of the blue color on the interior. This color is due to light reflected from outside. The roofs of sea caves are eroded by the waves, aided, if the entrance is closed at high tide, by the compression of the air in the cave. The roofs finally break through to the surface (just as do those of the

FIG. 160. Waves (at high tide) developing a sea cliff and a wave-cut beach or terrace. (Modified after D. W. Johnson, "Shore Processes and Shoreline Development," with permission of John Wiley & Sons, Inc.)

FIG. 161. Same shore as that shown in Fig. 160, but showing the wave-built beach exposed at low tide. (Modified after D. W. Johnson, "Shore Processes and Shoreline Development," with permission of John Wiley & Sons, Inc.)

underground caves that form sink holes).   During storms, water may be ejected through this roof opening, giving rise to *spouting caves.*

If the rocks along a shore contain vertical joints, erosion along these joints is usually rapid, whereupon the face of the cliff will become deeply indented.   As the erosion continues, vertical masses of rock will become separated from the cliff.   These masses are called *chimneys* or *stacks* (Figs. 163, 164, and 165).   During the process of separation, when the waves have cut through below the surface but there is still a rock connection at the surface, a *natural bridge* exists (Figs. 166 and 167).

Transportation.   The transportation of the materials contributed to the ocean, as well as of those acquired by its own erosive power, is accomplished by the *waves, the undertow and other shore currents, and the tidal currents.*   These forces are not equally developed along any given shore, but all function in some degree.   The methods of transportation are similar to those of the streams, *i.e.*, the material is moved by *sliding, rolling, saltation,* and *in suspen-*

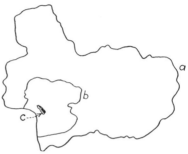

FIG. 162. Sketch shows how rapid wave erosion had reduced size of island of Heligoland in the successive years of 800 (*a*), 1300 (*b*), and 1910 (*c*).

sion.   The major part is moved on the bottom; for, because of the much slower movements of ocean water, any material in suspension settles out rapidly.   Owing to this fact, the water along a shore is fairly clear unless violently agitated during storms.

The material is transported toward the open sea by the undertow and other currents, or it may be shifted along the beach by the lateral shore currents.   If the direction of these currents is constant, the transported materials are all moved one way along the beach; but, if the currents vary in direction, the materials are shifted back and forth.

Deposition.   Just as velocity is essential in enabling the waves and currents to pick up and carry materials, so a decrease in velocity will mean the deposition of their load.   This loss of velocity is due dominantly to the shifting of the currents and waves into deeper or shallower water and, to a less extent, therefore, to the overloading of the ocean water by streams.   A shore current that in moving along a beach (*a*, Fig. 168) reaches a point (*b*, Fig. 168) where the shore turns inland to produce a bay will continue straight ahead (following a law of all moving bodies).   As it leaves the shore, however, it will enter deeper and deeper water.   This deep water is not moving; hence the velocity of the current will be checked.   As the materials that the current was shifting along the bottom will continue to follow the bottom, they will thus move downward

FIG. 163. Sketch showing how vertical joints favor the development of stacks along a shore.

FIG. 164. Stacks and sea cliffs, island of Capri, Italy.

out of the zone of strongly moving water and so will come to rest in the deeper water of the bay.   Smaller indentations along a coast will cause a correspondingly smaller checking of velocity and thus deposition on a minor scale.   If a current shifts from deep into shallow water, the consequent increased friction with the bottom will retard velocity and deposition will result.   The undertow, in moving seaward from the beach, encounters deeper water and, as it loses its velocity, deposits its load. In this way, it builds up the sea floor offshore and so can move material farther and farther seaward.   The very finest materials borne in suspension are carried many miles offshore (records show that materials from the Amazon River have been thus carried

FIG. 165. Wave erosion at the base of a stack, Alaska. (Photograph by W. W. Atwood, U.S. Geological Survey.)

several hundred miles out to sea), but nevertheless they finally sink downward beyond the moving water of the current, through the still water below, and at last to the sea bottom.

FIG. 166. Natural bridge developed along a joint by wave erosion, La Jolla, California. (Photograph by W. A. Tarr.)

For the most part, the material worn from the land is deposited along the beaches, but some is shifted offshore.   There are many variations from the normal movement seaward.   The waves that drive in on the shore move material up on the beach; the undertow drags it back. The battle is ceaseless, but the movement toward deeper water gains. Materials that are derived from the land, shifted seaward, and deposited are known as *terrigenous* (land-derived) *materials*.

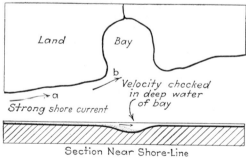

Features Formed by Deposition along the Shore. The deposits made along the shore by the ocean have numerous forms, the more common of which are *wave-built beaches, wave-built terraces, barrier beaches, spits, hooks, bars,* and *tombolos.* All of these deposits are the result of the mechanical work of the ocean.

The *wave-built beach* represents the major accumulation of material along a shore. The other features are, as we shall see, largely special extensions of the beach. The *wave-built terrace* (Figs. 159 and 161) results from the deposition in deeper water of material removed from the beach. If a beach is wide and nearly flat, large waves coming in commonly break a considerable distance offshore. At this place, a ridge of sand is usually developed as the waves and the under-tow shift material to this point from both sides. The ridge may be built above the water level by the help of storm waves and, if so,

FIG. 167. Natural bridge cut by waves in chalk on north coast of Ireland near Portrush. Note another natural bridge in headland seen through arch. (*Photograph by W. A. Tarr.*)

FIG. 168. Sketch showing deposition due to check in velocity of a current entering the deeper water of a bay.

becomes a *barrier beach* (Fig. 169). The lagoon back of a barrier beach gradually fills up, becomes a swamp, and finally the swamp also disappears; and thus the area has been reclaimed from the sea.

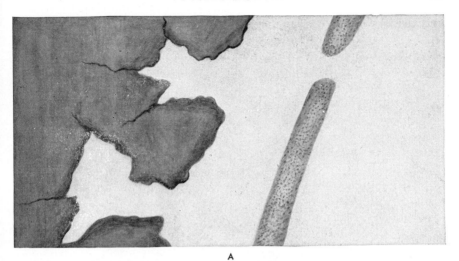

A

B

FIG. 169. Sketch showing position (A) and structure (B) of a barrier beach.

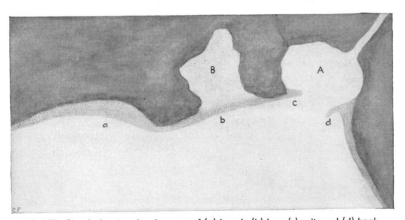

FIG. 170. Sketch showing development of (a) beach, (b) bar, (c) spit, and (d) hook.

As the shore currents move material along the beach, some form of deposition occurs wherever there is a change in the direction of the shore. If the shore line curves out toward the open sea, the shore currents fill in the inside of the curve and widen the beach, as at *a*, Fig. 170. The deposition that occurs as a shore current enters the side of a bay extends the beach out into the bay, and a *spit* (Fig. 170 *c*) is formed. If the spit is built across the bay, it becomes a *bar* (Fig. 170 *b* and Figs. 171 and 172)

and the bay becomes a lake or lagoon (Fig. 170 *B*). If the bar extends
from the mainland to an island, it is called a *tombolo* (Fig. 173). It
commonly happens that waves drive into a bay where a spit is being
built and deflect the shore current inward so that the spit becomes

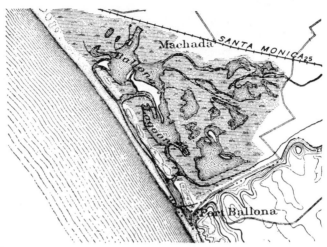

FIG. 171. Map showing bar and lagoon on California shore. (Part of the Redondo, California,
Quadrangle. Contour interval is 25 feet; 1 mile = 1 inch.)

FIG. 172. Bar built across a bay. Lagoon at back being filled up.

curved, forming a *hook*. A strong river current entering a bay (Fig. 170
A) during the formation of a spit may change it into an outward-curved
hook (Fig. 170 *d*).

All these depositional features are common along the seashore, especially if the coast has many indentations and the water is not too deep.
They are very numerous along the Massachusetts coast line, where the

waves have an abundance of soft, loose material to work upon. On the other hand, the Maine coast line is remarkably free from them, because the continental glaciers deepened the water along the shore and removed most of the soft rock, and the waves have been unable, as yet, to alter the hard rock that is exposed. Along the Atlantic Coast from New Jersey southward, depositional features are abundant.

FIG. 173. Air view of land-tied island produced by formation of a tombolo, Alaska. (*Courtesy of* U.S. Navy Air Service.)

The Changing Topography of the Coast

In studying the features due to erosion and deposition along the shore, we have seen how the ocean itself is constantly modifying and changing the topography of its coast. A glance at the map of any continent will show how the shape of the coast line differs from place to place (Fig. 174). The actual outline of the coast is due to the *work* (*both erosional and depositional*) *of waves and currents*, but this work may be interrupted and modified by three factors, *viz.*, *sinking of the coast, raising of the coast*, and *work of glaciers and streams*.

The Production of an Adjusted Shore Line. *The Work of the Waves and Currents.* The effectiveness of the work of the waves and currents along a shore depends on various factors, among which are the existing *irregularities of the coast line, the character of the rock*, and *the depth of the water* along the shore.

Projecting portions of land, such as capes, points, and other headlands (Figs. 163 and 164), are more vigorously attacked by the waves than are the rocks of the shore in reentrants, such as bays, sounds, and sea caves. The dominant modifications caused by the waves and currents, therefore, are the cutting away of the headlands and the deposition of the material in the quiet water of the nearest reentrant. This would mean a smoothing out of the shore line. If no other factors intervened and the waves and currents were thus allowed to complete their work, the final result would be an *adjusted shore line*, *i.e.*, one upon which the erosive work of the waves and currents was balanced by their depositional work.

An adjusted shore line, however, would not be perfectly straight unless the rocks of the shore were all of the same hardness. Thus, where the material is all sand, the shore line is straight or has long sweeping curves, as portions of the coast line of the Carolinas (Fig. 174) or of Texas. A coast line that is straight in general outline, however, has minor indentations known as *cusps* because of their resemblance to a crescent moon. Cusps are the result of the adjustment of the direction of the waves to the direction of the shore line.

The depth of the water is also a factor in the effect produced on a shore line. Waves have less eroding power in shallow water and, hence, in such places cannot cut the land so rapidly.

FIG. 174. Map of southeastern United States showing smooth and irregular shore lines.

During the early stages in the development of an adjusted shore line by the waves and currents, the irregularities are increased. This occurs very commonly by the production of spits and hooks (as can be seen at *c* and *d* in Fig. 170). Likewise, barrier beaches, whether connected with the mainland or not, increase the irregularities of a coast line. During and by the formation of stacks (see Figs. 163 and 164), the coast line is rendered more irregular and longer; and, when, by the deposition of the materials cut away, the stacks or islands are later tied to the mainland by tombolos (Fig. 173), the irregularity as well as the lengthening is further increased. Later, however, the spits and hooks are built entirely across the bays, forming bars; the lagoons back of the bars and barrier beaches become filled up; and, by more sediment being deposited along the tombolos, the land-tied islands become fully incorporated with the

mainland.   All this may result finally in producing a coast line of long
sweeping curves (Fig. 171).   The shore line of North Carolina is much
longer now than it will be when the lagoons back of the barrier beaches
along the shore are filled up.   Thus we see that the increase produced
in the irregularities of a coast line is temporary and, as the period of
filling in the indentations continues, a coast line of long sweeping curves
will be produced.   A good illustration of a shore line in the process of
change is seen in Fig. 175, which represents a part of the south coast of
Martha's Vineyard in 1846 and in 1886.   Such marked changes may
occur in a few years where the waves and shore currents are especially
active.

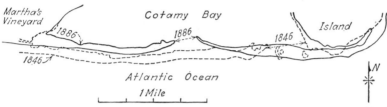

FIG. 175. Map showing shore line of Martha's Vineyard, Massachusetts, in 1846 and in 1886.   (After
Shaler, U.S. Geological Survey, 1885–1886.)

Effect of a Sinking Coast.   A factor that may interfere with the work
of the ocean in adjusting its shore line is the sinking of the coast.   The
effect that will be produced may be seen by a study of Fig. 176, which
shows a dissected area having an irregular shore line, and the same region
after the land had sunk (Fig. 177), showing how the sea had entered
the valleys of the rivers to variable distances depending upon the slope
or gradient of the valleys.   If the United States should sink 100 feet,
the mouth of the Mississippi River would be above the city of Vicksburg,
Mississippi, and a large area that is now along the river would thus be
submerged (Fig. 178).   If the downward movement should be 500 feet, a
vast area (black and stippled areas in the figure) would be submerged.
Valleys into which the sea enters owing to a sinking of the land are called
drowned valleys (Fig. 177).   Chesapeake Bay (a striking example) is the
drowned lower portion of the Susquehanna River.   The Potomac,
Rappahannock, and James rivers, which were formerly tributaries of
the Susquehanna, also have drowned valleys in their lower courses (Fig.
179).   Delaware Bay is the drowned end of the Delaware River.   The
lower end of the Hudson River was also drowned; in fact, the course of
the Hudson can be traced on the sea floor for about 50 miles out to the
edge of the continental shelf (Fig. 180).

Other lines of evidence of sinking shore lines are known.   Buried
fresh-water trees and sod have been found in the sea along the New Jersey
coast and elsewhere.   Man-made structures have sunk beneath the

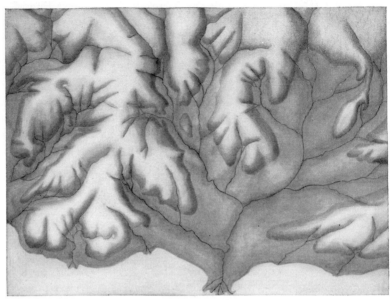

FIG. 176. A dissected area along a seashore.

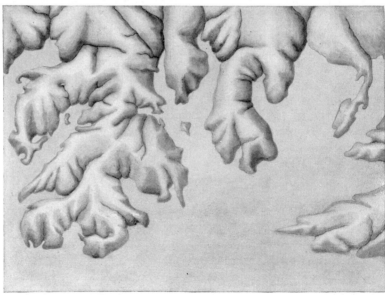

FIG. 177. Area of Fig. 176 after submergence. Shows drowned valleys and greatly lengthened coast line.

sea, and some, like the famous temple of Serapis at Pozzuoli, Italy, have been reelevated.

The result of a sinking coast is, therefore, to develop a shore line of numerous irregularities; hence the waves and currents must begin anew their work of adjusting the shore line. Projecting land masses must again be cut away and indentations filled out. Sinking of coasts and the consequent changes are going on constantly. The Atlantic seaboard in America is evidently sinking, at present, but so slowly that it can only be detected by careful observations extending over a long period of years.

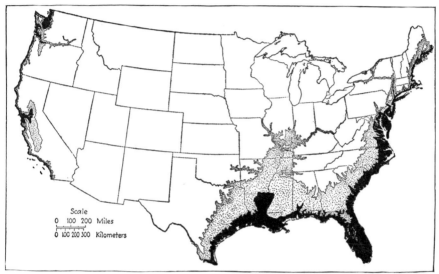

FIG. 178. Map of United States showing areas (black) that would be submerged if land sank 100 feet, and areas (stippled) that would be submerged if land sank 500 feet.

Effect of a Rising Coast. The effect of a rising coast is much different from that of one that is sinking. If the land rises (or, as is more probable, the sea level goes down), the shore line shifts seaward (see Fig. 78, page 87). The coast line formed by the emergence will be smoother than the old one because the deposition of material that has been going on offshore will, in varying degrees, have filled up the low places and left a smooth, uniform bottom. The important point about the outward shift of the seashore is that it stops the work of adjustment that has been going on at the higher level and starts it anew at a lower level. The amount of work necessary to bring about adjustment will, however, be much less on the fairly smooth emerged coast than on the deeply indented shore resulting from a submergence of the land.

Evidences that the land has been raised are readily discernible along many seacoasts. The coast of California from Oceanside (below Los

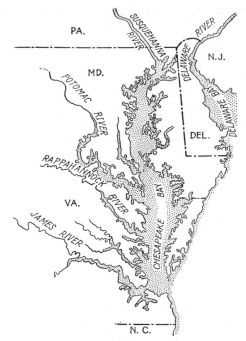

FIG. 179. Drowned valleys on Atlantic Coast.

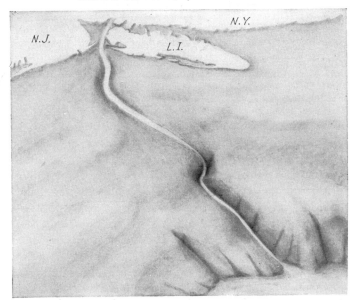

FIG. 180. Sketch showing drowned course of the ancient Hudson River. Note deep canyon at lower end.

Angeles) to San Diego and beyond is a good example. The raised beaches, spits, hooks, bars, and sea cliffs in this section all show that the coast has gone up. Wave-cut terraces or beaches are common along the Alaska coast, and in some of those at Nome, Alaska, gold placers have been found. One of these gold-bearing beaches is 22 feet above the present sea level, the next is 38 feet, and the highest is 78 feet.

The presence of wave-cut and wave-built terraces (Fig. 181) in the hills and mountains around Great Salt Lake shows that the water of the lake once stood much higher than it does today. These features show the evidences of wave action, just as it is seen today along seashores where wave-cut and wave-built terraces are being formed. The beaches

FIG. 181. Wave-built terrace formed along the old shore line of Great Salt Lake. (*Photograph by W. A. Tarr.*)

or terraces were abandoned as the water in the lake was lowered by evaporation. The succession of terraces shows that during periods of a fairly stationary water level, owing to the inflow's equaling the evaporation, the waves were able to build new beaches and terraces.

The Effect of Ice and Streams. Wherever the edge of the great continental *ice sheets* reached the sea in a region of considerable relief, the glaciers dug out the bottoms of the stream-made valleys and steepened their sides. When the ice melted, a very irregular shore line of numerous rocky headlands and many deep indentations was exposed. Moreover, as this type of irregular shore line developed best in fairly resistant rocks, a maximum amount of work for the waves and currents was produced, and thus the time necessary for the creation of an adjusted shore line was greatly lengthened. The deep, steep-sided valleys produced by the ice are known as *fiords*. The coasts of Norway, Greenland, and Alaska show large numbers of such features. The coast line of Maine is remarkable in being over 3,000 miles long (owing to its hundreds of bays and islands), though the direct line along the coast is only about 300 miles. This very irregular shore line was produced by the sinking of the shore in connection with the effect of ice on a stream-made topography. The waves have had very little effect on the rocks of this shore since the ice retreated.

Streams may produce irregularities in a shore line or make it straighter. A stream that is bringing more material to the ocean than the currents can move away builds a delta at its mouth, and so an irregularity in the shore line is produced. On the whole, however, the effect of streams is to produce a smoother shore line, for more of the material they contribute to the sea is used to fill up indentations than is used in the formation of deltas.

Summary. The topography of any coast is due primarily to the work of the waves and currents, which are tending to straighten its outline by cutting away the headlands and filling out the indentations. This process is interrupted, from time to time, by downward or upward movements of the land and is modified by the work of other physical agents, especially ice and streams. Allowing the agents of the ocean time enough, they will finally smooth out the irregularities of the coast and produce an adjusted shore line along which the work of erosion and deposition will be in balance.

The Topography of the Ocean Floor

The topography of the ocean floor is surprisingly well known, despite the fact that so little of our information has been gained by visual observation. Our knowledge was rapidly advanced during the Second World War as a result of the many precise depth measurements taken by ships following widely diverse courses. Improved underwater sound methods furnished continuous records of depths, and the locations of the recordings were checked by using electronic instruments. Consequently, accurate detailed information is available of the topography of the ocean floor near the continents, among the oceanic islands, and along lines crossing the oceans. We shall discuss the topography under three divisions: *the continental shelves, the continental slopes, and the floor of the deep ocean.*

The Continental Shelves. The continental shelves extend outward from the edges of the continents underneath the epicontinental seas (see Fig. 155, page 155). Most of them are under less than 600 feet of water, but some lie at much greater depths. The continental shelves differ greatly in width. On the east coast of North America, off Newfoundland, the width of the shelf averages about 240 miles, but a shelf has almost disappeared at Cape Hatteras, North Carolina. Below this point, the shelf widens to 70 miles, but narrows again almost to nonexistence along eastern Florida. Off the west coast of Florida, it is about 150 miles wide. Nowhere along the Pacific Coast of the United States does the width of a shelf exceed 20 miles. Most of the coast of Australia is bordered by a wide continental shelf lying at shallow depths. Its width exceeds 200 miles in many places. The widest shelf known underlies Barents Sea off the north coast of Norway. It extends approximately 750 miles to the island of Spitzbergen. Elsewhere in Europe, the shelf is narrower; for example, it is only 10 to 25 miles wide off the coast of Spain.

The continental shelves slope gently (less than $\frac{1}{10}°$ on the average) toward the ocean depths. Their surfaces, though fairly smooth over small areas, are commonly undulating, terraced, and irregular. The sediments lying upon them range in size from that of boulders to that of fine clay (see table, page 183). They include also organic substances and the materials that go into the formation of rocks such as limestones.

Continental Slopes. Whatever the width of the continental shelves, their descent is comparatively rapid to the deep-ocean floor. These steeper slopes are known as "continental slopes" (see Fig. 155, page 155). On an average, they incline 5° from the horizontal, though some inclinations exceed 20°. The continental slopes are the greatest relief features on the surface of the earth; some of them reach heights of 30,000 feet, which is far greater than the height of most mountain ranges. They are accounted for by relative upward and downward movements of the land and the ocean bottoms. Mud is the most common sediment on the slopes, although sand, gravel, and shells in abundance have also been found on them.

Submarine Canyons. Most of the continental slopes and shelves are cut by deep canyons. One that has long been known lies off the drowned valley of the Hudson River (see Fig. 180, page 174). It is called the "Hudson submarine canyon" and is about 2,400 feet deep and 3 miles wide. Off the Mississippi River delta, a wide canyon or trough penetrates the continental shelf for almost 30 miles. On the California coast, the Monterey submarine canyon, heading in Monterey Bay, extends seaward for 50 miles and then widens into a broad trough. The depth of this canyon exceeds 6,000 feet, and a portion of it resembles the Grand Canyon of Arizona. Submarine canyons have been found in the slopes and shelves of all the continents, so we know that their distribution is world wide.

The origin of the submarine canyons is not completely understood, though it seems probable (because most of them are apparent extensions of land-river valleys) that they were cut as land canyons and later submerged. Another theory, however, is that the submarine canyons were cut under water by seaward-flowing currents (so-called "turbidity currents"). It is known that during the glacial epoch the ocean level was considerably lower than it is at present, owing to so much water, in the form of ice, having been confined in the great ice sheets upon the continents. This explanation of a higher land level, however, could not account entirely for the cutting of canyons with the great depths of 6,000 feet. Apparently, considerable movement of the earth's crust would also have been necessary; which would presuppose, however, a higher mobility than the crust is thought to possess. The ultimate solution of the origin of submarine canyons, therefore, will probably have greater geologic significance than just the explanation of canyon erosion.

The Floor of the Ocean Deeps.　The topography of the deep-ocean floors, once assumed to be monotonously smooth, is actually comparable to that of land surfaces in roughness. In terms of large-scale features, the ocean floor is probably even more irregular than the land.

Although all three oceans are interconnected, high submerged ridges separate their basins. In the Atlantic Ocean, a vast midocean ridge extends from Iceland to Antarctica. It is a mountain range, about 6,000 feet high, lying beneath 9,000 feet of water. Transverse submarine ridges extend seaward from the continents on both sides of the Atlantic, and in the central areas the floor is characterized by deep basins interspersed with prominences.

The Pacific Ocean basin is roughly outlined by deep trenches that are more or less continuous. The deepest one known lies near the Philippines and is 34,440 feet deep. The ridges of the Pacific are equally prominent. A chain of them runs for more than 2,000 miles in a northwest direction from the Hawaiian Islands, and others, south and west of Hawaii, trend north and south or swing in wide arcs. Scores of flat-topped *seamounts* occur east, west, and south of Wake Island. Atolls and coral-reef platforms rise from the deep floor in the southwest Pacific.

The Indian Ocean floor is furrowed by long ridges and deeps, curved in an arc that is convex toward the east.

The great irregularities of the ocean floor should occasion no surprise, as the presence there of volcanoes has long been known and man has also been aware of the great earth movements that result, of course, in fractures. Moreover, whereas prominences of the land are being reduced by erosion, those on the deep-ocean floor are almost unattacked unless they rise to heights at which surface waves are effective. The smoothing of deep-sea topography is, therefore, due mainly to the deposition of sediment, which has been relatively minor in amount. If we could see through water as we can through air, the scenery afforded us on an ocean voyage would be the most spectacular on earth.

Mechanical Deposits on the Continental Shelves

No phase of the work of the ocean is more important than the formation of the large body of mechanically formed sediments that give rise

to the three important *clastic rocks: conglomerates, sandstones,* and *shales.*
Their formation will not be discussed here, however, as it is treated in
the chapter on sedimentary rocks.

Deep-sea Deposits

The deposits being made, at present, in the deep parts of the oceans
have been studied in all of the oceans. They are called *muds, clays,*
or *oozes,* and consist of materials from many sources. By far the larger
part of the material is *volcanic dust and pumice, cosmic or meteoritic
material,* and *organic material* (shells and the hard parts of swimming creatures, like sharks' teeth and the ear bones of whales). Some of the
material is derived from the land and is called *terrigenous.*

The *volcanic material* of deep-sea deposits may have been derived from
land or island volcanoes, as well as from the submarine volcanoes. The
fact that pumice will float for a long period of time permits its journeying
far from its source. Some material derived from *meteorites* has also been
found in deep-sea deposits.

The *organic remains* found in deep-sea deposits are of various kinds,
depending in part upon the depth of the water. Because calcium
carbonate is soluble in water, the calcareous shells of organisms will
largely disappear before they sink to a depth of 15,000 feet, and practically none of them will go below 20,000 feet. Below this depth, therefore, only the very insoluble parts of organisms occur. A single dredge
of material from a depth of 14,300 feet contained 1,500 specimens of
sharks' teeth and 50 ear bones of whales. Several kinds of "oozes" (as
these deposits of organic remains are called) are distributed over the
sea floor at varying depths. They are named from the dominant organism they contain. The common oozes, the depths at which they occur,
the area of the sea floor covered by them, and the percentage that area
is of the total are given in the following table:

DEEP-SEA OOZES

Kinds	Average depth, feet	Area covered, square miles	Approximate percentage of ocean bottom covered
Pteropod ooze............	6,264	400,000	0.28
Diatom ooze.............	8,862	10,880,000	7.80
Globigerina ooze..........	12,294	49,520,000	35.57
Radiolarian ooze..........	17,364	2,290,000	1.60

Terrigenous material is more abundant in the deposits nearer the continents, of course. This material has been carried out to the deep sea

by floating ice that comes from the polar regions and from glaciers that reach the sea, as well as by wind and currents.

Red *clay*, which is the most insoluble of the deep-sea materials, is widely distributed over the sea floor, the estimated area covered by it being 51,500,000 square miles. Much, if not most, of the red clay is the result of the alteration of the other deep-sea materials. It occurs at depths ranging from 13,350 feet to those of the deepest parts of the ocean.

Some minor deep-sea deposits are found, of which *manganese* and *phosphatic nodules* and a green mineral called *glauconite* are the most important.

The deep-sea deposits are thin, though they represent long periods of accumulation, as shown by the relatively large number of sharks' teeth and other organic materials occurring in them. Very few of these deposits have been found on the land.

CHEMICAL WORK OF THE OCEAN

The chemical work of the ocean is far less important than the mechanical work, as we have repeatedly noted. The chemical work includes *deposition* and *solution*. Of the two, deposition is by far the more important, consisting as it does in the formation of the *chemically formed sedimentary rocks: limestone, chert* and *flint, salt,* and *gypsum.* The formation of these rocks, however, is discussed in the next chapter.

Solution work, though of such minor importance, must be going on to some extent, as the water of the ocean is in constant contact with the materials along the shore. The finer fragments of the shore materials are undoubtedly altered, producing soluble substances of which some are soon deposited and others remain in solution.

CHAPTER 9

SEDIMENTARY ROCKS

We are now to consider the formation of the sedimentary rocks. The word "sedimentary," coming from the Latin word *sedimentum*, which means "settling," is applied to these rocks because during their formation the materials composing them settled through water (or the air) to different parts of the earth's surface. This process of accumulation goes on in any body of water (pond, lake, lagoon, or the ocean) just as long as material is supplied by the work of the wind, the streams, or the waves of the body of water itself. As originally used, the term "sedimentary rocks" designated those rocks composed of solid particles that could be seen settling in water. Later it was learned that some rocks were formed from material in solution in the sea water, and these are now included with the sedimentary rocks. Further studies have shown that deposits made upon the land by the wind or ice and those made along rivers and in lakes belong to the sedimentary rocks also. The great majority of all sedimentary rocks, however, were formed in the ocean or in bodies of water directly connected with it.

The sedimentary rocks are the most common ones at the surface of the earth. They are estimated to cover 75 per cent of the land surface, which leaves only 25 per cent for the igneous and metamorphic rocks together. In point of abundance in the earth's crust, however, the sedimentary rocks are insignificant, comprising only 5 per cent. Thus it will be seen that they form only a very thin layer at the top of the crust, the other 95 per cent of which undoubtedly consists predominantly of igneous rocks, though to how great an extent the metamorphic rocks may be present it is impossible to say. The sedimentary rocks on the earth's surface range in thickness from a thin film to 40,000 or 50,000 feet. We have good evidence for believing that at one time sedimentary rocks were much more extensive than they are at present. They probably covered nearly if not quite all of the other rocks of the crust and, if so, have been cut away in great quantities, exposing the igneous and metamorphic rocks below. This eroded sedimentary material has been redeposited elsewhere, in the same manner as materials derived from the weathering of the primary igneous rocks.

Since sedimentary rocks form so much of the land surface, they are utilized extensively by man for building and industrial purposes. Likewise, as they are now the chief rocks subjected to the agents of erosion, they have been carved into innumerable shapes. Some of these eroded areas are strikingly beautiful, such as those in Glacier National Park, Bryce Canyon, Utah (Fig. 182), and the Grand Canyon of the Colorado River (see Fig. 97, page 107). Aside from possessing elements of beauty and utility, however, the sedimentary rocks are of great importance in furnishing a record of past life and of the major physical events in the history of the earth. The life story is depicted in the fossils that are

FIG. 182. Bryce Canyon, Utah. (*Photograph by W. D. Keller.*)

found in the rocks, as we shall see in studying historical geology in the second part of this book. Other features of the rocks, such as their composition, color, and position, furnish information concerning the climate of past times and the changes that have occurred in the earth's crust.

The previous chapters on weathering, the work of the streams, and the ocean have amply prepared us for our present task, that of learning the details of the formation of the sedimentary rocks.

Source of the Materials in Sedimentary Rocks. If we considered only the primary source of the material in the sedimentary rocks, that source would be the igneous rocks; and, during the formation of the first sedimentary rocks, these *were* the only source. After some sedimentary rocks had been formed, however, they also were exposed at the surface and weathered and thus furnished material for other sediments. Rocks of the metamorphic group (Chap. 10) that are formed from both igneous and sedimentary rocks are exposed at the surface, weathered, and so also furnish further sedimentary materials. Thus we see that all the different kinds of rocks, igneous, sedimentary, and metamorphic, have been sources of material for the sedimentary rocks (see Fig. 237, page 232).

Kinds of Materials in Sedimentary Rocks. The materials that go into the formation of the sedimentary rocks are readily divided into two groups: one consisting of *solid particles* and the other of *substances* carried *in solution*. It will be recalled at once that the aim of the weathering process is twofold: to produce one group of substances that, because of their insolubility, necessarily consist of solid particles; and another group of soluble substances. Thus we see how directly the process of weathering is connected with the origin of sedimentary rocks. There is really a third kind of material (*i.e., carbonaceous material* derived from the air and from organisms) which enters sedimentary rocks. This material is less important in amount and is wholly unrelated to the two large classes of materials.

The Clastic Materials. The solid particles of which we have spoken are called *clastic materials* ("clastic" means "broken"). The term "fragmental" is also used, but the other name is the more common one. An accumulation of these solid materials produces a clastic rock.

The size of the clastic materials is shown in the following table. These sizes, as applied to the names of the materials, are purely arbitrary but are the ones commonly accepted by geologists.

SIZE OF CLASTIC MATERIALS

Kinds	Diameter, Millimeters
Boulders	Over 256
Cobbles	64 to 256
Pebbles	4 to 64
Granules	2 to 4
Sand	$\frac{1}{16}$ to 2
Silt	$\frac{1}{256}$ to $\frac{1}{16}$
Clay	Below $\frac{1}{256}$

Owing to this difference in size of the clastic materials, they are sorted by the action of various transporting agents; and, if the substances have about the same specific gravity, particles of about the same size will be deposited together. If the substances differ in specific gravity, however, larger particles of the lighter materials will be mixed with smaller particles of the heavier materials. Thus hematite, an iron oxide, is nearly twice as heavy as quartz, and consequently smaller particles of hematite will be deposited with larger fragments of quartz.

As ocean currents move offshore into deeper water, their velocity is checked, which results in deposition of the materials they are carrying.

The ideal sequence of this deposition would be first, and nearest the shore, the boulders, cobbles, and pebbles (these sizes are not commonly furnished by streams), next the granules and sands, and lastly the silts and clays. In reality, of course, this sequence is subject to many variations, depending upon the strength of the currents, the supply of materials, and other factors.

The shape of the particles of clastic materials, which ranges from round to sharply angular (Fig. 183), is as variable as their size. Long-continued wear during transportation produces rounded particles even of very hard minerals. Thus certain sandstones, notably the St. Peter

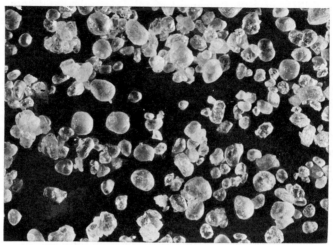

FIG. 183. Rounded and angular grains of quartz sand. The very round grains are from the St. Peter sandstone. Twelve times natural size. (*Photograph furnished by Frank Conselman.*)

sandstone found in Missouri and Illinois, consist, in considerable part, of nearly perfectly rounded grains of quartz. Under ordinary conditions quartz grains are not rounded in water to sizes smaller than $\frac{1}{10}$ millimeter in diameter, because the water around the grains breaks the blow. Wind can round grains to much smaller sizes. Rounded quartz grains have a dull appearance, known as a *mat surface*, owing to the fact that tiny chips have been broken off during rounding. A rock composed of sharp broken fragments, larger than sand particles, is called a "breccia" (Fig. 184). The material in such a rock had not been transported very far.

The clastic materials may be composed of any substance that can exist as solid particles. Fragments of all sorts of rocks, granite, gabbro, felsite, slate, marble, sandstone, and coal, are found in them. Specimens of 20 different kinds of rocks have been recognized in Missouri River sand. The mineral particles found in the clastic rocks are more numerous than the rock particles. Clay minerals and quartz are overwhelmingly abundant among the minerals of certain clastic rocks, though the micas, feldspar, hornblende, and the iron oxides are also common in those rocks. Rare minerals of interest in clastic rocks are gold, platinum, and diamonds and other gems. Occasionally particles of calcite, gypsum, and dolomite (fairly soluble minerals) are found in clastic rocks.

The Soluble Materials. The substances (aside from those present in mere traces) carried in solution to the ocean are comparatively few in contrast with the number of the clastic materials transported. The soluble substances are calcium carbonate, silica, sodium chloride, and magnesium, potassium, iron, and aluminum compounds. The table on

FIG. 184. Breccia composed of chert fragments cemented with asphalt. One-fourth natural size.

page 156 in the preceding chapter should be consulted for the amounts of each of these materials added. These substances are of varying solubilities in river water; and, as we shall see later in this chapter, some of them are very soluble in the sea water, and others are not.

The Carbonaceous Materials. The carbonaceous materials are dominantly carbon compounds, as their name implies. The carbon for their formation is derived directly from the air and from the decay of organic compounds. Plants take carbon dioxide from the air, making use of the carbon in their cells and liberating most of the oxygen. The plants are then used as food by animals. Accumulations of carbonaceous materials from plants (and possibly animals) may under very special conditions become coal or petroleum. Swamps and lagoons along shore are ideal places for the accumulation to take place.

Where Sedimentary Materials Are Deposited. Deposition of sedimentary materials may take place in all parts of the ocean, but actually most of the sedimentary rocks have been deposited in the shallower parts. At present, this deposition is largely restricted to the 10,000,000 square

miles of the epicontinental seas along the margins of the continents, but
in past geologic periods (during some of which the ocean submerged
50 per cent or more of the continents as they exist today) sediments were
deposited far inland from what are now the shores of the ocean.   As was
noted in our study of the ocean, material is now accumulating in the deep
seas, but most of these deposits apparently have no counterpart in any
of the sedimentary rocks.   The kind and amount of sediments deposited
in any one locality are controlled by the source of material, strength and
direction of the waves and currents, depth of the water, and distance
from the shore.

The sediments may be deposited adjacent to the shore and are then
called *near-shore deposits,* or they may be carried variable distances out
upon the continental shelf or beyond it and are then called *offshore
deposits.*   These terms are of value only as indicating the location of
deposition, for all kinds and sizes of material may be deposited from the
beach outward.   An ideal outward sequence probably does not exist.
At one place along a shore, a sand may be deposited, while a few miles
away along the same shore, there may be a deposit of clay.   Under
exceptional conditions (clear water at the shore), calcareous materials
may be deposited at the immediate shore, as, at present, along the coasts
of Florida and the Bahamas.   In general, the finest clastic materials and
the chemical (as well as some organic) materials are deposited at a distance from the shore.   Limestones require clear water for deposition.
Certain chemical deposits, such as salt and gypsum, are formed only in
restricted seas.   Broad, shallow interior seas have spread over the
continents of the past, and it was in such seas that most of the sedimentary rocks were deposited rather than in narrow epicontinental seas such
as those in which deposition is taking place at present.   Some of the
seas in the interior of North America were 2,000 miles across, though not
very deep.   In such seas, materials could be carried hundreds of miles
out from the land, and a single continuous deposit of sandstone, shale, or
limestone might cover many thousand square miles.

CLASSIFICATION OF SEDIMENTARY ROCKS

Based upon their origin, the sedimentary rocks may be readily classified
into three groups: *clastic sedimentary rocks, chemical sedimentary rocks,*
and *organic sedimentary rocks.*   These groups, arising as they do from the
products of weathering, may be shown graphically (study carefully the
chart on opposite page).

The Dominant Kinds of Sedimentary Rocks.   Though several kinds
are given in the chart, a world-wide study of sedimentary rocks has
shown that three kinds are most abundant.   These are, in the order of
their estimated abundance: *shales,* comprising 82 per cent of all sedi-

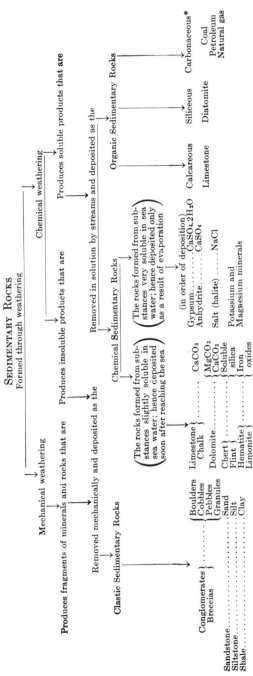

SEDIMENTARY ROCKS
Formed through weathering

Mechanical weathering

Chemical weathering

Produces fragments of minerals and rocks that are

Produces insoluble products that are

Produces soluble products that **are**

Removed mechanically and deposited as the

Removed in solution by streams and deposited as the

Clastic Sedimentary Rocks

Chemical **Sedimentary Rocks**

Organic Sedimentary Rocks

Conglomerates } .... { Boulders / Cobbles / Pebbles / Granules
Breccias }

Sandstone......Sand
Siltstone......Silt
Shale.........Clay

(The rocks formed from substances slightly soluble in
sea water; hence deposited
soon after reaching the sea)

Limestone } .... CaCO₃
Chalk }

Dolomite..........{ MgCO₃ / CaCO₃

Chert } .... Soluble silica
Flint }

Hematite } .... Iron oxides
Limonite }

(The rocks formed from substances very soluble in sea
water; hence deposited only
as a result of evaporation)

(in order of deposition)
Gypsum..........CaSO₄·2H₂O
Anhydrite.........CaSO₄
Salt (halite) ......NaCl
Potassium and
Magnesium minerals

Calcareous
Limestone

Siliceous
Diatomite

Carbonaceous*
Coal
Petroleum
Natural gas

* The carbon is derived dominantly from CO₂; hydrogen from water; other constituents, indirectly, through weathering and alteration.

mentary rocks; *sandstones,* 12 per cent; and *chalk, limestones,* and *dolomites,* 6 per cent (Fig. 185).   In this grouping, clays and siltstones are included with shales, conglomerates with sandstones, and chert and flint with the carbonate rocks.   All the other kinds of rocks form but a small portion of the grand total.   We must account for the greater abundance of these dominant rocks.

The great abundance of *shales* among sedimentary rocks is explained by the fact (as we saw under "Weathering") that the dominant mineral in the average igneous rock is feldspar, which breaks down to various clay minerals, as do other aluminum-bearing minerals in igneous rocks. Since the majority of all the clay minerals go into the composition of shale,

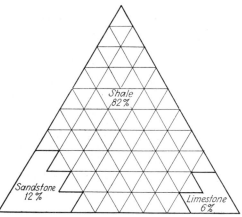

FIG. 185. Diagram showing the percentages of each of the major classes of sedimentary rocks. Each small triangle equals 1 per cent.

and as they are the most abundant minerals formed during the weathering of igneous rocks, we see at once that shale *should* be the most abundant sedimentary rock.

Sandstones rank second in abundance because they consist dominantly of quartz, a very hard, insoluble mineral that forms about 20.5 per cent of the average igneous rock.   The main loss of this quartz during weathering is by the abrasion of the grains, but, on account of its extreme hardness, even abrasion takes place very slowly.

The abundance of *chalk, limestone,* and *dolomite* is accounted for by the fact that calcium and magnesium carbonates are the most abundant substances of the soluble products of weathering, together with the fact that their very slight solubility in the sea water causes their early deposition. *Chert* and *flint* are very abundant in some of the carbonate rocks.   We have noted in discussing the weathering of igneous rocks that, of the silica set free, a part was carried in solution to the sea, and it is a part of this silica that was deposited so abundantly as chert and flint.

Thus we see that the abundance of certain compounds in the original rocks leads during the weathering process to their concentration in other forms (the sedimentary rocks) at the surface.

The Gradations among Sedimentary Rocks.   The chart of the classification of sedimentary rocks given above shows at a glance where each of them belongs.   Inasmuch as the deposition of the various sedimentary materials is taking place all the time in the waters surrounding the continents, a certain area may be receiving one kind of material, adjacent areas very different kinds, and some areas none.   The deposit at one place may consist essentially of one material, a pure sand, clay, or limestone, but it is very evident that the deposition of any one material does not cease abruptly at a certain point and another type begin abruptly at that point.   The deposition of clastic materials depends upon the velocity of the transporting agent.   As this velocity gradually decreases, so also does the size of the particles deposited.   Grains of a deposit of sand may, therefore, gradually change in size along the shore, grading into a coarser deposit (pebbles or boulders) in one direction, or into a finer deposit (a silt or even a clay) in the opposite direction.   Seaward, the change is a decrease in size of particles (Fig. 186); sand thus grades into a clay.   However, the currents that are transporting materials are not uniform from day to day; hence there is inevitably some mingling of sizes.   As a result, sandstones may contain some clay and are called *shaly* or *argillaceous sandstones*, shales may contain sand and are called *sandy* or *arenaceous shales*.   Such rocks are gradation products.

Gradations exist in chemical and organic rocks also.   The deposition of a limestone may be taking place (chemically or organically) adjacent to the deposition of clays or sands (Fig. 186), whereupon a zone of gradation will exist between the adjacent types of materials.   As a result, there are limestones that contain shale (*shaly limestones*) or sand (*sandy limestones*).   This type of gradation results in a mixture of insoluble materials (the sand or clay) with those materials (the calcium carbonate) deposited from solution.   These gradations are shown graphically in Fig. 187, which should be carefully studied.

The gradations just discussed are all lateral changes, but vertical gradations also exist.   A sandstone may grade upward into a shale or a shale into a limestone.   These changes are brought about in a number of ways, as will be shown more fully in the historical part of this volume.   A gradual deepening of the water over a deposit of clastic materials would result in the beginning of deposition of finer materials.   So for a time, fine and coarse particles would mingle, which would produce a gradational phase, as, for example, a sandstone that contained considerable clay; or a gradual clearing of the water would start the deposition of some calcium carbonate along with the clay that had been going down, which would result in a gradational phase between a limestone and a shale. Other factors that influence gradation of one material into another, not only vertically but also laterally, are changes in the distance of the deposition from shore, in the direction and strength of currents, and in the source and character of materials.

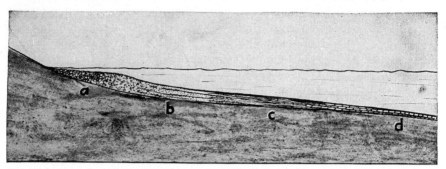

FIG. 186. Sketch showing ideal lateral gradation of one sedimentary rock into another: (a) conglomerate into (b) sandstone into (c) shale into (d) limestone.

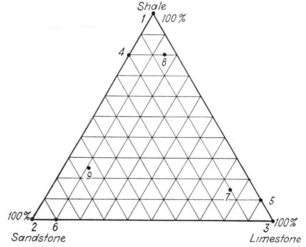

FIG. 187. Diagram showing relationship of the three principal sediments. (1) 100 per cent shale; (2) 100 per cent sandstone; (3) 100 per cent limestone; (4) sandy shale (80 per cent shale and 20 per cent sand); (5) shaly limestone (90 per cent limestone and 10 per cent shale); (6) calcareous sandstone (90 per cent sandstone and 10 per cent limestone); (7) sandy, shaly limestone (75 per cent limestone, 15 per cent shale, and 10 per cent sand). Determine the rock names and the percentages of each constituent for (8) and (9).

It should be noted, however, that, although gradations do exist, the different sedimentary rocks are, on the whole, surprisingly pure. The vertical transition of one type of sedimentary rock into another is usually sharp, and even the lateral change takes place in a surprisingly narrow gradational zone.

ORIGIN OF THE SEDIMENTARY ROCKS

The three principal methods by which the sedimentary rocks have originated have been indicated in the classification chart given on page 187. This chart shows a broad grouping of the rocks according to the present prevailing trend of thought, although there is no unanimous agreement among geologists as to the origin of all of the sedimentary rocks. We cannot go into great detail in this volume, but the broader outlines of the origin of the *clastic, chemical,* and *organic* sediments will be given.

The Origin of the Clastic Sedimentary Rocks

The clastic materials carried by streams, wind, and ocean currents are deposited whenever the velocity of the moving agent becomes insufficient to transport the particles farther. Deposition by streams and wind may occur on the land or in lakes, but, as such deposition is of minor importance, we shall discuss only the deposits made in the ocean.

Whatever the velocity of a river current may be, when the stream enters the quiet water of the ocean, its velocity is checked, and deposition takes place. The result of this deposition may be a delta, though most of the material dropped will be immediately shifted by the waves and shore currents to quieter water along the shore or into deeper water offshore, the result in either case being deposition.

Formation of a Conglomerate. The coarsest material being shifted by the waves is deposited along the beach, and if the size of the particles is above 4 millimeters in diameter (*i.e.*, pebble, cobble, and boulder sizes; see table, page 183) a conglomerate is formed (Fig. 188). A sea in encroaching upon the land may greatly widen the area of beach deposits so that a conglomerate bed of considerable extent may be formed.

Formation of a Sandstone. The particles of the materials known as "granules" and "sand" are smaller than 4 millimeters in diameter (see table, page 183) and hence are carried farther out than the coarse materials and eventually form beds of sandstone (Fig. 189). Though these materials may be carried offshore for miles, most sandstones are formed near shore. The thickness of the deposit will vary with the supply of sand, the strength of the currents, and the slope and configuration of the shore line.

Sandstones are commonly made use of for building purposes wherever they occur, and many of them are very attractive stones.

Formation of Siltstones and Shale. The finest particles (diameters below $\frac{1}{16}$ millimeter), those of silt and clay, are carried the farthest and are deposited in the deep, quiet waters beyond the reach of the waves and strong shore currents. However, if the land adjacent to a shore is low

FIG. 188. Conglomerate.

FIG. 189. Thick bed of St. Peter sandstone at mine entrance, Pacific, Missouri. This sandstone is being mined for use in making glass. (*Photograph by W. A. Tarr.*)

lying and the water shallow, silt and clay may be deposited up to the shore. These silts and clays become siltstones and shales after consolidation. As silt particles are intermediate in size between those of sand and of clay (see table, page 183), siltstone forms a gradational phase between a sandstone and a shale. Siltstones are really quite abundant, though they are generally designated as "shales." Probably 10 per cent of the total 82 per cent of shales consists of siltstone. Lagoons are the seat of the deposition of much of these fine materials. When exceptional floods or storms occur, coarser materials may be carried much farther out than is normal and thus sand may be deposited over clay. When normal conditions are restored, clay is deposited over the sand. In this way interbedded sandstones and shales are formed. Fine clays settle faster in the sea water than in fresh water, due to their having been coagulated into larger particles by the action of the salts in the sea. This fact would thus favor deposition nearer shore in sea water than in lakes.

On account of the great abundance of shale at the earth's surface, man has adapted the rock to many uses. In the manufacture of brick, tile, and other clay products, shale is widely used, and much of it is used also in making Portland cement.

Summary. The deposition of the materials of the clastic rocks is due primarily to a decrease in the velocity of the transporting agent. The particles being transported are sorted; the larger and heavier ones are deposited first and then those of the successively smaller sizes down to the finest clay particles.

Origin of the Chemical Sedimentary Rocks

The sedimentary rocks formed by the precipitation of the soluble substances brought to the sea comprise one of the most interesting groups of rocks. Most of them, such as limestone, salt, gypsum, and iron minerals, are extensively used by man. On the whole, the origin of the rocks of this group is well understood, though much research is still needed to make clear many of the details of the methods of their formation.

The soluble substances carried to the sea may be placed in two groups: one comprising those substances that are slightly soluble in the sea water and thus are rapidly deposited, and the other comprising those very soluble substances that accumulate in the sea water and are precipitated only under special conditions. The substances in these two groups are given in the lists below:

Substances Slightly Soluble in Sea Water and Thus Quickly Precipitated	Very Soluble Substances Accumulating in Sea Water
Calcium carbonate	Sodium chloride
Magnesium carbonate	Calcium sulfate
Silica	Magnesium sulfate
Iron minerals	Magnesium chloride
	Potassium sulfate
	Potassium chloride

Substances Slightly Soluble in Sea Water. The materials that are rapidly removed from the sea water are the most abundant of the soluble substances carried to the sea annually.

Calcium Carbonate and the Rocks It Forms. Calcium carbonate is the most abundant of all the soluble compounds added annually to the sea, yet there is little of it in the sea water, which shows that it is rapidly removed. The removal is accomplished in two ways, chemically and organically (discussed later). At one time in the earth's history, one of these methods of the formation of limestone was, on account of the existing conditions, the predominant method; and at another period, another one.

Evaporation or any other process (such as a rise in temperature) that removes carbon dioxide from the sea water causes the chemical precipitation of the calcium carbonate (*calcite*). Upon its precipitation, the calcite settles to the sea floor as an extremely fine-grained mud. While the rock that results from this deposition is still soft and porous, it is known as *chalk* (if it contains much clay, it is called *marl*); later, through consolidation, it becomes a hard, firm *limestone*, which though fine grained may later become coarse grained through crystallization. These chemi-

FIG. 190. Oölites from Great Salt Lake. Enlarged six times.

cally precipitated limestones may contain some fossils, as the calcium carbonate present in the sea water furnishes a favorable environment for those organisms that make use of calcium carbonate in their shells. The shells of the organisms accumulate, of course, along with the chemically precipitated calcium carbonate. Not uncommonly, as the calcium carbonate is being deposited, it forms small rounded grains known as *oölites*.[1] These are really tiny concretions. The floor of the bathing beach at Great Salt Lake is composed of such oölites (Fig. 190). A limestone consisting of these grains is known as an *oölitic limestone*.

Magnesium Carbonate and the Rock It Forms. The magnesium carbonate that is added to sea water is not removed so fast as the calcium carbonate, as some of it is changed into the soluble magnesium sulfate and chloride and so accumulates in the water. A part of the magnesium carbonate, however, unites with calcium carbonate and forms *dolomite* [$CaMg(CO_3)_2$]. Dolomite is as common as limestone among the older geologic formations. The two rocks resemble each other so closely that most people call both "limestone." Dolomite, however, is harder and heavier than limestone, but the best way to distinguish between them is by the hydrochloric acid test. Limestone dissolves rapidly (fizzes) in the acid, and dolomite, unless in a fine powder, is scarcely affected. Many dolomites are unfossiliferous, but some contain a few fossils, usually in a poor state of preservation.

Silica and Its Resultant Rocks. The second most abundant of the soluble substances added to the sea water annually by the rivers is silica, which constitutes 11.8 per cent of these materials. As sea water

---

[1] A term recently proposed for the individual grains is *oöid*.

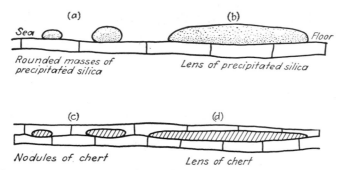

FIG. 191. Sketch showing masses of silica (a and b) accumulating contemporaneously with limestone on the sea floor and the resulting chert (c and d) after burial.

FIG. 192. Nodules and lenses of chert (light gray) in Burlington limestone, Columbia, Missouri. (*Photograph by W. A. Tarr.*)

contains only a small amount of silica, it is evident that nearly all of this silica is deposited. In contrast with the prevalent use of calcium carbonate made by animals in the construction of their hard parts, very few organisms of the sea make such use of silica. The larger part of the silica is, therefore, chemically precipitated. When streams are bringing clay to the ocean, much of the silica is deposited with the clay (it is a partial cause of the stickiness of clays); but, if the river waters are clear (carrying only materials in solution), the silica brought into the sea accumulates until it reaches the saturation point, whereupon the salts in the sea water cause its precipitation on the sea floor in the form of a colloidal or jellylike mass containing water. This precipitation of the silica takes place at the same time and in the same areas on the sea floor as does that of the calcium carbonate (Figs. 191, 192, and 193). The masses are rounded (Fig. 191, *a*); or, if the amount of silica precipitated is large, it is spread out on the floor as lenses (Figs. 191, *b*; and 192) or beds (Fig. 193). As other sediments are usually deposited over the rounded masses while they are still soft, they are flattened on account of the

FIG. 193. Chert bed (back of notebook) in Cretaceous limestone, Tivoli, Italy. (*Photograph by W. A. Tarr.*)

pressure, though some masses become hard before burial and so retain their original shape. The hardened masses are called *nodules*, or *concretions*, and *lenses* (Figs. 191, *c* and *d*; and 192). Precipitated silica thus gives rise to the very abundant and widely occurring white *chert* (Figs. 192 and 193) and black *flint* (Fig. 194) of limestone, chalk, and dolomite. The association of chert and flint (both are varieties of quartz and occur most commonly in the form of nodules) with calcareous deposits is just what would be expected, for both silica and calcium carbonate require clear water for their precipitation. The occurrence of chert and flint with calcareous rocks is always with the purest forms of those rocks; for, if enough clay were present to form a shaly limestone, for example, the silica would go down with the clay, leaving none for the formation of chert and flint. Chert and flint may contain calcareous fossils that became enclosed in them while the silica mass was soft. Such fossils are usually very well preserved, as the silica gel protected them from destroying agents. Some of these fossils have been changed later to quartz by silica replacement.

Because chert and flint break readily into chips with sharp cutting edges, they have been used by man since the time of the stone ages, first as tools and later as a means of lighting fires. They may even be used for building materials, as shown in the accompanying picture (Fig. 195) of a church constructed of flint nodules.

Iron Minerals. Only a very small quantity of iron is carried to the sea annually, owing to the low solubility of the iron minerals. An abundance of decaying organic matter in the presence of these minerals, however, favors their solution. Some of the iron is removed as *hematite* (Fe_2O_3), and a smaller quantity as the *iron carbonate* ($FeCO_3$); for, though the carbonate is the more soluble, if oxygen enters the solution (as it commonly does), the iron will be oxidized and deposited as hematite soon

FIG. 194. Flint nodule in the chalk, South Coulson, Surrey, England. Note the thin white coating of nodule. (*Photograph by W. A. Tarr.*)

FIG. 195. Church constructed of flint nodules, Cambridge, England. (*Photograph by W. A. Tarr.*)

after reaching the sea. Rarely, the conditions of solution on the land favor the removal of iron in quantities sufficient to form a bed of hematite, *limonite*, or, very rarely, of the iron carbonate (*siderite*). Hematite not uncommonly has replaced the calcium carbonate of shells on the sea floor, and the bed of iron ore thus contains fossils. Calcareous oölites are also replaced by iron oxides, or the iron mineral may assume the oölitic form as it is deposited. The world's most important supplies of iron ore come from sedimentary deposits, notable among which are those of the Lake Superior region (Fig. 196), the Clinton iron ore of the Appalachian region, the Lorraine iron ores of France and Germany, and (probably) the great Brazilian iron deposits.

Substances Soluble in Sea Water. In considering the soluble mineral content of sea water (see table, page 156), we found that *sodium chloride* (27.2 parts per thousand), *magnesium compounds* (5.54 parts per thousand), *calcium sulfate* (1.26 parts per thousand), and *potassium compounds* (0.863 part per thousand) are present. The fact that the present sea water contains these compounds in large amounts is evidence of their high solubility. These substances continue to accumulate until special conditions make possible their precipitation.

Sodium Chloride and Its Deposits. Sodium chloride has apparently been accumulating in the sea water since the beginning of the ocean.

FIG. 196. Iron ore from Lake Superior district. Light bands are hematite. Dark bands are jasper (chert containing hematite). One-fourth natural size.

From time to time during the past, *salt* has been deposited, but the total quantity thus removed is only a small fraction of what remains in the sea. Salt is so soluble in water that the only common way of removing it is by evaporation, and it would not be deposited from sea water until about 90 per cent of the water had been removed. The deposits of salt show that they were formed in isolated bodies of sea water that evaporated until deposition took place. The evaporating body of water could be a bay or inland sea, and it might even be so closely connected with the main body of water as to receive influxes of sea water during storms. These influxes of fresher water would stop deposition until evaporation had again concentrated the water, but they would add to the total amount of salt present. The salt is deposited in beds that, for the most part, are only 10 to 30 feet thick, but rarely may be hundreds of feet thick. It is possible also that the waters of lakes could evaporate until they became so saturated with salt that it would be deposited. Figure 197 shows salt in a dried-up lake or playa in north central Nevada. Such salt deposits are common in shallow lakes that dry up during a part of a year. If Great Salt Lake were to evaporate, it is estimated that it would deposit 400,000,000 tons of salt.

Calcium Sulfate and the Rocks It Forms. Calcium sulfate is not so soluble in water as sodium chloride; therefore, as a body of sea water evaporates, *gypsum*, the rock that calcium sulfate forms, is deposited before salt. Calcium sulfate forms two different deposits: one, the common gypsum ($CaSO_4.2H_2O$), and the other, *anhydrite* ($CaSO_4$). Though both are known to be deposited as sea water evaporates, gypsum is much more common.   Gypsum occurs in three forms: a fine-grained massive rock, *alabaster;* transparent crystals, many two feet long, *selenite;* and a fibrous aggregate, *satin spar* (Fig. 198).   The occurrence of pure

FIG. 197. Salt plain in central Nevada.   (*Photograph by W. A. Tarr.*)

FIG. 198. The three common varieties of gypsum.   Satin spar (at top), alabaster (left), selenite (right).

gypsum in thick beds of widespread extent has led to the conclusion that the process of its concentration must have been repeated, some evaporation having occurred in a shallow basin from which the water flowed to another basin, where it was further evaporated until finally gypsum was deposited in a very pure form.

Deposits of gypsum are usually associated with those of salt, but not always; for example, in the red beds of western United States thick beds of gypsum occur without salt. It is used for making wall plasters and plaster of Paris.

Magnesium and Potassium Sulfates and Chlorides. The most soluble of all substances in sea water are the magnesium and potassium sulfates and chlorides; hence they remain in solution after all the other substances are deposited, and their deposition occurs only when all the water is evaporated. The final concentrated solution from which they are deposited is known as the *bittern.* It is an interesting fact that potassium is present in the original rocks in an amount only slightly less than that of sodium, yet in the sea water it is only about one-thirtieth as abundant. This is explained by the fact (already mentioned under "Weathering") that most of the potassium is sorbed by the clay particles and, therefore, remains in the soil or goes into the formation of shales.

Apparently the complete evaporation of a body of sea water has occurred only a few times in the earth's history and then very locally. The world's largest deposits of potassium and magnesium salts are at Stassfurt, Germany. A smaller deposit occurs in France. Similar deposits of potassium and magnesium salts are located in eastern New Mexico and western Texas. These deposits supply the needs of the United States for potassium salts and furnish some exports. The chief use of potassium salts is for fertilizer. Magnesium compounds are also used as fertilizer and in increasing amounts as the need for magnesium in certain soils is being recognized.

Summary. As a body of sea water evaporates, the first mineral to be deposited is gypsum, next salt, and lastly, with complete evaporation, the magnesium and potassium minerals.

Origin of the Organic Sedimentary Rocks

The third method by which sedimentary rocks are formed is through the life processes of certain organisms. Both animals and plants contribute to the formation of these rocks. We shall discuss the organic sediments, however, according to the kind of material deposited, *i.e.*, *calcareous*, *siliceous*, and *carbonaceous*. One of these groups, the carbonaceous, furnishes a material that has proved to be indispensable in modern civilization.

Calcareous Deposits. Organisms play a very important part in the origin of some limestones. A vast number of creatures living in the ocean (and fresh waters, also) build their hard parts out of calcium carbonate. One has only to note the large number of shells along a sea shore to realize the abundance of such forms. These creatures are probably removing the larger part of the calcium carbonate added to the sea annually. Where the temperature, clearness of the water, and food supply are suitable, they live in vast numbers (as do the corals about some islands and along some continents). When these organisms die, their hard parts remain and eventually accumulate in sufficient amounts to form a bed or layer. If wave action is considerable, the shells may be broken up, forming calcareous gravel, sand, or mud. These accumulated materials become *limestone*. If all the shells are completely broken up and pulverized, the limestone will not show fossils, but, usually, fossils are more or less abundant in organic limestones (Fig. 199). Unless a

FIG. 199. Fossiliferous limestone.

limestone consists predominantly of fossils, it is not possible, by any physical methods yet known, to distinguish with certainty between an organic and a chemically precipitated limestone, as the latter may possibly contain some fossils also. Texture, mode of occurrence, and associated rocks are the criteria used, at present, in deciding between them. Chalk had always been regarded as an accumulation of the shells of minute organisms, but studies have shown that only a small percentage of the rock consists of organic remains, the major part being a chemical precipitate.

Various calcareous oozes are being deposited on the floor of the deep sea, at present, but most of these deposits have no counterparts in the rocks of the land.

Siliceous Deposits. Deposits of siliceous organic remains are, for the most part, unimportant. Some deep-sea oozes are siliceous, but few deposits occur on the land. The one siliceous deposit of any abundance is composed of diatom remains. Diatoms are small plants that use silica for their hard parts. Where they live abundantly in the sea water, thick beds of their remains may accumulate. Such deposits, called *diatomite*, are known in many parts of the world, but the largest are those of California, where beds hundreds of feet thick occur. Some men are of the opinion that some of the petroleum found in California was derived from these tiny organisms. Certain sponges have siliceous skeletons, but they do not accumulate in sufficient abundance to form beds.

Carbonaceous Deposits. There are two important carbonaceous deposits: *coal* and *oil*. The former is wholly of vegetable origin, but both plants and animals have probably contributed to the formation of the latter.

Formation of Coal. Coal is the result of an accumulation of plant remains under such conditions that the plant tissues are converted into a deposit rich in carbon. The most favorable place for such a process is a swamp in which the vegetation grows abundantly and is submerged under water as it dies. Submergence prevents dry rot (seen in logs in forests), which completely destroys plant remains. The vegetation in the water undergoes a slow decay, and this process is aided by anaerobic bacteria that eliminate the oxygen and hydrogen of the plant tissues while concentrating the carbon. The material is then buried under other sediments and still further compressed and altered until it becomes a bed of coal. The kind of coal formed depends upon the character of the vegetation and the degree of its alteration in the swamp and after burial. Anthracite, or hard coal, has undergone the greatest changes.

Formation of Petroleum or Oil. Petroleum, although a liquid, belongs in the group of sedimentary deposits. It is a very complex mixture of hydrocarbons, and in the condition in which it comes from the ground consists of varying amounts of benzene, kerosene, gasoline, lubricating oils, paraffin, and asphalt. It is now generally believed that the origin of petroleum is organic and that both plants and animals have contributed to its formation. Just where all the changes that produced it took place is not definitely known, but the following appear to be likely possibilities. (1) Oil drops may have been formed within the organism, been released upon its death, and then buried. (2) The oil may have been formed during the decay of the organism on the floor of the swamp, lagoon, or sea and then buried. (3) Organic material may have been buried in the muds and after the burial been altered into petroleum. The formation of natural gas is largely due to subsequent reactions within the oil. After the oil was buried, it migrated through the rocks and accumulated in large quantities in porous rocks (usually sandstone or channeled limestone) called *reservoirs*. The formation and accumulation of petroleum took place in deposits made along shores, for it is there that life was most abundant.

CONSOLIDATION OF SEDIMENTARY ROCKS

During our discussion of the origin of sedimentary rocks, we have seen that the sediments are deposited as soft, loose materials. The materials composing prospective conglomerates and sandstones, for example, though packed closely by wave and current action, contain nothing between the grains to hold them together. The changes that convert the deposits of sediments into hard firm rocks are both *mechanical* and *chemical*. The many methods of consolidation can be tabulated as follows:

Mechanical methods of consolidation
    a. Pressure of overlying rocks
    b. Drying of deposits
Chemical methods of consolidation
    a. Cementation by
        1. Calcium carbonate
        2. Silica
        3. Iron oxides and the clay minerals
    b. Crystallization

Pressure. Mechanical consolidation due to pressure takes place as more sediments are deposited above a given bed. The weight of the overlying deposits forces the particles of the bed below closer together (except in sandstones and conglomerates). This squeezing eliminates much of the water still present in the materials.

Drying. The other mechanical method of consolidation is drying. As the rocks dry, the water that was not squeezed out by the pressure of beds above is eliminated. The deposit might thus become a porous rock unless further consolidated by pressure or other means of consolidation. Coal is a rock that has been both greatly compressed and dried, as many feet of plant remains are necessary for the formation of one foot of coal.

Cementation. Cementation is a very important means of chemical consolidation, especially in the coarser clastic rocks, the conglomerates and sandstones, and more rarely in coarse accumulations of organic remains. These coarse-grained rocks are very porous and water circulates through them easily, as we have seen in studying ground water. If this water is carrying material in solution, it may be deposited between the grains of the rock. The deposition of the material, or *cement* as it is called, may be uniformly distributed through a rock, or it may take place only in certain parts where conditions for precipitation are most favorable. If the amount of the cement is small, it may be deposited locally, forming a concretion (see Fig. 131, page 138). The most common cements are *calcium carbonate, silica,* the *iron oxides,* and the *clay minerals* (other materials occurring rarely). When the pores of a rock are filled with cement, circulation of water through it ceases. Deposition in rocks may occur from the surface downward; but, as we learned under "Ground Water," it is especially common in the saturated zone below the water level (called the "zone of cementation" because of this fact).

Calcium Carbonate. The most common cement in sedimentary rocks is calcium carbonate, as would be expected, for it is the most common mineral constituent of the average ground water. Some sandstones become completely cemented with calcium carbonate and so contain a high percentage of it.

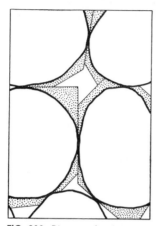

Silica. Silica also is a very common cement. It enters the rocks in solution and is deposited as quartz. Therefore, in a sandstone composed of grains of quartz rounded by erosion, the grains may start to grow again; and, if there is not enough silica to fill up the interstices between them, crystal faces may develop on these rounded quartz grains (Fig. 200). These faces can be seen as tiny glistening points on the surface of a broken piece of sandstone.

FIG. 200. Diagram showing crystal faces (stippled) of quartz developed on rounded grains of sandstone during cementation.

A sandstone cemented with silica is known as *quartzite,* which can be distinguished from sandstone because it breaks *through* the grains, whereas sandstone breaks *around* the grains. This is because the cement in a quartzite is as strong as the quartz grains and the break therefore goes evenly through both.

Iron Oxides and Clay Minerals. The iron oxides, hematite and limonite, and the clay minerals occur as cements in sedimentary rocks, though less commonly than calcium carbonate and silica. Iron-bearing concretions are common.

Crystallization. Crystallization is the chief means of consolidating the chemical sediments. Limestones, dolomites, chert and flint, and salt and gypsum all change from the very fine-grained rocks formed by precipitation into crystalline masses. In some rocks the change in size of the grains has been so insignificant that the crystals or grains cannot be distinguished even with a microscope. This is true for chert and flint, chalk, and some limestones. In other rocks the crystals are large, producing coarse-grained rocks. Salt and gypsum may be very coarse grained. A bed of gypsum in western Oklahoma contains crystals 6 inches long (Fig. 201). The process of crystallization is simply the growth of the larger particles in a mass of fine material at the expense of the smaller particles. The small grains pass into solution in the water that is still in the rock faster than do the larger grains, and this material is redeposited upon the larger grains because, on account of their size, they have a greater ability to attract the material in solution. Thus the rock grows coarser in texture as long as solutions are present.

FIG. 201. Bed of gypsum composed of large crystals of selenite, western Oklahoma. (*Photograph by W. A. Tarr.*)

FEATURES OF SEDIMENTARY ROCKS

Certain characteristic features are common to sedimentary rocks and thus are of assistance in identifying them. Most of these features were formed during the deposition of the sediments but others were formed subsequently. These features are as follows:

Bedding	Mud cracks
Cross-bedding	Fossils
Ripple marks	Oölites
Current	Concretions
Wave	Stylolites
Rill marks	Color
Rain prints	

Bedding. Sedimentary rocks are typically bedded deposits. During their formation, they were spread out on the sea floor as sheets or layers of variable lateral extent. Some beds are remarkably persistent, covering vast areas, though not to the same thickness throughout; others are merely local and may be measured in hundreds of square feet. The thickness of the beds ranges from less than that of a sheet of paper to 10 and, rarely, more than 100 feet. The vast majority of beds are from a few inches (Fig. 202) to a few feet in thickness (Fig. 202). The very thin beds are called *laminae* (see Fig. 145, page 146). The top and bottom of a bed are normally nearly parallel, though some bedding is so uneven as to give rise to so-called *nodular bedding* (Fig. 203).

The bedding in rocks is due: (1) *to differences in the kinds of material deposited,* as would exist between a bed of shale and a bed of limestone;

FIG. 202. Thick-bedded (lower) and thin-bedded (upper) sandstone in Wyoming. (*Photograph by E. B. Branson.*)

(2) *to differences in the sizes of the particles deposited,* as those existing between layers of coarse- and fine-grained sandstone; or (3) *to variations in the color of the materials deposited,* as those between light- and dark-gray layers of limestone.

Cross-bedding. Normally the bedding of sediments is essentially parallel but in the coarser clastic sediments two sets of bedding planes are not unusual. In Fig. 204A, *a* and *a* represent the normal bedding planes, and *b* the shorter bedding planes that cross from *a* to *a*. A rock bedded thus is termed *cross-bedded* (or *cross-laminated*). Cross-bedding is developed in a deposit when the currents forming it are strong and frequently change direction. Thus in A of Fig. 204, strong currents have carried material rapidly offshore, producing a cross-bedded layer having a steep front. Strong currents created by storms may scour out depressions in the sea floor, which, as the currents lose their velocity

FIG. 203. Nodular bedding in limestone, Boone County, Missouri. (*Photograph by W. A. Tarr.*)

and begin to deposit, are filled up, producing cross-bedding (Fig. 204, B). Not uncommonly, the cross-bedding between successive layers lies at different angles, owing to changes in the direction of the current producing it. Cross-bedding is most common in sandstones (Fig. 205) but occurs in some limestones (Fig. 206) also.

FIG. 204. Sketch showing development of cross-bedding.

Ripple Marks. As the currents move over the sea bottom, they shift the particles along with them. If most of the material is rolled along, variations in the size of the grains will cause some particles to move faster than others, and thus a depression at right angles to the current will be developed between the faster moving particles and those lagging behind. These depressions will be rapidly deepened, and soon the surface will be covered with a series of roughly parallel depressions and the

FIG. 205. Cross-bedding in sandstone near Lander, Wyoming.   (*Photograph by E. B. Branson.*)

FIG. 206. Cross-bedding in limestone near Ha Ha Tonka, Missouri.   (*Photograph by William Warner.*)

intervening ridges.   Such a surface is *ripple marked*.   Ripple marks are formed very commonly wherever moving water has clastic materials to work upon.   The ripple marks differ in size, but in sands of medium-sized grains they are commonly ¾ inch to 2 inches from crest to crest.   Rarely, the distance from crest to crest may be several inches.   There are two common types of ripple marks: *current* and *wave*.

Current ripple marks may be made either by a current of water (Fig. 207) or by wind, although those made by the latter agent are rarely preserved in sedimentary rocks. In cross section, current ripple marks have the typical shape shown at *a* in Fig. 208. To produce the ripple mark of the figure, the current must be moving to the right. The material is dragged up the gentle slope and rolled down the steep slope, and thus the ripple mark advances to the right.

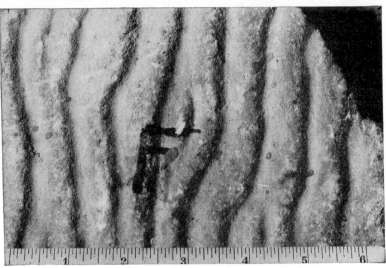

FIG. 207. Current ripple marks in the St. Peter sandstone, Missouri. Which way was the current moving?

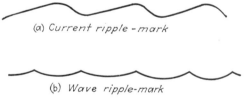

(a) *Current ripple - mark*

(b) *Wave ripple-mark*

FIG. 208. Diagram of current and wave ripple marks.

Wave ripple marks are produced by the up-and-down movement of the water caused by a wave along a shore. Wind does not make wave ripple marks. The two sides of a wave ripple mark have similar slopes (Fig. 208*b*) and the ridges are sharp, although when these features are found preserved in the rocks the sharp crests have usually been cut off by later movements of the water.

Rill Marks. Rill marks are depressions scoured out by water that runs back down the beach after the breaking of a wave. If the depressions that are made are filled by sand before the next high tide, they may be preserved in future sedimentary rock.

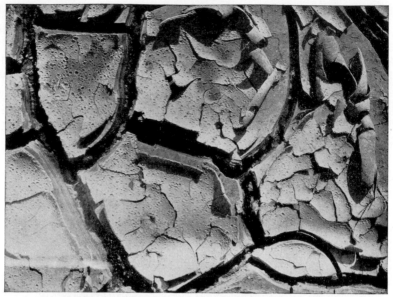

FIG. 209. Rain prints, mud curls, and mud cracks in clay, Versailles, Missouri. (*Photograph by W. A. Tarr.*)

FIG. 210. Cracks in mud flats along the Missouri River, central Missouri. Size shown by hammer at left. Some of these cracks were 2 feet deep. (*Photograph by W. A. Tarr.*)

Rain Prints. Raindrops that fall on fairly firm silts and clays form impressions, which, if preserved, become features of sedimentary rocks (Fig. 209).

Mud Cracks and Mud Curls. Mud cracks and mud curls (Fig. 209) are formed as a result of the drying of an exposed deposit of clay, silt, or sand. Many cracks thus formed extend downward for 2 feet or more, especially in the silts and muds along rivers (Fig. 210). Cracks along rivers eventually become covered with water and filled with other material (Fig. 211), which preserves them if the deposit is buried. Broad mud flats along the seashore that are submerged only during storms at high tide are favorable places for the development of mud cracks and, also, for their preservation as features of sedimentary rocks. Mud curls develop in laminated muds. They are caused by the faster drying of the surface of a layer, which, therefore, shrinks more than the lower part and so curls upward (Fig. 209).

Fossils. The presence in a rock of fossils of any sort, such as shells, bones, teeth, and tracks, can safely be interpreted as indicating a sedimentary rock. A few occurrences of fossils in tuff beds are known, but

FIG. 211. Fossil mud cracks near Pennington Gap, Virginia. (*Photograph by W. A. Tarr.*)

it is easy to prove the volcanic origin of such beds. These beds were formed by the falling of volcanic dust into a body of water containing animals and plants, which were thus incorporated with the volcanic material.

Oölites. Oölites are distinctive features of sedimentary rocks, but they have already been described as small calcareous concretions that may form during the deposition of calcium carbonate. The calcium carbonate of the oölite may be replaced by silica and form siliceous oölites (Fig. 212).

Concretions. Concretions are common features of sedimentary rocks. We have already discussed (page 139) those concretions that are formed in a rock by ground water long after the deposition of the rock, but there is another group of concretions that are formed at the same time (contemporaneously) as the rocks enclosing them. These concretions consist of many different materials, but most commonly of calcium carbonate, silica, or pyrite. The concretions may be round, elliptical (Fig. 213),

oval, lenticular, nodular, or irregular; in fact, their shape may be similar
to that of the subsequent concretions (see Fig. 134, page 140). In size,
they range from tiny concretions smaller than peas to lenticular masses
several feet (Fig. 214) in length and as much as 3 feet in thickness.

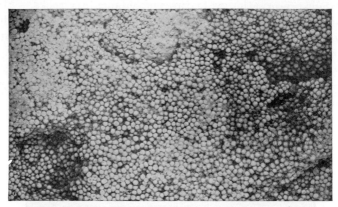

FIG. 212. Siliceous oölite (natural size) from Washington County, Missouri. (*Photograph by W. A. Tarr.*)

FIG. 213. Calcareous concretion in Lias shale, Dorset coast, England. Note curvature of beds around the concretion, which is evidence of its contemporaneous origin. Concretion is 15 inches long. (*Photograph by W. A. Tarr.*)

Contemporaneous calcareous concretions are common in shales and
clays. These concretions are chemical precipitates, like many limestones.
The calcium carbonate is precipitated directly on the sea floor, the growth
of the concretion starting about a central point and more material being
added on the outside.

The chert and flint nodules occurring in limestone, chalk, and dolomite are contemporaneous concretions. Their origin has been discussed
and illustrations of them given on pages 195, 196, and 197.

Pyrite occurs as concretions in all kinds of sediments but is especially abundant in shales, carbonate rocks, and coal. The surface of a pyrite concretion may be covered with crystal faces of the mineral.

Contemporaneous concretions occur dominantly along or within a given bed (Fig. 215). Their persistence in this respect makes them of value as criteria in determining beds of the same age, even though they

FIG. 214. Lenticular calcareous concretion from Lias shale, Dorset coast, England. Note layer of cone-in-cone on exterior of concretion.

may be miles apart. Such a widespread distribution in itself indicates that the concretions were deposited at the same time as the beds.

Stylolites. Stylolites are very common and interesting features of sedimentary rocks, usually of limestone and dolomite and rarely of sandstone and quartzite. They have already been considered (page 132) under the discussion of the work of ground water, the agent to which they owe their formation.

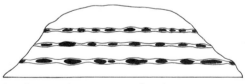

FIG. 215. Sketch showing the normal arrangement of contemporaneous concretions along a bed.

Color of Sedimentary Rocks. The color of a sedimentary rock is due to the inherent color of the minerals composing it or to an extraneous coloring matter introduced at the time of the deposition of the rock or later. The vast majority of sediments possess one of three dominant colors or mixtures of them in which the shade of color depends upon the proportions of the different colors. These three colors are white, black, and red. Mixtures of black and white materials produce a gray rock, small amounts of black material producing a light-gray (the characteristic color of most limestones) and large amounts a dark-gray rock. White materials mixed with red produce pink rocks.

Black sedimentary rocks are due to the carbonaceous material remaining after the decay of organic matter. On weathering (chemically), however, a gray limestone usually becomes buff, yellow, or red. This is because iron minerals were included with the calcareous materials when the limestone was deposited. In the presence of carbonaceous material, however, iron exists as white or colorless compounds. During the weathering of limestone, however, when ground water containing a large quantity of oxygen enters the rock, the carbonaceous material is oxidized to carbon dioxide (CO_2), which escapes; whereupon the colorless iron compound is oxidized to hematite (Fe_2O_3), which is red. The color of hematite is so dominant that a very small amount of it will color the rock a faint shade of red. By uniting with water, some of the hematite will form the iron oxide limonite ($Fe_2O_3.nH_2O$), which produces the yellow and brown colors of the weathered rocks. Mixtures of hematite and limonite produce orange and purple colors. These two iron oxides are very common coloring agents of sediments. The great series of red beds of western United States and of other countries owe their color to the presence of hematite. Orange and green colors are produced in sedimentary rocks by various means, some of which are not fully understood.

WEATHERING OF SEDIMENTARY ROCKS

The same agents of weathering, mechanical and chemical, that attacked the igneous rocks act upon the sedimentary rocks, but with somewhat different results, as we shall see, because the sediments themselves are composed of the products of weathering.

Conglomerates, as the name indicates, may be composed of any kind of rock or mineral. As a result, each boulder or pebble will weather into the materials that the rock or mineral it represents would weather into. A conglomerate composed of boulders, cobbles, and pebbles of granite would weather into the same products as a granite, but one composed of particles of different types of igneous rocks, or the different kinds of sedimentary rocks, would weather into all the different products that the weathering of the different rocks present would produce.

Sandstones, however, are composed dominantly of quartz grains, themselves a product that was unaffected by chemical weathering; hence, disintegration (by the removal of the cement if any is present) is the chief change, the sandstone becoming a sand again.

Shales are composed predominantly of insoluble clay minerals produced by the weathering of certain igneous rocks; hence, when the shale itself is weathered, it becomes again a loose aggregate of clay minerals. Any chemical change is minor in amount. The soil over a shale is a clay soil, which grades directly and almost imperceptibly into the shale.

Limestones, chalk, and *dolomites,* being soluble in ordinary ground water, pass back into solution during weathering. Such results of weathering are evident in exposures of limestone, the surface being roughened, pitted, and channeled (Fig. 120, page 131). Some channels are many feet deep and not uncommonly are connected downward with an underground passage or even a cavern. As the limestone or other carbonate rock passes into solution, any insoluble impurities, such as chert, flint, clay, iron oxides, or quartz grains, are left behind and form the mantle rock. This material is usually red (especially over dolomites), because even the very small amount of iron present in a fairly pure limestone is converted into hematite during weathering and, being greatly concentrated in the mantle rock, colors it red. Over some dolomites, red soils may contain as much as 10 or 15 per cent of hematite. Such soils may accumulate until they are many feet in thickness. The soil, of course, is not so red as the rest of the mantle rock on account of the organic matter it naturally contains. Some limestone soils are even black, owing to an abundance of organic matter.

The *chert* and *flint* associated with carbonate rocks are relatively insoluble and so are concentrated in the mantle rock and soil during weathering. In some areas of carbonate rocks containing much chert (some limestones contain 50 per cent of chert), the chert accumulates on the surface (especially the slopes of the hills, from which the fine residual soil is easily washed away) until it completely covers it. Such chert-strewn hillsides look from a distance as though they were snow mantled. They are waste land. Some of the chert will find its way into the streams and become disintegrated into gravel.

Such soluble rocks as *salt* and *gypsum* readily pass back into solution during weathering, leaving behind any impurities they contain to help in the formation of soil.

Some sedimentary rocks containing *iron minerals* in amounts insufficient to pay to mine the iron may undergo enrichment as a result of the weathering of the rocks. The insoluble iron oxides are left behind and the more soluble materials associated with them are removed. This type of enrichment has changed the original iron-bearing sediments of the Lake Superior region into the high-grade ores found there. Lateritic deposits formed at the surface may be rich enough in iron to mine. These deposits (see page 77) represent one of the end products of weathering.

In the weathering of sedimentary rocks, as in the weathering of igneous rocks, the formation of a productive soil is of the first importance to man. The famous bluegrass region of Kentucky owes its productive-

ness to its limestone soil.   A soil well suited for agricultural purposes
is the sandy loam produced by the weathering of a combination of sandstones and shales.

SUMMARY

The products of the weathering of the primary igneous rocks (as well
as some secondary rocks) are transported to the ocean, sorted, and
deposited, resulting in a series of sedimentary rocks.   Some of these
rocks consist of fragments of various sizes, and others are of chemical
or organic origin.   These sedimentary rocks possess various features
that are distinctive of them as deposits made in water.

CHAPTER 10

METAMORPHIC ROCKS

Rocks that have suffered intense folding at great depths or those occurring near the contact of large intrusive bodies with older rocks commonly possess structural features that are different from those of the igneous and sedimentary rocks. A careful study of these rocks shows likewise that, though some of the original minerals of the earlier rocks are still present, others have been changed into different minerals. The new rocks are called *metamorphic rocks*, since "metamorphic" means changed in form or character. Two important lines of evidence led to the recognition that these rocks had originated through changes in older rocks. One was that the minerals and structural details of the altered rocks could, in some mountainous areas, be traced into less altered phases that still showed features of the original rocks. The other line of evidence was the discovery, made through chemical analyses, that, although the altered rocks look vastly different, actually they have the same chemical composition as certain sedimentary or igneous rocks from which, for other reasons, it was thought they might have been derived (Figs. 216 and 217).

There are two types of *metamorphism: regional* and *contact.* Regional metamorphism consists of slow changes due to the normal pressure, heat, and solutions that exist everywhere within the earth's crust and of other changes, probably more rapid, that are caused by folding and crumpling (Fig. 218A) of the rocks. Contact metamorphism is due to the exceptionally high temperature, pressure, and very strong solutions that are connected with injection of magma into a rock (Fig. 218B). Alterations produced during contact metamorphism are very marked adjacent to intrusions but die out, as a rule, within half a mile. Most metamorphic rocks have been formed by regional metamorphism; hence our discussion will be concerned mainly with that type of change. Contact metamorphism is of economic importance, however, as it produces some of our valuable metal-bearing deposits.

Where Metamorphism Occurred. Numerous attempts have been made by geologists to divide the crust of the earth into zones in which certain changes in the rocks occur (Fig. 219): for example, the outer zone

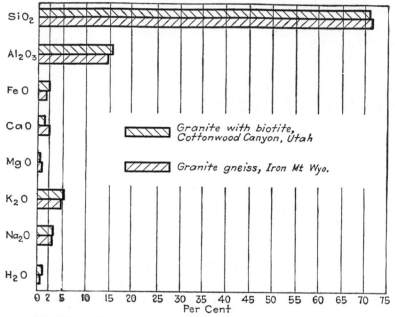

FIG. 216. Diagram showing similarities in composition of granite and gneiss.

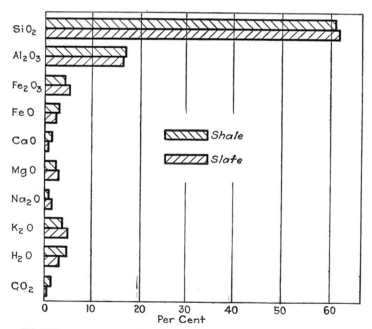

FIG. 217. Diagram illustrating the similarity in composition of shale and slate.

of weathering and below it the zone of cementation. Needless to say, such zones have arbitrary limits; the zone of weathering, for example, ranges from a few inches to hundreds of feet in thickness.   In the discus-

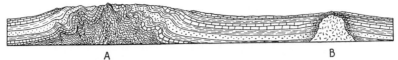

A   B

FIG. 218. (A) Folding and crumpling such as produce regional metamorphism; (B) contact metamorphism around an igneous intrusion.

sion that follows, we shall refer to the *zone of metamorphism*, but it should be understood that it begins at the various depths below the surface at which metamorphism begins.

The occurrence of metamorphic rocks in the central part of mountain ranges, in which extensive erosion has exposed them, and the additional fact that the surface or near-surface sedimentary and igneous rocks are fresh unaltered material indicate that metamorphism usually occurred at a considerable distance below the surface.   That this distance is not necessarily great has been proved in many mountainous areas, one being the Appalachian region, where the depth has been measured and found to be within a few thousand feet of the surface.   We can thus deduce something about the amount of pressure and heat that caused the formation of metamorphic rocks.

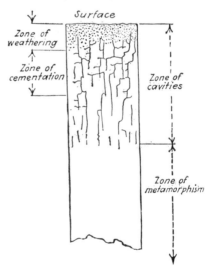

FIG. 219. Diagram showing zones in outer part of the earth.

THE AGENTS OF METAMORPHISM

The alterations that occur in rocks and minerals are both chemical and physical. The *chemical agents* of metamorphism, *water* and *gases*, change the existing rocks and minerals into new ones; and *pressure* and *heat, physical agents* of metamorphism, bring about flattening, elongation, and other changes of the rock constituents.   It will be seen in our discussion of metamorphism that most of the alterations are produced partly by chemical and partly by physical means and, moreover, that the chemical and physical agents may both be operative at the same time in producing such alterations.   Thus it will not be possible wholly to separate the discussions of chemical and physical metamorphism.

Chemical Agents. The chemical changes are caused largely by water, though it is aided by the various acids and gases it contains and by heat. Under special conditions, such as the injections of lava into a rock, the metamorphism may be very intense due to the high temperatures in connection with strong acids and gases that may be present. Deep within the crust, the heat might be so great that all solutions would be converted into gases, and if so, the metamorphic effects would be intensified. At these great depths, pressure, another physical agent of metamorphism, would aid the chemical agents in their work by crushing the rocks into smaller grains that would be more easily attacked.

Water and Gases. Water is such an effective agent of metamorphism that even cold water can bring about changes (as we have seen under "Weathering"). However, as hot water has a much greater efficiency, deep-seated metamorphism is the more marked. When the temperature is high enough, water is converted into steam, which is also able to take part in the chemical changes. Such gases as oxygen, carbon dioxide, sulfur dioxide, chlorine, or fluorine greatly increase the ability of water to accomplish chemical changes. The changes take place slowly, of course; but, as the time element in geologic processes is ample, great changes are finally accomplished.

The water in the rocks may have been included in them originally, such as the water in shales or sandstones; it may be contained in hydrous minerals, such as the clay minerals; or it may have worked its way into the rocks from below or above. When a shale or other water-bearing sedimentary rock becomes deeply buried, the heat causes the liberation of water from the hydrous minerals. This process, while altering the hydrous minerals, liberates some of their water, which aids in bringing about the chemical changes. In the deeper zones, carbon dioxide would be liberated, and during the breaking up of pyrite by solutions sulfur dioxide might be released. Through all these means, water and gases may be made available for chemical work.

The Physical Agents. *Heat* and *pressure* are very important agents in producing metamorphic changes. Pressure operates everywhere in the earth's crust but is, of course, more effective at the greater depths, where heat also produces its greatest effects owing to the higher temperatures existing there. In the outer 40 to 50 miles, movement (flowage) may be produced in the solid rocks. Such movement is an important factor in the formation of the banded rocks.

Heat. Tests made to determine the temperature in deep wells in many parts of the world prove that there is a slow increase in temperature downward. The rate is different in different areas: where there has been recent igneous activity the temperatures are high near the surface (Fig. 220); in others they are low. At depths of 20,000 feet, the temperatures, if uninfluenced by igneous rocks, are probably much the same. In a deep well in Pennsylvania, the temperature of the rocks just below the surface was 10°C. and at the bottom of the well, at a depth of 7,756 feet, it was 77°C. The temperature was 77°C. at 8,300 feet in a well in the Big Lake oil field in Reagan County, Texas. In some deep (6,000 to 7,000 feet) mines, temperatures are 44 to 49°C., and special means of ventilation to cool the mines must be employed.

The average rate of temperature increase downward has been estimated to be 1°C. for 100 feet; at that rate the boiling point of water should

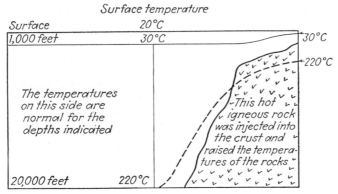

FIG. 220. Diagram showing increase in temperature due to an igneous intrusion.

be reached at about 8,500 feet. In the two wells mentioned above, however, the temperature at such a depth was much below the boiling point of water; in fact, several wells have been drilled to depths of 10,000 feet or more in which the boiling point of water was not reached. It must be inferred, therefore, that the rate of 1°C. for 100 feet represents too high a temperature increase downward, though the rate is probably affected by many factors that we are unable to evaluate or possibly of whose existence we have no knowledge. The important fact is, however, that any rock occurring at depths of a mile or more exists under conditions of high temperature. Deep within the earth, the temperature is probably thousands of degrees; but, as the great pressures there prevent expansion, the rocks cannot become liquid except locally.

Pressure. We know that pressure increases downward owing to the weight of the column of rock above any given point. This pressure can easily be computed as follows. The average specific gravity of the outer part of the earth is commonly considered as 2.7. Using this figure and the weight of a cubic foot of water (62.5 pounds), the weight of a cubic foot of average rock is found to be 168 pounds and the weight of a column of rock, 1 foot high and 1 inch square, 1.16 pounds. The pressure on 1 square inch at a depth of 1,000 feet would thus be 1,160 pounds; at one mile about 6,000 pounds; and at 10 miles 60,000 pounds or 30 tons. (The pressure at the center of the earth is estimated to be

FIG. 221. Crumpled gneiss.

45,000,000 pounds per square inch.) These great pressures would aid in producing profound changes in a rock. Experimental studies have

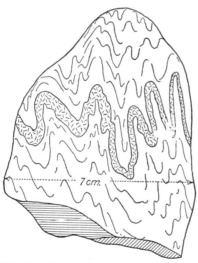

FIG. 222. Sketch of a dike 18.5 centimeters long crumpled into a space of 7 centimeters.

shown that at a depth of approximately 11 miles the strongest granite known would probably flow like asphalt. Below this depth an opening could not exist in the earth's crust. Rocks weaker than granite would flow at depths much nearer the surface; in fact, certain shales would flow within 1.5 miles of the surface. This actually occurred in a deep well in Pennsylvania, the shale flowing and crushing the iron casing in the well as though it were a paper tube.

If the pressure in the metamorphic zone is sufficient to crush the rocks, they should show evidence, such as folding and crumpling, of having flowed or moved. This evidence of flowage (Fig. 221) is present in many metamorphic rocks. Dikes and sills (the tabular masses of igneous rocks that are intrusive in other rocks) are normally straight (see Fig. 17, page 21), but in metamorphic areas they are much folded and crumpled (Fig. 222).

The pressures within the earth's crust (Fig. 223) are *uniform,* or *directional,* which is, of course, nonuniform.   Uniform pressure is effective in reducing the volume of a substance, and nonuniform, or directed, pressure leads to movement and changes the shape of minerals, as we shall see later.

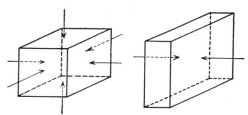

FIG. 223. Diagram at left illustrates uniform pressure; diagram at right, directional pressure.

THE RESULTS OF METAMORPHISM

The agents of metamorphism induce a wide variety of changes that result in the development of many different metamorphic rocks.   Despite the great diversity, however, both the changes produced and the resultant rocks may be classified into the few groups shown in the following table:

EFFECTS OF METAMORPHISM

The Change Produced	Example of the Resultant Metamorphic Rock
Coarse banding	Gneiss
Thin banding	Schist
Formation of new minerals	Garnet gneiss
	Chlorite-muscovite schist
Recrystallization	Marble
Thermal hardening (baking)	Hornfels

The details of the results of metamorphism will now be discussed in terms of the individual changes.

Chemical (Mineral) Changes.   The chemical changes through which new minerals are produced are the most important changes in the formation of metamorphic rocks.   These changes are going on constantly, though usually slowly.   The number of new minerals that are formed is large and a full discussion of their formation would be out of place here. We can follow the process of a few of the simpler changes, however, and thus have some idea as to how the metamorphic agents accomplish their work.   As a rule, *if a new mineral forms it must be stable under the new physical conditions* (see *law of stability,* page 65).   Thus the clay minerals formed at the surface of the earth are unstable when moved far below and so are altered to minerals that are stable there.   This principle of the alteration of minerals should be kept in mind throughout our discussion of metamorphism.

The Change of Limestone to Marble.   Probably the simplest chemical change is that of a limestone or dolomite to marble, as this alteration involves the formation of no new minerals. Marble is coarser grained than limestone and so the change has been simply one of small grains into large ones. As the original calcite grains in the limestone differed in size, the smaller grains went into solution faster than the large ones and the material was deposited on the larger grains. Thus it is another example of large grains' growing at the expense of smaller ones, such as we have seen in discussing the formation of the sedimentary rocks. As the alteration of the limestone proceeds, the fine-grained limestone becomes the coarser-grained marble (Fig. 224). This change, which is a common one in metamorphism, is known as *recrystallization*.

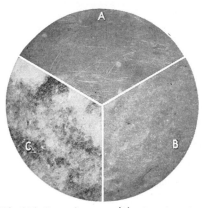

FIG. 224. Dense limestone (A), altered to fine-grained limestone (B), and then to marble (C)—all changes due to recrystallization.

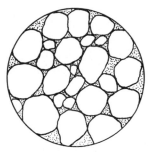

FIG. 225. Diagram showing grains (white) of a sandstone cemented with quartz (stippled) to form quartzite.

The Change of Sandstone to Quartzite. The *cementation* of the grains of a sandstone by quartz is a simple sedimentary process that is included by some authors under metamorphism. It does not belong here, however, as it merely involves the carrying of silica in solution and its deposition as quartz upon the grains of sand (also quartz) until the openings in the sandstone are filled (Fig. 225). This process is mere cementation, which may occur from the surface of the earth downward. Sandstones and quartzites do undergo metamorphism, however, but their alteration, being due to pressure, will be noted under the discussion of physical changes.

The Change of Shale to Slate and Schist. The alteration of shale to slate and schist is a much more complex process, as it involves several changes. Shale consists predominantly of clay minerals, soluble silica, potassium, and water. Some shales contain quartz, mica, and iron oxides, also. After a shale is buried and subjected to increasing heat, the first change is a loss of water. This simple alteration (called *dehydra-*

tion), alone, hardens the shale, and if no other change occurs a hard flintlike rock called *hornfels* or *baked shale* (Fig. 226) results.

During metamorphism, part of the water of the clay minerals is driven off by heat and so is able to aid in the chemical changes. The potassium of the shale unites with the remainder of the water, the alumina, and

FIG. 226. Hornfels or baked shale from Breckenridge, Colorado.

the silica of the clay minerals to form little scales of *muscovite mica*, which is the dominant constituent of most *slates*. Some shales do not contain enough potassium, however, to form mica from the clay minerals, whereupon their alumina and silica unite, forming large dark crystals which give the rock a spotted appearance. One variety (staurolite) of these crystals occurs as crosses, which in Virginia and other places are collected

FIG. 227. Staurolite crystals. One-half natural size.

and sold as "fairy crosses" (Fig. 227). Had pyrite been present in the original shale, it might have been recrystallized during the metamorphism into larger pyrite crystals (Fig. 228). The dark color of black slates is due to the formation of *graphite* scales from carbonaceous material in the original shale. If the original shale was yellow, it contained limonite, which during metamorphism would lose its water and become hematite, and thus a red slate would be formed. This is not all of the story, however, for pressure (as we shall see in studying physical metamorphism) causes the flakes of mica to assume a parallel arrangement, which gives to slates their property of splitting into sheets.

If a slate is subjected to further metamorphic action by hot solutions, the larger scales of mica will grow at the expense of smaller ones and a mica *schist* will result.

The Change of Granite to Gneiss. The alteration of granite, or any other igneous rock, to a metamorphic rock is by far the most complex metamor-

FIG. 228. Pyrite cube embedded in a black slate. One-half natural size.

phic process. The quartz is not altered, as a rule, but may be badly crushed; the feldspar, however, may undergo marked changes, the most common of which is the alteration into muscovite mica. If the igneous

FIG. 229. Garnets (12-sided form). One-half natural size.

rock contains mafic minerals, such as hornblende or pyroxene, they are altered to hornblende needles (pyroxene becomes hornblende), chlorite, biotite mica, or *garnets* (Fig. 229). A gneiss (originally a granite) containing garnets 6 inches to a foot or more in diameter occurs in the Adirondacks. Garnets are very common in all kinds of metamorphic rocks, and some of them are used as gems (Fig. 230).

Summary. Solutions, aided by heat, take material from one mineral and add it to another to form a new mineral, thereby producing a new type of rock (metamorphic rock). Many different minerals are formed, but the most common ones are micas, hornblende, chlorite, garnets, and quartz. In the formation of some metamorphic rocks, material is added from another rock nearby; in the formation of others, no material is added or removed, one mineral merely changing into another or one mineral grain merely growing larger at the expense of a smaller grain of the same mineral.

Physical (Structural) Changes. A striking characteristic of most metamorphic rocks is that they are *banded* or *foliated* and have the property of cleaving more or less readily along these bands or planes. This banding and cleavage are due to the movement (shearing) and recrystallization that are induced by the physical agent pressure.

FIG. 230. Garnets in schist from Wrangell, Alaska. One-fourth natural size.

The banded character of metamorphic rocks is utilized in naming the two most common types, gneiss and schist. If the bands in the rock are fairly coarse ($\frac{1}{8}$ to $\frac{1}{4}$ inch in thickness), the rock is a *gneiss* (Fig. 231); if the bands are thin and the rock cleaves readily, it is a *schist* (Fig. 232). A *slate* (Fig. 233) has this cleavage property very highly developed and may thus be split into remarkably thin sheets.

Banding the Result of Directional Pressure. Directional pressure involves movement and shearing and is the dominant factor in forming the banded, cleavable rocks. The new minerals that develop during chemical metamorphism are, as a result of directed pressure, dominantly flat, tabular, or elongated bladelike forms. The common minerals that have these shapes are *muscovite, biotite, chlorite, talc* (a hydrous magnesium silicate), and a bladed variety of *hornblende*. These minerals develop

FIG. 231. Gneiss.   Note elongated feldspar crystals.   One-half natural size.

with their flat sides at right angles to the direction of the pressure; thus, as

FIG. 232. Schist.   Note thin banding and garnet crystals.   One-half natural size.

was noted in discussing the formation of slate, the directional pressure caused the mica to become parallel, giving the slate its cleavage. Cleavage planes developed by metamorphism in a folded sedimentary rock are generally independent of the bedding planes and may be at right angles to the direction of the pressure (Fig. 234).

In those minerals which do not undergo chemical changes, the grains are either crushed and elongated (Figs. 231 and 235) by the pressure and movement or are compelled to rotate or flow until they are parallel to each other. It is thus that gneiss, consisting as it does chiefly of crushed and elongated quartz and feldspar grains, possesses a coarser banding than a rock that is composed of tabular metamorphic minerals. Pure sandstones and quartzites are crushed as a result of directional pressure, and, although the banding developed is poor, they are known as

FIG. 233. Slate split into two sheets, each $\frac{1}{4}$ inch thick.

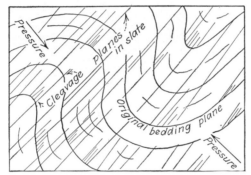

FIG. 234. Sketch of section of slate quarry, showing how cleavage planes of the slate are at right angles to the pressure and independent of the bedding planes.

quartz schists. If the sandstones and quartzites were clayey, considerable mica might form and so good schistose banding would be developed. If no banding developed, however, the metamorphosed sandstone or quartzite might be called a "quartzite."

The mottled varieties of marble are the result of directional pressure and the accompanying movement. This movement is made possible by the fact that calcite and dolomite have perfect cleavage in

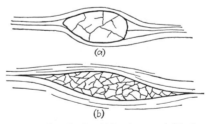

FIG. 235. Sketch of pebble of quartz (a) before and (b) after crushing and elongation.

three directions. As a result of the flowage or movement, the rock is twisted and crumpled until all evidence of the bedding planes of the limestone from which the marble originated is lost.

In the restricted space in which metamorphism occurs, it is inevitable that there should be crowding and jamming of rock masses. This results in the folding and crumpling characteristic of the metamorphic rocks (Fig. 221, p. 222). Thus directional pressure and its accompanying movement not only cause the parallel banding characteristic of metamorphic rocks but also the folding and crumpling seen in all kinds of metamorphic rocks. As directional pressures operate chiefly nearer the surface where upward movement is possible, folded and banded metamorphic rocks are most abundant in the crust. They are especially abundant, of course, in the intensely folded strata of mountainous regions.

Massiveness the Result of Uniform Pressure. When a new mineral formed by chemical metamorphism is subjected only to uniform pressure during its formation, the mineral crystal will be nearly equidimensional,

FIG. 236. Serpentine. One-fourth natural size.

such as cubes of pyrite (Fig. 228), twelve-sided garnets (Figs. 229 and 230), or staurolite crystals (Fig. 227). All these minerals are very dense and heavy as their atoms have been forced close together by the uniform pressure, which, therefore, accomplishes volume reduction. These minerals are common in schists and gneisses where they develop after the formation of the banding that is caused by directional pressure. The growth of these later minerals under the conditions of uniform pressure is due to a continuation of the chemical changes, the new minerals forming out of the materials around them.

Two common *massive* (*i.e.*, not banded or foliated) *metamorphic rocks* are *marble* and *serpentine*. The massiveness of marble is due to the fact that its formation (which we learned is a recrystallization of limestone) is accomplished under conditions of uniform pressure. Serpentine (a hydrous magnesium silicate) also is formed under uniform pressure, but by the alteration of minerals (like olivine) rich in magnesium. Serpentine is a green mottled rock (Fig. 236). Both marble and serpentine are widely used for building purposes. Another massive metamorphic rock developed under uniform pressure is *greenstone*. It is formed when the dark mafic minerals in a gabbro or basalt alter to chlorite, which gives the rock its green color. It may be noted that if a greenstone later becomes involved in directional pressure it may be converted into a chlorite schist.

CLASSIFICATION OF METAMORPHIC ROCKS

In the previous chapters on igneous and sedimentary rocks, tables of the names of the more common rock types were developed. Tables of value may now be constructed which will include these earlier rocks with their metamorphic derivatives. It must be remembered, however, that there are hundreds of varieties of gneisses just as there are hundreds of kinds of granites, and that there are many kinds of schists, slates, and marbles. Therefore, many names are applied to a given metamorphic rock; for example, there are biotite gneisses, hornblende gneisses, garnet gneisses, and garnet-biotite gneisses. Muscovite and biotite schists are especially common and are usually called "mica schists." There are also garnet schists and garnet-muscovite schists.

The following table shows the dominant types of metamorphic rocks that are derived from the igneous rocks:

METAMORPHIC ROCKS DERIVED FROM IGNEOUS ROCKS

Igneous Rocks	Metamorphic Rocks
Granite, diorite	Gneiss, schist
Gabbro	Hornblende gneiss, hornblende-chlorite schist
Peridotite*	Talc schist, chlorite schist, serpentine
Felsite, felsite porphyry	Mica schist
Basalt, basalt porphyry	Chlorite schist, hornblende schist, talc schist, greenstone
Volcanic glass, tuff	Mica schist

* An igneous rock rich in olivine. Introduced here because of the economic value of some of its metamorphic products.

Some of the metamorphic rocks formed from the sedimentary rocks are shown in the following table:

METAMORPHIC ROCKS DERIVED FROM SEDIMENTARY ROCKS

Sedimentary Rocks	Metamorphic Rocks
Conglomerate	Gneiss
Sandstone and quartzite	Quartz-hornfels, quartz schist, quartzite
Siltstone and shale	Slate, mica schist, hornfels
Limestone and dolomite	Marble
Iron ores (limonite and hematite)	Specularite schist, magnetite* schist, magnetite ore
Coal	Graphite

* Magnetite is a black magnetic iron oxide.

SUMMARY

Metamorphism is the alteration of some previously existing rock by pressure, heat, and water, usually under the conditions that exist at considerable depths. The metamorphic agents are always in operation beneath the surface, converting minerals into others that can exist under the pressure conditions at that place. The new minerals are generally more complex in composition than the original minerals. The combined results of the metamorphic processes are the metamorphic

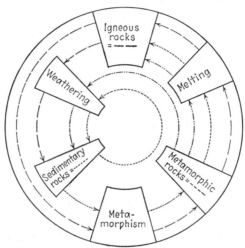

FIG. 237. Diagram representing rock cycle.

rocks with their many new minerals and structures. They form a group of rocks that are very abundant in many parts of the earth's crust.

The end of metamorphism would be attained when the temperature became high enough (between 600 and 900°C.) to melt the metamorphic rocks, whereupon they would become a liquid magma, which, upon cooling, would become some type of igneous rock again. This would complete the cycle of igneous rock to sedimentary rock to metamorphic rock and back to igneous rock again, as is shown in Fig. 237. This sequence of events has undoubtedly taken place many times.

CHAPTER 11

SNOW AND ICE

Ice and snow have indirectly accomplished geologic work of importance over a considerable proportion of the earth's surface. Other agents, such as wind and running water, operate in every climate and altitude, but over the warm areas of the earth, snow is rarely present and is ineffective as a geologic agent. In regions where snowfall is heavy, most of the work accomplished is by the indirect method; *i.e.*, melt water from the snow does geologic work as running water. In mountain areas snow itself in the form of snowslides does destructive work. At times during the geologic past snow has been much more widely distributed over the globe than it is now.

Snowslides. On steep mountain slopes snow may accumulate to such depths that its weight is too great for its grasp on the surface. The drift starts moving with an almost imperceptible creep, speeds up, and gaining momentum, plunges down the slope, twisting and breaking even the largest trees and carrying with it great quantities of loose rock. Many an Alpine village has been destroyed by such an avalanche, and slides are not uncommon on all mountains high enough to have permanent snow.

The slide remains as a rock-filled snowbank until the snow melts, and then its effects become evident. A great bare patch on the mountainside almost free of loose rock indicates the path of the slide, and a heterogeneous mass of rock and twisted trees marks the end of the avalanche. The many snowslide scars and accompanying heaps of rock waste in the Rocky Mountains bear mute witness to the local efficacy of snow as a destructive agent. However, the changes accomplished by snowslides are insignificant as compared with those brought abou by snow that changes into ice and forms glaciers.

Snow Fields. In high altitudes and latitudes there are large areas within which snow persists the year round, and, although large patches within such areas may be bare during part or all of the year, the permanent drifts are known as "snow fields" (Fig. 238). Drifts persist although evaporation and melting may greatly restrict the size of the snow patches. The primary factor that determines the formation of snow fields is the excess of snowfall over waste (melting and evaporation); it follows that of two areas at the same altitude one may have a snow field and the other, because of the smaller snowfall, may be bare during much of the year.

The *snow line* is an imaginary line connecting the lowest margins of snowdrifts that persist throughout the year. At the equator in South America the snow line is at an elevation of about 18,000 feet; in Mexico, about 14,000 feet; at the northern boundary of the United States, about 10,000 feet; and 35° from the poles it is at sea level, at some places.

FIG. 238. Snow fields and a glacier in Alaska. (*Official photograph, U.S. Navy Air Corps.*)

As snowfall exceeds waste in snow fields, it is evident that in such places the snow mantle increases in thickness from year to year. It is also evident that there is some limit beyond which the increase cannot go, as otherwise all the water of the earth would be locked up in snow fields. This limit is determined by the weakness of the ice, which lacks the strength to hold its shape under the weight of the accumulating snow and spreads out beyond the confines of the snow field into lower altitudes or latitudes where melting checks further advance. As an example, consider an area like Greenland and suppose that the snowfall were 10 feet per year and 9 feet were lost by melting and evaporation.[1] In 5,000 years the snow would accumulate to a depth of 5,000 feet, which

[1] At the rate of 1 foot excess snowfall over waste per year, all of the water on the earth would be piled up on Greenland in one-fifth the time it would take to base-level the North American continent at the present rate of erosion.

would be sufficient to cause movement of the snow field. As the temperature would be higher near the sea, the melting would be greater and the snow would be thicker on the interior of the island than near the water. The weight of 5,000 feet of snow and ice would be so great as to crush the ice at the bottom and tend to make it move laterally. The outward movement of the snow becomes a necessity, obeying ordinary physical laws.

GLACIERS

A mass of snow and ice set in slow motion on land by its own weight is called a *glacier* (Fig. 239). Glaciers will form wherever the yearly

FIG. 239. An Alaskan glacier. (*Official photograph, U.S. Navy Air Corps.*)

snowfall exceeds the yearly waste long enough for the snow to acquire sufficient weight to start movement in the mass. Areas with small snow fields may have no glaciers, but the distribution of glaciers is nearly the same as that of snow fields. Glaciers are present in high mountains of equatorial regions; toward the poles they are at lower and lower levels, reaching sea level, in some places, as far as 35° from the poles. In tropical and temperate regions, glaciers form only in mountain valleys and for that reason are called *valley glaciers*. In frigid regions, land areas at low altitudes may be covered with glaciers. Such low-altitude glaciers covering large areas (Greenland is a good example) are called *continental glaciers*.

Glacial Ice. Although glaciers form from snow, they are made up of solid ice. Throughout the almost infinite variety in the shape of snowflakes, certain broad characters are constant: all are flat, thin, and lace-like. The delicate ice crystals, however, change rapidly once they have reached the earth. Ice evaporates, even though the temperature of the air is below freezing; the delicate points of the flakes waste away, and at the same time there is a tendency for recondensation about the central, more solid part of the flake. These two processes, waste of delicate points and growth of center, convert the flakes into tiny spheres. The change from fluffy to granular snow at the surface, in a few days at the most, is common in temperate climates. The process is hastened by rise in temperature, and a short melting period, each day, quickly converts a considerable depth of flakes into grains with little total loss to the mass through melting. In a snow field a steady granulation of the snow continues throughout the winter, and the residue at the end of the summer is completely grained. A piece of clean glacial ice does not show the spheres even under the microscope, but the structure remains throughout the life of the glacier and when the ice partially melts it breaks down into small spheres. It would seem that the cementing ice had slightly different properties than the spherical ice, and possibly this accounts, in part, for the motion peculiar to glaciers. We might liken the mass to grains of sand cemented by a somewhat plastic cement.

This graining is only an incident in the conversion of snow to solid ice. Even slight melting at the surface of the snow furnishes water that descends to refreeze in the pores. Apparently no considerable thickness of grained snow can exist without being thoroughly cemented in its lower part. Pressure on the lower part of the granular snow from the overlying snow tends to compact the lower part into ice. The combined granulation, melting, refreezing, and pressure tend to make the ice of the snow field and glacier nearly as dense as that resulting from the ordinary freezing of water.

Glacial ice is compact and in a real sense rigid. A stone in its midst is as firmly incorporated as one frozen into the ice of a pond. Glacial ice snaps and cracks under stresses that tend to deform it just as does ordinary ice. Even so, it molds itself into the tortuous curves of valleys very much as though it were a viscous liquid.

One of the most striking features of glacial ice is stratification, a layered structure that comes largely from the mode of origin of the ice. Each year a layer of ice is added, which is the remnant after the waste of the year's snowfall. At least a small amount of dust settles on the surface of the snow to give to the yearly layers a laminated appearance. Most of the sediments freed by the year's melting accumulate on the surface to mark by an exceptionally dirty band the end of the active melting season. Where snow accumulates in a steep-walled mountain valley, much coarse debris may be released by spring thaws and may roll down to the ice surface in the valley (Fig. 240).

Glacial Motion.   To say that we understand glacial motion would be misleading, although many peculiarities of the motion are common knowledge.   For instance, warm glaciers (near the melting point), and therefore wet glaciers, move faster than cold, dry glaciers; or, again,

FIG. 240. Lower end of a glacier with a thin mantle of gravel, sand, and clay.   Stratification is seen in the vertical front.   (*Official photograph, U.S. Navy Air Corps.*)

glaciers may override obstructions and actually move uphill for short distances, provided that they are sufficiently long and thick.   Most evident is the fact that glaciers do not slide as a unit down valleys, although minor parts of a valley glacier are pushed like a great rasp along the valley bottom and sides.

We can appreciate the distinctive movement of glaciers by visualizing a great icecap like that of Greenland.   Let us assume that at the center

ice has accumulated to a thickness of several thousand feet.   The ice
in the lower part of this pile is under pressure so great that it must move
laterally, developing a thrust that is transmitted to the margins.   The
ice at the margin is thin, for the position of the margin is determined by
melting, which is compensated for by forward movement of the ice.   The

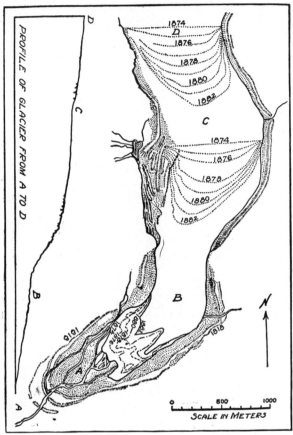

FIG. 241. Map of the Rhone Glacier, Switzerland, showing differential ice movement.   The middle
of the glacier moves most rapidly.   (From Emmons, Thiel, Stauffer, and Allison, "Geology," after
Heim.)

great pressures maintained at the center of the cap are lacking at the
margin where the ice is shoved forward—actually pushed over the underlying rock.   Gravity is the direct cause of the lateral movement of the
margin, but freezing of water within the ice is of some importance and,
possibly, a close second to gravity.   All waters resulting from the melting
of surface ice tend to descend through cracks to refreeze at lower levels
and, in expanding, add to the rigid thrust.
   Another factor, probably of some importance in the movement, is the

alternate expansion and contraction of the ice with seasonal or more rapid temperature changes. Numerous crevasses permit the descent of comparatively warm air and water, and it is likely that the temperature of the ice varies from time to time even at considerable depths. Movement by expansion and contraction seems particularly adapted to valley glaciers in which the weight from thickness is not great. When the ice cools with exceptional rapidity, it contracts, not as a continuous unit but by cross-cracking into many units. Snow, rock debris, and ice formed from surface melt tend to fill the cracks, and the linear expansion accompanying a subsequent rise in temperature is possible only as the ice moves downward or outward.

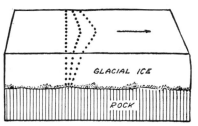

Rate of Movement. Judged by most standards, all glaciers move slowly, and it has been only in comparatively recent times that movement has been recognized as one of their characteristics.

A young Swiss, Louis Agassiz, was the first to prove definitely the movement of glaciers. While a boy he noticed in some of the valleys of the Alps that the relationship of bodies of ice to landmarks on the

FIG. 242. Diagram showing differential movement within a valley glacier. Stakes driven in a straight line across the top of a glacier in a short time show a curve down-valley. Pegs placed on the side of the glacier demonstrate that the top moves faster than the bottom. (*From Emmons, Thiel, Stauffer, and Allison, "Geology."*)

sides was not constant. He drove stakes in the valley outside the ice and stakes in line with them on the ice, and found that with the lapse of time the relationship of the stakes changed; those on the ice moved down-valley while the others remained stationary. Agassiz was of an inquiring turn of mind and was not satisfied with finding out merely that the glacier moved. He also measured the rate of movement of the glaciers on which he worked and demonstrated that the middle of the ice moved faster than the sides (Figs. 241 and 242).

In the warm season, a forward movement of a few inches per day is, perhaps, average for the ice near the margin of a glacier, and a movement of a few feet per day is rapid. It is scarcely believable that with such slow movements a glacier can be a powerful agent of transportation and mechanical weathering.

EROSION BY GLACIERS

The former presence of a glacier in a region is recognized by its erosive effects in valleys, on hills, and on level areas. A glacier accomplishes erosion, however, only by means of rock fragments incorporated within it, so before the erosive work can start the glacier must obtain these tools.

The Glacier Acquires Its Tools. As the first snows fell that were to make a glacier, they rested upon mantle rock, either residual or transported, probably, in the main, residual. Melting and refreezing took place frequently; the mantle rock came to have a cementing material of ice, and the projecting boulders and pebbles became frozen into the lower part of the glacier. In addition to the rock material frozen in the bottom, there are other rock materials throughout the entire ice mass. Even in the coldest regions the wind carries a certain amount of dust, and this falls with the snow. At some places volcanic dust settles widely over the snow surface and may even make beds of dust in the glacier. During the eruption of Katmai, dust settled on several glaciers; in some places several feet thick.

The glacier finally becomes a mass of granular ice, banded here and there with dust layers. In valley glaciers another factor enters into their composition. During the summers snow melts or rain falls and washes materials down the sides of the valleys and out onto the forming glacier; thus the valley glacier may have coarse material scattered through it almost from top to bottom. Some glaciers are in steep-sided valleys and debris falls directly upon them from the cliffs. The thicker the valley glacier becomes, the more nearly it fills the valley, the less likely it is to receive materials from the sides, and the cleaner the upper ice is compared with the lower. If one could observe a section of this newly formed glacier, he would see, at the bottom, mantle rock cemented with ice; above that, ice intermingled with rock debris of various kinds; and higher in the glacier, mainly ice and some fine material.

The glacier is now a mixture of ice, boulders, pebbles, sand, silt, and clay. As it starts to move, the mantle rock frozen into the bottom moves with it, as part of it, and makes a sort of rasp of the glacier bottom. The glacier does not usually push this mantle rock out of place, however, but in a sense creeps over the top of it. The glacier advances on to more mantle rock, freezes to it, and makes it part of its load. Melting is constantly taking place near the edge of the glacier, and water runs down and refreezes in the pore space of the mantle rock, which is then picked up. Many miles of the glacier may pass over the mantle rock before all of it is absorbed.

Erosion Starts. After all of the mantle rock has become part of the glacier and the bare rock is exposed underneath, the rock-shod mass begins to scour fine material from the solid rock and pluck or break off projecting pieces. Imagine the effect of a mass of ice thousands of feet thick, shod with sand, pebbles, and boulders, moving slowly over a bare rock surface. Probably the effect is not so striking as one may imagine, as the glacier moves so slowly that the actual amount of down-scouring is small, and the total effect is more like that of sandpapering in finishing woodwork than like planing or chopping the wood. The sharp pebbles and boulders are pressed down hard enough to make scratches even in such rock as granite, and, as the ice is moving in one general direction, the scratches on the rock surface are nearly parallel. It is only relatively resistant rock that will retain such scratches. In some places glaciers move over soft shales and other rocks that contain many cracks or joints and are tilted so that the ice strikes the under part of the layers and tends to peel them up. Under such conditions great quantities of material are plucked and removed by the glacier, and it may actually overload itself (or pick up more material than it can carry).

Summary of How a Glacier Acquires and Uses Its Tools. 1. Snow freezes to the mantle rock on which it falls and makes that mantle rock a part of the glacier.

2. The glacier picks up more mantle rock as it advances.

3. Using the rock fragments picked up, the glacier scours and plucks materials from the solid rock over and against which it moves.

4. The wind blows material on it while it is forming, and thus wind-blown materials occur throughout the entire mass.

5. Particularly in valley glaciers, materials are washed or slump onto the top.

Factors Influencing Rate of Erosion by Glaciers. On account of their great *weight* it seems that glaciers should be powerful plucking and scouring agents, but such eroding power depends on several qualities, of which thickness of the ice or weight is important. *Rate of movement* is important, and, as the ice moves slowly, its plucking and scouring power is small compared with its weight. A glacier heavily *shod with hard rocks* erodes faster than one with little load. Plucking and scouring are faster on *rough surfaces* than on smooth ones if the roughness is not so great as to retard motion. Both processes reduce *soft rocks* much faster than hard; thus shale is cut down several times as fast as granite. *Rocks* that are slightly *dipping in the direction of ice movement* are plucked much faster than horizontal beds or those dipping against movement. *Rocks* that are *closely jointed* are plucked much faster than rocks with widely-spaced joints, and *thin-bedded rocks* faster than thick-bedded.

Effects of Glacial Erosion

Cirques. Some erosional features produced by glaciers are conspicuous. At the heads of glaciers occurring near the tops of mountains, the ice scours directly downward and forms steep-walled depressions, having the shape of an amphitheater, known as "cirques" (Figs. 243 and 244). Cirques are the most striking topographic features of mountains that have been intensely glaciated. Some have walls more than a thousand feet high. The Uinta Mountains of northern Utah contain

FIG. 243. A cirque in the Wind River Mountains, Wyoming. (*Photograph by W. D. Keller.*)

FIG. 244. Drawing of a cirque, the highest walls about 800 feet.

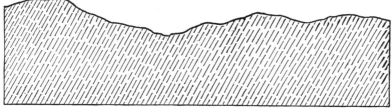

FIG. 245. An unglaciated mountain valley and a cross-section of the same valley.

FIG. 246. The valley shown in Fig. 245 filled with a glacier.

numerous large cirques, although the glaciers that formed them have long since disappeared.

U-Shaped Valleys. As glaciers move down mountain valleys, they modify the irregular features formed by streams and change the narrow-bottomed valleys to wide U-shaped valleys (Figs. 245, 246, 247, and 248).

The valley shown in Fig. 249 has not been glaciated. It was formed in the same rock formations, in the same mountains, and by a stream

about the same size as was the glaciated valley of Fig. 250.   A comparison
of these pictures shows that the glaciated valley is much wider and more
rounded at the bottom than the nonglaciated valley.   Some of the
material scoured off in forming the U-shaped from the V-shaped valley
has become rock flour, and some of that plucked off has become boulders,
cobbles, and pebbles.

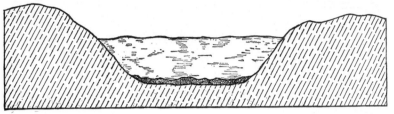

FIG. 247. A cross-section of the glacier-filled valley shown in Fig. 246.

FIG. 248. The same valley as in Fig. 245 after the glacier has melted away.   A hanging valley on
the right.

Unlike streams, glaciers may scour places upstream deeper than some
downstream, and thus create rock basins in their valleys.   Such basins
are rarely deep, and many of the lake basins of glaciated valleys were not
formed by scouring but by deposition.   Projecting knobs of rock are
likely to be smoothed and scratched by glaciers.   Granite areas that
have been glaciated are so smooth as to make walking over them hazard-
ous.   In walking from nonglaciated to glaciated granite, one would
be able to tell the difference by the rough footing over the one and the
smooth over the other.   In the Alps, where glaciers have moved through
valleys composed of dolomite, they have scoured off the small knobs,
leaving conspicuous, small, oval hillocks.   From a distance these look
like flocks of sheep and the natives call them sheep rocks, "roches
moutonnées."

FIG. 249. The unglaciated valley of Little Popo Agie River 10 miles south of the valley shown in Fig. 250. Both valleys were formed by streams of about the same size, and both were cut in the same kinds of rocks. Glaciation caused the difference in shape. (*Photograph by E. B. Branson.*)

FIG. 250. The valley of Big Popo Agie River, a U-shaped valley about 800 feet deep. The ridges across the valley are small terminal moraines. (*Photograph by E. B. Branson.*)

Hanging Valleys. Some valley glaciers have deepened the valleys that they inherited from the streams. A valley heading in the mountains is filled with ice far below the snow line, but the tributary valleys below the snow line contain no glaciers, and those above the snow line have glaciers of less eroding power than the main glacier. As tributary valleys are not deepened so rapidly as the main valley, they are left high above the main valley when the glacier recedes. Such features are known as *hanging valleys* (Figs. 248 and 251); they contain waterfalls (Fig. 251) in early stages and are one of the evidences of former glaciation.

Scouring by Continental Glaciers. Scouring accomplished by continental glaciers is much less than that produced by valley glaciers. The thickness of mantle rock was so great that most continental glaciers did the greater part of their work in merely removing it. Where a glacier crossed a wide valley, it may have done considerable scouring as it moved up the far slope. The summits of ridges between deep valleys, the tops

FIG. 251. A hanging valley on the side of the valley shown in Fig. 250. (*Photograph by E. B. Branson.*)

of hills, and level places where there was only a small amount of mantle rock were scoured by the continental glaciers of North America. When one imagines ice thousands of feet thick over most of the northern part of North America, and that ice in steady motion, he is likely to assume that all of the region over which it passed was deeply eroded. However, the average depth of the morainic material over the area covered by the North American continental glaciers is less than 20 feet. The average depth of mantle rock outside of glaciated areas is about 10 feet. As the glaciers must have handled the mantle rock, the total amount of erosion or downward cutting by them was probably not more than 10 feet.

Glacial Scratches on Bedrock. Glaciers leave numerous subparallel scratches on the bedrock over which they move (Fig. 252). If not covered with mantle rock, these weather off within a few hundred years or within a few thousand at the most.   Scratches that may be seen as remnants of the work of the continental glaciers of North America (which disappeared 40,000 or 50,000 years ago) have had glacial drift over them that has been removed recently.   The sides and bottoms of glaciated

FIG. 252. Glacial scratches on a rock ledge at Clinton, Massachusetts. (*Photograph by Alden, courtesy of U.S. Geological Survey.*)

valleys are likely to show longitudinal troughs with scratches in them. The troughs may appear like the work of a carpenter who planes a deep groove and then sandpapers it smooth.

Deposition by Glaciers

The former presence of glaciers in a region is recognized by the deposits that are left when the ice has melted.   Most of these deposits are *unstratified*, but some are rudely *stratified*, having been worked over by water, and it is difficult to distinguish between them and bouldery stream deposits, as lack of good stratification is also characteristic of the coarser deposits of alluvial fans.   Moreover, swift streams may move materials as large as some of the large glacial boulders.   The geologist examines the deposit for every possible evidence of glaciation, but the best distinguishing feature is the unsorted character of glacial materials, coupled with the stratification of stream deposits.   In most glacial deposits boulders and cobbles are well separated by clay, but in stream deposits boulders and cobbles touch one another.

Character of Drift.   Some parts of glaciers are nearly half composed of material other than snow and ice, and other parts contain only a small amount of foreign material.   After a glacier has melted back and left its load on the ground, it is easy to examine the materials that it carried.

In size these materials range from diameters of 50 feet or more in boulders to the small sizes of clay particles. (Masses several hundred feet in diameter are known.) Glacial boulders as large as 40 or 50 feet in diameter are exceptional; those 10 feet in diameter are by no means uncommon; and, on first examination, boulders 1 to 5 feet in diameter seem to make up the main part of the materials.

Drift is a technical term used to designate all materials that have been handled directly or indirectly by the ice, and fine materials such as gravel, sand, silt, and clay make up most of it. Much glacial drift is called

FIG. 253. Glacial deposit showing variety of sizes of rock fragments. (*Photograph by E. B. Branson.*)

boulder clay, because it contains boulders in the midst of the clay. Glacial materials may be characterized as extremely heterogeneous in size (Fig. 253).

As a glacier contains fragments of all the kinds of rocks over which it passed, the drift represents a great variety of rocks. The larger boulders are made up of the harder rocks, such as granite, gneiss, quartzite, and the more resistant limestones; most limestones, the sandstones, and the less resistant types of igneous rocks are represented by granules and the finer fragments. The sands, silts, and clays are derived mainly from the weathered mantle rock that the glacier picked up. As the larger pieces of rock are moved along in the glacier, some of them are rubbed against the underlying rock, and thus their lower sides become flattened and scratched, but they are apt to be turned over and so become flattened and scratched on other sides (Fig. 254). Many boulders in the drift have such *flattened and scratched surfaces*, which are, probably, the most characteristic features of glacial boulders. As drift is dropped directly from the ice, it is not sorted and so shows no stratification except where it is worked over by water.   Glacial boulders are subangular (*i.e.*, almost angular) in contrast with stream boulders, which are rounded. As most glacial boulders are unrelated in kind to the rocks of the region

FIG. 254. A glacial boulder showing flattened surface, scratches, and subangular shape.

FIG. 255. Erratic boulders of Grenville marble near Fine, New York.   (*Photograph by W. A. Tarr.*)

in which they are found, having been brought from distant places, they are commonly referred to as *erratics* (Fig. 255).

Although present in smaller quantity, the material scoured off the solid rock by the glacier is more characteristic of drift than are the fine materials obtained from the weathered mantle.   Glaciers powder rocks as they scour them and produce white material called *rock flour*.   However, the scoured material does not appear white when mixed with the other fine materials in the drift, as it is colored by them. Only by microscopic examination and chemical tests is it possible to distinguish between rock flour and the residual clays originating in the mantle rock. The latter are composed, largely, of clay minerals; the former is composed of a large variety of minerals but lacks the clay minerals. The rock flour is not made up of so fine particles as is the clay of the weathered mantle.

Waters issuing from glaciers are likely to be milky-looking on account of the ground-up rock fragments they contain. The milky nature of the water may persist for many days, even after the water has passed through several lakes, which act as settling basins. It is only the extremely fine materials that stay in suspension for many days. The fine material due to chemical weathering is much less likely to give color to glacial water than the rock flour.

Deposits of drift may become cemented and so form solid rock or *tillite*. The first discovery of a deposit of this kind was made by a geologist working north of the Great Lakes in Canada, where a stream had cut down several hundred feet in solid rock. After examining the rock carefully, he decided that it had originated as a glacial deposit. A glacier of one of the earlier geological periods had deposited the drift which had later been cemented. Such solid-rock drift has been found in many places in the world. Some of it is among the oldest of the sedimentary rocks and indicates that glaciation started at a very early period in the earth's history. This is evidence that the earth has not been growing colder gradually but has had periods of cold followed by periods of warmth.

Summary of Characteristics of Drift. 1. Heterogeneous in size of materials (huge boulders to clay).

2. Heterogeneous in kinds of materials, all kinds of rocks that the glacier passed over.

3. Many subangular boulders.

4. Many boulders have flat faces.

5. Many of the boulders, cobbles, and pebbles have scratches on them.

6. Not stratified, except the minor parts deposited by water.

7. Some of the fine materials are mechanically weathered (rock flour).

8. Boulders may be embedded in clay, silt, and sand several feet from other boulders.

Unstratified Glacial Deposits

The occurrence of unstratified deposits in a region is significant evidence of the former presence of a glacier in that region. The deposits, known as *moraines*, are made up of materials that the glacier carried and dropped at the edge, sides, and bottom of the ice. According to these

FIG. 256. A glacier forming a terminal moraine. The edge of the glacier was at one time thick enough to project above the top of the moraine. (*Photograph by Russell, courtesy of U.S. Geological Survey.*)

FIG. 257. A simple terminal moraine in Bull Lake Creek Valley, western Wyoming. The moraine is about 1½ miles long and about 100 feet high. (*Photograph by E. B. Branson.*)

positions of deposition, moraines are known, respectively, as *terminal, lateral,* and *ground moraines.*

Terminal Moraines. *Of Valley Glaciers.* The materials piled up at the edge of a continental glacier or at the end of a valley glacier make terminal moraines (Figs. 256 and 257). These form where the end or edge of a glacier remains stationary for some time, a condition resulting when the advance of the ice exactly equals the waste from melting and evaporation.   For example, if the ice moves forward 5 feet per day and the edge melts back the same amount per day, all the load in the 5 feet is piled up in one ridge.   If such a condition should persist for 100 years, all of the load in more than 30 miles of ice would be piled up in one ridge. This ridge would be irregular in height and width.

Most terminal moraines are not such simple ridges, however, as the ice edge does not remain stationary, but, after forming one ridge, may retreat slightly and irregularly (or not at all in some places) and pile up a second ridge a few hundred feet back of the first ridge.   This process may be repeated many times (Fig. 258).   The irregular retreat of the edge may leave the ridges in contact at some places, resulting in a series of interlocking ridges (Fig. 258).   The depressions between the ridges may become sites of small lakes, and the highest parts in the ridges may form conspicuous knobs.

Of Continental Glaciers.   Few terminal moraines of continental glaciers are more than 50 feet high, but, as most of them are made up of several ridges, some are several miles wide.   If the ice edge retreats slowly and builds up deposits back of the terminal moraine, there may be no sharp line of demarcation between such deposits and the terminal moraine. A person crossing from one to the other might not notice any change in topography (Fig. 259) or composition of drift.   Terminal-moraine topography may be recognized under such conditions, however, by the presence of *kettles* (deep, narrow depressions without outlets that may be occupied by lakes) and knoblike hills between the kettles (Fig. 258).   The association of such hills and depressions has given rise to the name *knob and kettle topography.*   The kettles might be mistaken for sink holes but for the bouldery clay on their sides and the lack of solid rock in place near them.   Most of them are larger than sink holes, also, and their margins are less sharply defined.

A simple-ridge terminal moraine, 50 to 100 feet high, constitutes a conspicuous feature in an otherwise level topography.   As the edge of the glacier was not long stationary in forming such a ridge, no thick alluvial apron (outwash plain, see page 259) formed in front (Fig. 260).   If the deposits back of the ridge are thin, the moraine stands out nearly its entire height above the surrounding region.

A glacier may thus form many terminal moraines while its edge is retreating; the continental glaciers that covered the northern part of the United States formed hundreds of them.   If, however, the edge of the ice advanced again, it would pass over its own terminal moraines and either pick up or spread out the materials.   There is, therefore, no way of determining how many times some of these glaciers advanced and retreated or how many terminal moraines they formed.   Special features of terminal moraines, called "kames," are discussed under "Stratified

FIG. 258. A terminal moraine made up of interlocking ridges. In the notch in the glacier a kame is forming. Between the ridges are depressions without outlets (kettles). At the right of the moraine is an outwash plain.

Deposits," as they are composed of drift that was deposited by glacial waters.

Lateral Moraines. Along the sides of valley glaciers material is deposited much as it is in the front, though, as the edge does not fluctuate so much as the front, a lateral moraine is likely to be made up of a single, irregular ridge. In mountain valleys lateral moraines may look like railway embankments (*i.e.*, smooth-topped ridges). The moraines are discontinuous where the glacier moved through narrow places in the valley. Where a glacier filled a valley, the highest part of the lateral moraine may have formed on the upland at the valley edge (Fig. 246).

FIG. 259. A section through ground moraine and a low terminal moraine with the outwash plain at the left.

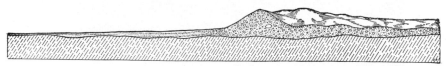

FIG. 260. A section through ground moraine, high terminal moraine, and outwash plain.

Valleys more than 1,000 feet deep may have such marginal moraines, and this has given rise to the statement that some lateral moraines are more than 1,000 feet thick, whereas, though they may have a vertical extent of 1,000 feet, their thickness is nearer 100 feet.

As continental glaciers cover such large areas, all their end moraines are considered as terminal and not lateral moraines.

Ground Moraines. The ground moraine occupies all of the areas covered by the glacier, but small parts of it are covered by terminal and lateral moraines. Much of the material of the ground moraine was deposited under the glacier as the bottom of the glacier melted or as the glacier became overloaded. As the ice was unequally loaded, the ground moraine, in some places, is thick and, in other places, thin or absent. The top of most ground moraines, however, was deposited in the same way as the terminal moraines, *i.e.*, at the edge of the glacier as the edge melted back and the materials were dropped. Consider a glacier advancing 1,000 feet per year and the edge melting back 2,000 feet per year. All of the load in 2,000 feet of the glacier would be deposited over 1,000 feet of the ground, and that would become ground moraine. Only in those places where great areas of the ice sheet stranded and melted down without the edges really melting back would the ground moraine all be deposited from the bottom of the ice.

Topography of Ground Moraine. The topography of the ground moraine is dependent largely on the topography of the land on which it was deposited. Where the glacier moved over a rough area, *i.e.*, one of mature topography (Fig. 261), the valleys were filled, or partially filled, the tops of the hills were scoured off, and little or no morainic material was left on them. The filling of the valleys in some places and partial filling in others left great numbers of depressions without outlets, which were deep enough to become the sites of lakes. Most of the lakes of Wisconsin, Michigan, New York, Canada, and the New England states

FIG. 261. Ground moraine over mature topography. The relief is about 200 feet. Before glaciation, this topography was that of Fig. 92.

were formed in this way. Lake Chelan in Washington and the finger lakes in the central part of New York are striking examples of stream courses that were nearly parallel to the movement of the glacier and were deeply scoured, but not filled very much. Where glaciers moved across valleys, they made irregular deposits and created many lakes.

If ground moraine was formed on a nearly level surface, its topography was determined by the distribution of the load in the glacier. Where the load was large there are hills, and where small there are depressions. The topography thus comes to consist of low hills unrelated to stream valleys, and shallow depressions without outlets. The depressions may become the sites of lakes. Such topography is normally not very rough.

In some areas elongated hills, known as *drumlins*, form conspicuous features of the ground-moraine topography (Figs. 262 and 263). These hills are composed of ordinary, unstratified drift (Fig. 264), and must

have been deposited when the ice was nearly stagnant, but there remained
enough movement to elongate them in the direction the glacier was
moving.   The drumlins of an area are marked by a notable uniformity in
size, as well as in shape.   Drumlins attract the attention of anyone
interested in land surfaces, whereas the ordinary ground moraine is
somewhat monotonous in its topography.   In height drumlins range
from a few to 150 feet, but most of them are 70 to 80 feet high.   Most
drumlins are from $\frac{3}{4}$ to 2 miles long and from $\frac{1}{4}$ to 1 mile wide.   In

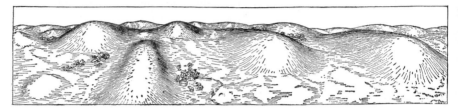

FIG. 262. Drumlins viewed from the ends.

FIG. 263. Drumlins viewed from the sides.

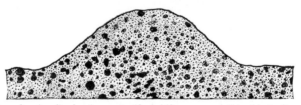

FIG. 264. Section of a drumlin showing unstratified drift; coarse particles black; fine particles white.

parts of central New York and Wisconsin, drumlins are so numerous that
the entire topography consists of them and the intervening depressions.
   In some regions drift occurs in considerable amounts unaccompanied
by any of the features of the usual glacial topography.   In northern
Missouri, for example, the drift is 50 feet thick in places, but no glacial
topography can be identified.   In going northward from Missouri
through Iowa, one travels continuously over drift and finally comes
upon topography of terminal- and ground-moraine types, made up of
drift that is indistinguishable from that in Missouri.   The drift in Missouri was deposited by a glacier that had withdrawn (perhaps for hundreds of thousands of years) before a new glacier advanced into the

region to the north and formed the deposits that still show glacial topography. Streams have cut valleys through the Missouri drift and destroyed all of the features of glacial topography, but since the time of formation of the Iowa drift the amount of erosion has been so small as to leave most of the glacial features.

Stratified Glacial Deposits

Continental glaciers, such as those that occupied North America as far south as the Ohio and Missouri rivers, had a great deal of water running over them, through them, and underneath them. In the southernmost 300 or 400 miles, melting must have equaled or exceeded snowfall, and thus the glacier gradually decreased in thickness southward. It was supplied from the north with ice thousands of feet in thickness. By the time its edge reached the Ohio River, it was only 200 or 300 feet thick, but it also received the snowfall and rainfall of the regions over which it came. It had, therefore, lost several thousand feet of ice through melting; also, there ran over it and under it water from the snowfall and rainfall of the region. As the ice of glaciers is cracked and porous, large streams cannot form and exist for a long time on the top and so most of the drainage is by subglacial streams.

The water under the ice ran through and over great quantities of loose material. It worked over some of the material and partially stratified it. The fine materials were carried on and the coarse ones left behind by the water, and thus patches of partially sorted drift were created. In addition to these patches, two distinct topographic features, *eskers* and *kames*, were formed of stratified drift.

Eskers and Kames. Glacial streams running in channels under the ice, or in fissures in the ice, may become so heavily loaded that they block their own channels with gravel but carry most of their fine materials to the edge of the glacier. If they block their channels at the time when the ice is practically stagnant because of having melted down to an insignificant thickness, the resulting deposits form ridges (something like railway embankments) running in the direction that the ice is moving. Such ridges, called *eskers* (Figs. 265 and 266), are not common features, as most of them are destroyed by ice movement about as soon as they form. The gravels and finer materials are really stream deposits, but also, as streams came in contact with the larger materials, they sorted them out, leaving the boulders behind and carrying the clay, silt, sand, and granules forward. Such a stream, emerging at the edge of the glacier, melted the ice above it and so formed a canyon in the ice (Fig. 258) just back of the glacier edge. It proceeded to fill the canyon with gravel, carrying the sand, silt, and clay forward and depositing them beyond the terminal moraine. The water finally found a new outlet and abandoned

FIG. 265. Woodworth Glacier, Alaska. (1) An esker; (2) outwash plain and terminal moraine; (3) glacier front; (4) glacial scratches and ridges; (5) lake in ground moraine. (Photograph by Bradford Washburn, courtesy of Harvard University Institute of Geographical Exploration.)

the canyon that it had filled with gravel.   After the ice had melted and left the terminal moraine disconnected with the glacier itself, the gravel that had been in the ice canyon became an unusual feature, both topographic and structural, of the terminal moraine.   It formed a hill of sorted gravels (Fig. 267), rather than of heterogeneous material of all sizes, in the back edge of the terminal moraine.   Such hills of sorted gravels have been called *kames* (Figs. 268 and 269).   Many kames are not in the back part

FIG. 266. An esker near Clinton, Massachusetts. *(Photograph by Alden, courtesy of U.S. Geological Survey.)*

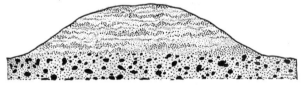

FIG. 267. Cross-section of an esker composed of stratified sand and gravel, resting on unstratified drift.

of terminal moraines, as, after they form, the edge of the ice may retreat a little and build another ridge back of the kame.   If a kame had formed next to the outermost edge of the Bull Lake moraine described on page 261 and all of the other ridges had been built back of it, the kame would really be in front of the main part of the terminal moraine.

Outwash Plains.   As the terminal moraine formed, a great deal of water ran over the top, down through the main mass, and out from under the ice.   Part of the water was organized into streams and part was merely unorganized runoff.   With the loose material of ground and terminal moraine available, each little stream loaded itself heavily and built a small alluvial fan against the terminal moraine where its velocity decreased.   As the alluvial fans grew laterally, they united and formed an *outwash plain,* which sloped gently away from the moraine. Some outwash plains became nearly as high as the moraine itself at the part that connected with the moraine, whereupon it rendered the moraine inconspicuous on its leeward side (Figs. 259 and 265).

Use of Glacial Gravel. Gravels from eskers, kames, and outwash plains have been used extensively as road metal and ballast for railroads. Such gravels are cheap because they may be taken out with a steam

FIG. 268. A kame and part of a terminal moraine. Few kames are as symmetrical as this one Height nearly 200 feet. (*Photograph by H. L. Griley.*)

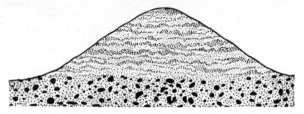

FIG. 269. Cross section of the kame shown in Fig. 268 illustrating stratification within the kame in contrast with unstratified drift below.

shovel and do not need to be crushed or sifted, and they are good because they are composed of the more resistant materials carried by the glacier and sorted out by the streams. A glacier that moved only over sandstones and shales, would not furnish good gravels, but the glaciers of North America moved over great areas of igneous and metamorphic rocks and hard limestones and thus secured fragments of resistant rocks.

A Typical Example of Valley Glaciation

Considering only the scouring and plucking in mountain valleys gives one a wrong impression of the appearance of a glaciated valley. One may travel up such a valley from the end of the old glacier nearly to the source without noticing any conspicuous feature produced by glacial erosion, as most of such features, excepting the cirque, are likely to be covered with deposits made by the glacier. As one starts up a glaciated valley, the first feature that attracts his attention is the terminal moraine (Fig. 270). This may be of the simple-ridge type or of interlocking ridges. A description of one glaciated valley that displays all of the ordinary

features of glacial deposition and erosion may present a better picture of
such features than generalizations can give.   Such a valley is that of Bull
Lake Creek, a tributary of the Big Wind River, about 100 miles south of
Yellowstone Park.   The outer part of the terminal moraine of this valley
is on the banks of the Big Wind River.   The terminal moraine is about
3 miles in width, being made up of an intricate network of some 25 interlocking ridges.   The edge of the ice must have shifted 25 or 30 times
while the moraine was forming.   Depressions ⅛ mile across and 100 feet
deep are present, and much shallower, smaller ones are common.   Isolated
hills rise 100 to 200 feet above the deepest depressions.   Some ridges
are distinct for half the length (distance along the ridges from one side
of the valley to the other) of the moraine.

FIG. 270. The terminal ridge of the moraine in Bull Lake Creek Valley, Wyoming, where it is cut by a
highway.   (Photograph by E. B. Branson.)

The moraine formed a huge dam across Bull Lake Creek and created
a lake basin.   The stream has cut through the moraine to some 50 feet
below the general level, but the lake is still 8 miles long.   The final ridge
built by the glacier in this moraine is more than ¼ mile up the valley
from the rest of the ridges, and it cuts the lake nearly in two.   From the
ends of the terminal moraine, lateral moraine ridges project up the sides
of the valley at the valley margins.   The glacier filled the valley to overflowing and built its lateral moraines on the extreme edge.   The valley is
1,000 feet deep, and the lateral moraines form the uppermost 100 feet or
so of the margins.

From the terminal moraine one may travel upstream 8 miles before
encountering any other conspicuous glacial feature.   Boulders of various
types are scattered over the valley floor, but these might have been
brought in by the stream.   A simple ridge, shown in Fig. 257, stretches

across the valley 8 miles upstream from the terminal moraine. The ridge is about 100 feet high and about 1½ miles long (the length is from one side of the valley to the other). The edge of the ice must have remained stationary for a long period of years to produce such a ridge, which is in no way different from the ridges of the other terminal moraine except in its simplicity. A short distance upstream from this moraine, the bedrock is granite and the valley takes on an entirely different aspect. It is deeper and narrower and has been less affected by glaciation, although the granite has been considerably smoothed. Glacial scratches appear in only a few places on the granite, as they have been obscured or com-

FIG. 271. Glacial lake in a U-valley below the cirque. *(Photograph by Carl C. Branson.)*

pletely removed by weathering, though weathering has not roughened the surface to any appreciable degree. A few lake basins have been scoured out of the granite (Fig. 271), but most of the numerous lakes present are due to the glacial deposits.

One finally comes to the glacier itself, 4 miles long, at the very top of the mountains save for a few projecting peaks and ridges. The glacier comes from a huge cirque. In this part of the mountains, cirques are not conspicuous, on account of being filled nearly to the rim with snow and ice; but 40 miles south, in the same range, as the cirques contain little snow and ice, they form striking topographical features. Where the glaciers have disappeared, the top of the mountain remains as a narrow, sharp-crested, discontinuous ridge. The heads of glaciers have worked backward from either side, cutting the cirques farther and farther and finally leaving only a narrow ridge between. This type of topography can be seen only at the tops of strongly glaciated mountains.

SPECIAL EFFECTS OF GLACIATION

Destruction of Glacial Lakes. In looking at a map of North America, one is struck by the great number of lakes present in Canada, the northern Middle States, the northern Central States, and New England. With all the lakes plotted, it might seem possible to draw the line between the glaciated and unglaciated parts of North America from the lakes alone. This line, however, would be far from accurate for, as explained in an earlier paragraph, some of the glacial advances are older than others; and, moreover, stream topography has superimposed itself upon glacial topography, reducing the areas to maturity in terms of stream erosion. As all of the upland is in slopes in mature topography, no place for lakes exists except along the flats of the river bottoms. The glacial lakes, therefore, disappeared before the region attained full maturity. Many glacial lakes fill up with the fine materials they receive from streams, slope wash, and, to a minor extent, the wind.

Changes in Drainage. Changes of drainage resulting from glaciation have been mentioned in a former paragraph but need to be emphasized further. In all of the glaciated areas, valleys occur that are inconsistent within themselves, *i.e.*, they may have wide flats for a considerable distance, and then narrow rapidly to valleys not much wider than the stream itself. The Mississippi between Montrose, Iowa, and Keokuk, Iowa, is an example (Fig. 272). On examining the region the geologist finds that the stream has a wide flat in its preglacial valley and that its present valley is narrow where drift has filled the old valley and has forced the stream to take a new course over solid rock. Where a stream is forced out of its drift-filled valley (Fig. 273) and, taking a course over hard rock, enters an open valley over a bluff, falls and rapids are formed. The falls of the New England states and of New York (Niagara is the most conspicuous example) are due largely to changes in drainage caused by glaciation. In glaciated regions some streams flow long distances at low grade where under normal development they would flow short distances at high grade.

Economic Effects of Glaciation. Glaciation has had profound effects on the habitability of many parts of the earth. In some regions it has smoothed the topography and made the land more suitable for agriculture; in others it has produced such roughness as to make the land useless for all but grazing purposes. In some areas it has enriched the soil by furnishing ingredients needed by plants; in others it has piled nonproductive clay, sand, and boulders on soils that had been rich.

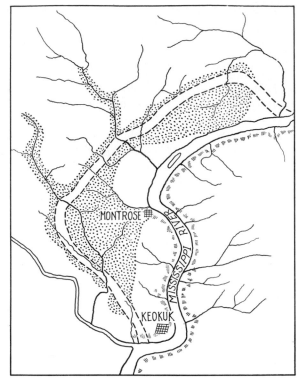

FIG. 272. Map of the Mississippi River near Keokuk, Iowa, showing changes in the river course.   The old river course is outlined by dashes; the preglacial valley is stippled.   The valley is little wider than the stream between Montrose and Keokuk where the river took a new course because the old valley was filled by glacial drift.

FIG. 273. A valley filled with terminal moraine so that it might force a river to change its course. (*Photograph by Schrader, courtesy of U.S. Geological Survey.*)

By creating abundant water power, glaciation has been largely influential in making New England a manufacturing region. In some places rich ore and coal deposits have been covered so deeply with drift that their exploitation has been made difficult if not impossible.

THE THEORY OF CONTINENTAL GLACIATION

At this time it seems incredible that anyone could account for erratic boulders, scratched boulders and pebbles, scratched solid rock, and great deposits of drift in any way excepting by glaciation. However, it is worth recalling that little more than 100 years ago the principle accepted today that the events of the past are to be interpreted on the basis of the present had not been formulated, and fanciful explanations of natural phenomena were common.

A geological book[2] published in the United States in 1889 stated that "there are probably no evidences of glacial action upon the continent of North America where they do not now exist, except in a few places in the Rocky Mountain region," but this book was about the last of its kind. The supposition that all of northern North America was once covered with water and that floating ice carried out the drift was not regarded as impossible by some theorists.

The conception that much of the north temperate region of the world had once been covered by glaciers was of slow growth even after the idea was promulgated. Louis Agassiz, whose measurement of glacial motion has been mentioned in a former paragraph, was responsible in the main for the acceptance of the continental-glaciation hypothesis. After studying the movement of glaciers and some of the deposits at the lower end of glaciers in the Alps, he traveled northward to find how far the Alpine glaciers had extended at an earlier period. After passing the last terminal moraines, he continued northward for a long distance without seeing any evidences of glaciation and finally came again to terminal-moraine topography with erratic boulders scattered over it. As he had crossed a considerable region where no glacial boulders and no glacial topography existed between this topography and the Alps, he knew that these moraines had not been formed by Alpine glaciers. As a matter of fact they could not have been formed by any glaciers from the south, and there were no mountains to the north sufficiently high to account for the formation of Alpine glaciers. After he found that these moraines covered wide areas he came to the conclusion that a continental glacier coming from the north had once covered the region.

This seemed a fanciful and even impossible hypothesis and it was not accepted immediately by geologists or other scientists. If it had not been that Agassiz was a well-recognized zoologist and paleontologist, he would not have had the opportunity to present his ideas about glaciation

[2] S. A. MILLER, "North American Geology and Paleontology."

as convincingly as he did.   He was invited to go to England to give a series of lectures on zoological subjects, and while he was there some of the local geologists accompanied him into the field and found, even there, boulders and other evidence of glaciation that had escaped the attention of the local workers.   He succeeded in convincing some of the geologists that his hypothesis was, at any rate, worth investigating.   In America some geologists accepted the idea of continental glaciation with enthusiasm, whereas others would have nothing to do with it.   Agassiz welcomed the opportunity to come to America and examine the materials that had been identified as glacial drift and to help with the establishing of the theory of continental glaciation.   He became professor of zoology in Harvard University and was one of the most influential scientists in America during his lifetime.

CHAPTER 12

THE WIND

Wind is air in motion. Although air is only about $\frac{1}{800}$ as dense as water, the wind possesses remarkable ability to accomplish gradational work. The degree to which the wind is effective depends upon its velocity. Large quantities of fine earth materials are moved far and wide by the wind. A complete study of the atmosphere would include many factors, such as climatic effects and temperature, but we are primarily interested in the air as a geological agent.

Wind Velocities and Resulting Pressures. Velocities of the different types of winds are shown in the following table:

Type of Wind	Velocity, Miles per Hour
Light to gentle breeze	1 to 9
Fresh breeze	10 to 14
Strong wind	15 to 22
High wind	23 to 30
Gale	31 to 40
Strong gale	41 to 60
Hurricane	60 and above

When wind attains a velocity of 70 miles per hour, it becomes highly disruptive. Hurricanes in Florida and Puerto Rico have reached velocities of 125 to 150 miles an hour. The highest wind velocity so far (1951) reported in the United States is 231 miles an hour, which was recorded April 12, 1934, at the observatory on Mount Washington, New Hampshire.

Winds of the higher velocities exert great pressure on the sides of buildings and are capable of demolishing strong structures. The following table from Milham's "Meteorology" gives the pressure exerted by the wind at different velocities.

Velocity, Miles per Hour	Pressure, Pounds per Square Foot
5	0.12
10	0.50
20	2.00
40	8.00
80	32.00
150	112.50

THE GEOLOGICAL WORK OF THE WIND

The gradational work of the wind is accomplished essentially by *mechanical* means, though the air aids indirectly in producing a certain amount of *chemical* work, also, which has been discussed under "Weathering."

Mechanical Work

We are all familiar with the ability of the wind to do mechanical work, for we have watched it whirl leaves and paper about, felt it drive dust in our eyes, and probably felt the sting of sand grains driven against our faces. Just as with the other physical agents, the first step in the accomplishment of work by the wind is *getting a load*, then *transporting* it great or small distances, and finally *depositing* it.

Getting a Load. The ability of the wind to pick up loose particles is due to eddies and crosscurrents produced in the air by objects on the surface. Whenever the currents are directed downward to the surface, they disturb loose material; and, if the particles are small enough to be lifted, they are deflected upward into the air.

Loose Material on the Surface. The immediate source of a load for the wind is the loose material (soil) of the surface. The dry surface of a plowed field, the flood plain and channel of a river, a beach, a dried-up lake or playa, a desert area, a gullied hillside, or any other surface unprotected by vegetation or not continuously moist furnishes material for the wind to pick up.

Abrasion. The wind secures a part of its load, however, by greater efforts than those of merely picking up loose material, *i.e.*, by abrading the surface over which it moves. To accomplish this, the wind must, of course, have tools, *i.e.*, something it can drive against a rock to grind off particles. Its chief tools are the dust (dry silt and clay) and sand particles it has picked up from the loose material on the surface.

Most of the abrasive work is done by driving sand grains against a surface, the finer dust particles being of use chiefly in polishing the abraded surface. For the most part, the particles worn off are small (of dust size) and are immediately swept away by the wind. A part of the material may be sand, however, as, for example, the grains furnished during the abrasion of a sandstone. The cement of the sandstone usually wears away first, so the sand grains are free to be picked up by the wind.

During the process of eroding a surface, the chief tools of the wind, *i.e.*, the sand grains, also become worn. The original sand grains may have been angular but soon their corners are worn off and finally they are reduced to well-rounded grains (see Fig. 183, page 184). The wind can form perfectly rounded sand grains of quartz to sizes as small as 0.15 millimeter in diameter, which is about one-fifth the size of the smallest grains that can be rounded by water. The constant chipping off of small bits from the surface of a sand grain leaves it minutely pitted, with a consequent frosted appearance.

Injected Material. Although most of the load of the wind is acquired by its own efforts, occasionally material is injected into it. Vast quantities of volcanic dust have been blown into the atmosphere by violent volcanic eruptions, of which the Krakatoa explosion is an excellent example (see page 39).

Summary. The wind gets its load first by picking up material it finds loose on the surface and then by picking up the particles it has eroded in

FIG. 274. Current ripple marks made by wind in volcanic ash, Irazu, Costa Rica. *(Photograph by E. B. Branson.)*

using the first material as tools. Additional materials are contributed to it during volcanic eruptions.

Transportation. The wind transports material in three ways: by *rolling,* by *jumping* or *saltation* (*i.e.,* moving the material along the surface in a series of short jumps), and in *suspension.*

Rolling. A wind that is moving straight forward effectively rolls sand grains along the surface. As the particles are being rolled along, ripple marks are quite commonly produced. The process of their formation is identical with that of water-made current ripple marks. Some eddies in the wind and variations in the size of the particles being moved cause the formation of alternating shallow depressions and low ridges (Figs. 274 and 207, page 209). The ripple marks advance with the wind by the grains' rolling up the gentle windward slopes of the small ridges and then rolling down the steeper leeward slopes into the depressions. In a stiff breeze, the forward motion of ripple marks can easily be detected.

Saltation. Great quantities of desert sand are transported by a combination of impact and saltation (*i.e.,* jumping or leaping). The process begins usually where sand grains are being picked up by the wind as it moves across an irregular land surface.   As these grains are carried forward, they fall and with a combined downward and forward motion strike other loose sand grains still on the ground.   The impact from the falling grains drives those still on the surface up into the air stream, and they, in turn, are blown forward.   The energy which they have thus acquired

FIG. 275. A dust storm in Prowers County, Colorado, March 21, 1937.   It was a typical "dust-bowl" storm, making artificial light necessary in midafternoon.   Wind velocity was about 30 miles per hour at the ground.   (*Photograph by courtesy of the Soil Conservation Service of U.S. Department of Agriculture.*)

is passed on to other grains which they hit as they descend.   Hence, each moving grain, after advancing a few inches, starts another grain on to its short jump.   The combination of countless individual hops over a surface gives rise to an apparently smooth advance of the sand. Vertical and cross currents of the wind, produced by irregularities of the land and objects upon it, may increase or otherwise modify the saltation produced by a straight-moving wind.

Suspension.   Whenever the velocity of the wind is sufficiently great, particles may be carried in suspension.   The greater part of the sand grains so carried are transported within a few feet of the ground because the lower currents, being relatively slow currents (owing to the numerous obstructions they encounter on the surface), are unable to lift the greater part of the sand particles to the higher currents that might be able to transport them.

Dust that is carried upward into the faster-moving wind above may be transported great distances. A strong wind blowing for 2 or 3 days in one direction in the semiarid southwestern part of the United States produces, as a result of transported dust, a haziness of the air and highly colored sunsets and sunrises in windward regions. The dust particles that fall in the polar regions and upon vessels in mid-ocean are transported in the swift upper currents. The red rains (called "blood rains") of northern Italy furnish a very interesting example of long-distance transportation. Strong winds starting in the desert area of northern Africa, where they pick up the minute particles of hematite worn off of the sand grains of the desert, sweep across the Mediterranean; and,

FIG. 276. Sand deposited around sagebrush west of Lovelock, Nevada. (*Photograph by W. A. Tarr.*)

as they cross the Alps, their moisture is condensed to rain that carries the red particles down upon northern Italy. The transportation of wind-blown dust is world wide. It has been said that every square mile of the land surface of the earth has received dust particles from every other square mile, a statement quite within the realm of probability.

Dust storms (Fig. 275) or sand storms are the moving days for immense quantities of material, but the wind is busy moving material in the intervals between storms, though the distance may be short.

Deposition. In order to bring about deposition by the wind, all that is needed is to decrease its velocity until the sand or dust particles can no longer be moved. This decrease in velocity may be brought about by obstacles on the surface, such as fences, trees, and houses, or it may take place because the force that set the wind in motion has ceased.

The first grains to be dropped, or to cease being rolled, are the largest particles, of course, and so on down through the scale of sizes. Minute particles of dust, less than $\frac{1}{256}$ millimeter in diameter, continue to settle out of the air long after the wind has ceased blowing.

Common sites of deposition are small depressions and areas along fences and around bushes (Fig. 276), shrubs, trees, and larger objects if any are available. Forested areas, as well as grasslands, receive much fine wind-blown material, which soon becomes mixed with the local soil and loses its identity. Mountainous regions adjacent to deserts receive large quantities of dust, though most of it soon finds its way into the streams unless the region is covered with forests. If an abundance of material is available, it is possible that deposition may start without the aid of an obstacle or a depression as a starting point.

Results of Wind Work

The results of wind work are twofold: *erosive* and *depositional*. On the whole, the depositional features are the more common, but in certain areas the results of wind erosion are striking and abundant.

Erosive Features. Wind transporting sand is a natural sandblast. Its effect on the land surface can be likened to the effect that would be produced by rubbing an immense sheet of sandpaper over that surface. Any object the sand moves over or against is abraded. Wind-worn surfaces and other effects of abrasion are thus produced.

Wind-worn Stones (Ventifacts). One of the striking results of wind action is the carving and shaping of stones. Such wind-worn products are called *ventifacts*. The wind, in driving sand against the side of a stone, carves and smooths it, developing a flat face, which, if the material composing the stones is not of uniform hardness, is apt to be pitted (Fig. 277A). If the wind varies in direction, faces may be developed on other sides of the stone. Thus one, two, three, or more faces may develop. The faces are rarely of the same size or shape. When two of them intersect, a sharp edge is formed. If a single edge appears on the sandblasted stone, the latter is called an *einkanter* (a German word that means "one edge"). A wind-worn stone commonly has three faces, and thus three edges, and so is called a *dreikanter* (Fig. 277B).

Rock Smoothing and Carving. Abrasion by the wind produces smoothed rock surfaces. These surfaces, even though very large, are apt to be pitted. The pits range in size from minute irregularities of the surface to depressions several feet across (Fig. 278).

In desert regions, a surface of unusual mosaic character, known as *desert pavement,* may occur. It is produced on fragment-covered surfaces by the wind's carrying away the smaller particles and leaving behind those of cobble size, which become tightly packed; whereupon the wind, sweeping its load of sand across the cobble surface, wears it smooth.

Since the cobbles consist of different kinds of rocks having various colors and shapes, the "desert pavement" is a natural mosaic.

If there are marked differences of hardness in the materials of a rock, various fantastic shapes (Fig. 279) may be produced by wind erosion.

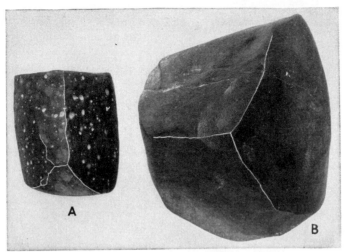

FIG. 277. Wind-worn stones. (A) Pitted einkanter; (B) dreikanter.

FIG. 278. Wind erosion in sandstone, southeastern Colorado. *(Photograph by W. A. Tarr.)*

A sandblast of the wind, by cutting irregularly into the rocks, produces isolated, rounded hills, which usually have steep lower slopes because the greatest amount of cutting is found near the bottom. Talus slopes are absent in areas of much wind abrasion because of this great amount of cutting near the bottom of the slopes. The wind may also bore through a thin ridge or wall of rock and form a *natural bridge* (Fig. 280).

Depositional Features. The material collected and moved by the wind forms two dominant types of deposits, each of which owes its characteristics to the distinctive size of the materials composing it. Wind-blown accumulations of clay and silt are called *loess*, and those of sand (rarely of clay) are called *dunes*. The two deposits are not usually closely associated.

FIG. 279. Grotesque sandstone remnant produced by wind abrasion, southern Utah. (*Courtesy of U.S. Geological Survey.*)

Loess Deposits. Loess consists dominantly (about 75 per cent) of quartz grains of silt size and clay. Very few of the grains are larger than those of silt. Fresh-water or land snail shells are found in loess. The material is usually buff to yellow in color and is remarkably porous. Loess possesses the property of standing with steep or vertical faces, as may be seen along highways that have been constructed through it (Fig. 281).

The largest deposits of loess in the United States occur on both sides of the Mississippi River from Louisiana and Mississippi north to Illinois and Iowa; along the Missouri River; and, locally, along other rivers in the central Mississippi Valley. It is found widely distributed in central Europe; and, in Asia, it occurs in Mongolia, Tibet, and China.

FIG. 280. Natural bridge carved by wind in sandstone, south of Moab, Utah. (*Photograph by W. A. Tarr.*)

In the United States, the loess deposits are thin, averaging between 10 and 20 feet in thickness and but rarely attaining a thickness of 50 to 100 feet. Those of Europe are also thin, but thicknesses of 300 feet are reported in China. Because of the softness of loess and the consequent ease with which it is excavated, great numbers of people in the loessal regions of China live in houses that are really caves dug in the loess.

FIG. 281. Typical vertical face of loess west of Red Oak, Iowa. (*Photograph by W. A. Tarr.*)

Loess soils are wonderfully fertile and so are intensively cultivated wherever they occur.

As to origin, it is now generally agreed that loess is due to wind action. The loess of America and Europe is found along rivers, where it is thickest and coarsest near the rivers and is unrecognizable as loess more than 100 miles from them. This distribution points to the river bed as the source of the material, as can scarcely be doubted by anyone who has watched the wind sweeping clouds of clay and silt up from the dried flood plain of a river on to the bordering uplands. Most of the loess along these rivers was deposited during and following the glacial period, as all the rivers were then greatly overloaded with the fine material obtained from the melting ice. The loess of Asia apparently had its source in the deserts (such as the Gobi) of the central part of the continent. From these regions, the wind carried dust to the south and southeast and deposited it in the greatest abundance in the province of Kansu. The Yellow River, or Hwang Ho, of China flows through this area and owes its color to the enormous amount of yellow loess it is transporting. Likewise, the sea into which it drains (via the Gulf of Pohai) is known as the Yellow Sea.

Although essentially all loess deposits were formed wholly by wind action, there are a few, small, imperfectly stratified deposits that are probably due to the settling of dust in shallow lakes or ponds.

Dunes. Dunes are accumulations (mounds or hills) of sand. The term "sand" as used in this connection refers only to the size and not to the kind of materials present.

The *size of the particles* in most dunes ranges in diameter from 0.05 millimeter (the smallest size in which the separate grains can be distinguished by the naked eye) to 4 millimeters (the diameter of the particles of fine granules).

The dominant *shape of the grains* of dune sand is rounded, but angular material also occurs and possibly in greater abundance than has been supposed. As previously noted, rounded sand grains of quartz usually have a frosted surface.

The *composition* of most dune sand is dominantly *quartz*, though small quantities of any of the minerals forming or occurring in rocks may be present. Locally, there are dunes that contain little or no quartz. Dunes composed of *gypsum* sand occur in New Mexico; others composed of *calcareous oölites* occur in the Bahamas and Bermudas; some composed of *calcareous shells* are found in the Bermuda and Hawaiian Islands; and low dunes of dried *clay* are found in Montana (Fig. 282). In order to make complete our list of materials that occur in dunes, we should include the *snow* of snowdrifts.

Dunes (Fig. 283) range from a few to 400 feet or more in height and from a few square feet to several square miles in area. In desert regions, heights of 200 to 400 feet are common.

With a moderate wind and an abundant supply of sand, the longer axis of a dune will be at right angles to the direction of the wind (see Fig. 284A), but a strong wind in the same area will develop dunes elongated parallel to the direction from which the wind is blowing (see Fig. 284B). Less commonly, where the wind is nearly unidirectional, *barchanes*, or *crescent-shaped dunes* (see Fig. 284C and Fig. 283), may form.

All sand dunes *migrate* to some degree unless they become so covered with vegetation that the wind no longer has access to the sand. Migration is accomplished by the wind's blowing the sand up the gentle windward slope (a, Fig. 285) and allowing it to roll down the steeper (up to 33°) leeward slope (b, Fig. 285).   As material is shifted from the windward to the leeward sides, the dune moves in that direction (shown by the dotted line in the figure).   If the direction of the wind varies, the

FIG. 282. Clay dunes, northern Montana.   (*Photograph by W. A. Tarr.*)

FIG. 283. Crescent-shaped sand dunes near Biggs, Oregon.   A dominantly unidirectional wind blows from left to right.   (*Photograph by Gilbert, U.S. Geological Survey.*)

direction of dune movement varies with it.   The rate of movement of dunes is slow, rarely exceeding 25 feet per year.

Migrating dunes may advance over forests, farms, houses, railroads, and highways and may even bury villages and cities.   The fact that dunes buried many cities of the ancient civilizations (Babylonian, Chaldean, and others) of southern Asia and thus prevented the complete destruction of the cultures of those periods has been a great aid to later generations of mankind in the work of unraveling the history of those civilizations.   The advancement of dunes over good farm land or other valuable property may be checked by planting such grasses and shrubs as will grow in sand.   Figure 286 shows dune migration being checked with the growth of vegetation.   In many sandy areas of western United States, the movement of the sand has been started when, the region

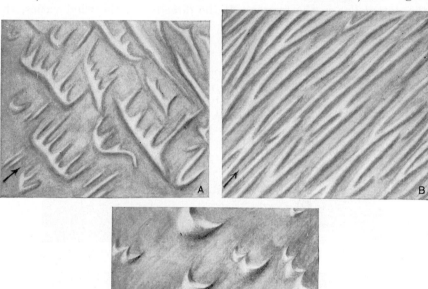

FIG. 284. Sketches showing different types of sand dunes.

having been opened up for settlement, the covering of grass and trees was removed in preparation for tilling the soil.

Sand dunes have a world-wide *distribution*, and, although they are more numerous in arid regions, they are present also in moist areas.

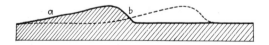

FIG. 285. Sketch showing the movement of a sand dune.

Dunes are found along rivers throughout western United States, and also on uplands far from rivers if a source of sand, such as a sandstone, is available.   From large sandstone areas in Oklahoma and Kansas, the wind has obtained sand with which it has built adjoining belts of dunes. Further downward cutting by the wind in these regions is now prevented by the fact that the sandstone contains so much salt and gypsum. These two minerals absorb and retain so much moisture that in rainy seasons the wind cannot blow the material away, and in dry seasons they form a crust that prevents the wind from picking up the material. In this way the salt plains (see Fig. 197, page 199) of these regions have been developed. Dunes are found along the seashore and along lakes. Where there is an abundance of sand, dunes along the ocean have formed a belt many miles wide. The dune belts along lakes (such as Lake Michigan) are narrower because the supply of sand is less.

FIG. 286. Vegetation getting a foothold on a dune. Movement will eventually be checked. Note current ripple marks on dune. Which way was the wind blowing that formed them?

Wind Placers. As we have already seen, the work of the wind is not always destructive, and placers formed by the wind are another example of this. As different minerals have different specific gravities, the removal by the wind of the lighter grains may bring about a concentration of the heavier minerals; and, if any of the heavy minerals is economically valuable, the accumulation or placer may be an important source of that mineral. Some of the gold placers of Western Australia (an arid region) were formed in this way by the wind.

Volcanic Dust Deposits. Volcanic dust is carried long distances by the wind and forms deposits that are valuable as abrasive material because of the extreme fineness and sharpness of the particles. The volcanic dust deposits in north central Kansas and southern Nebraska are examples. Volcanic dust usually forms fertile soils. The wheatlands of eastern Oregon and Washington are composed of this material.

CHAPTER 13

STRUCTURES AND DIASTROPHISM

Rock patterns of all kinds are called structures. These contrast to the arrangement of grains or crystals, which are textures. Depositional structures, such as bedding, ripple marks, and nodules, have been discussed in Chap. 9 of this book. The larger structures brought about by movements in the earth's crust are the subject matter of the present chapter.

Joints. Cracks or joints are common structures, as they affect all rocks. Most joints are nearly vertical, and nearly all rocks have two sets, trending nearly at right angles. Some rocks are jointed so closely that it is difficult to obtain a piece more than 3 or 4 inches in diameter, and it is highly exceptional to find 100 feet of space between joints. An architect wishing to use pieces of rock 50 feet long is restricted in his choice of material, as jointing has limited the size of blocks. Most joints were formed during earth movements. There is no part of the earth that has not moved up or down many times during earth history. The movements were commonly very slow, but they produced almost innumerable earthquakes,[1] and the repeated passage of vibrations through the rock created joints, just as the progress of earthquake vibrations through a building makes cracks in it. It may seem doubtful or impossible that regions far from mountains and from recent earthquakes have ever been affected by great shocks, but even such regions as the Mississippi Valley have, within historical times, had serious earthquakes that actually created joints and enlarged those already present.

Near the surface of the earth, joints may be closed or remain open. They may be filled with weathered materials or widened by solution. Joints cannot extend into the zone of flow, as the rock is not strong enough to maintain cracks. Few joints have great vertical extent; it is the joint group that reaches deep, rather than a single joint. Below groundwater level they may be filled with calcite, quartz, pyrite, and other materials deposited from solution. Such cemented joints are weak places, and new earth movements are likely to cause a break along them.

[1] See New Madrid earthquake (p. 316).

Some igneous rocks crack while cooling, and a close network of joints results, as explained on page 45. Such joints may range from horizontal to vertical, as they formed at right angles to the most rapidly cooling surface.

Faults. Along some of the cracks in the rocks, differential movement takes place, *i.e.*, the rocks on one side of the crack move in a different direction or a different amount from those on the other. This is called

FIG. 287. A fault. Along an almost vertical crack, the rocks at the right have moved downward about 18 inches more than those at the left. Note that there is no gap along the fault.

faulting (Fig. 287). Consider a north and south crack several miles long. On the west side of the crack the uplift is 1,000 feet, and on the east side 2,000 feet. The amount of differential movement (or *displacement*) is 1,000 feet. The same amount of displacement would have resulted if the west side had remained still and the east side had risen 1,000 feet, or if the east side had not moved and the west side had gone down 1,000 feet. Along this crack, the east side might have moved north or the west side south, or vice versa, giving rise to horizontal displacement. Horizontal movement occurred along the fault that caused the California earthquake of 1906, and railroads and fences that crossed the fault were offset the amount of the horizontal movement, at one place as much as 23 feet, although vertical displacement was less than one foot in most places.

Displacement along a fault ranges from a fraction of an inch to 15 miles or more. Displacements of 200 to 3,000 feet are by no means uncommon in mountainous regions. The length of the fault line, *i.e.*, the length of the crack along which the movement takes place, varies even more than the amount of displacement. The fault that created the California earthquake of 1906 has been traced for nearly 300 miles. Faults a few inches long are not uncommon. The crack along which movement takes place may range in direction from vertical to horizontal, more commonly being nearer to vertical. The fissures along which faults occur do not remain open in the deeper zones and are not likely to gape near the surface.

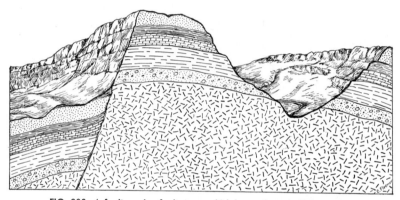

FIG. 288. A fault, and a fault scarp which has undergone little erosion.

Fault movements are likely to crumble and break rocks adjacent to the fissure. Just as a glacier moving over a surface plucks and scours rocks, so one mass of rock moving over another, along the fault, plucks, scours, and crushes. Along large faults the pressure of one wall against the other is almost inconceivably great, and the downward pressure of a glacier 5,000 feet thick is very small compared to it. The movement of one rock against the other, even though the amount of movement is only a few inches, may smooth the surfaces until they are sleek as glass. Such surfaces are known as *slickensides* and are very common along faults.

Fault Scarps. Where one side of a fault remains higher than the other, the displacement may give rise to cliffs, which are called *fault scarps* (Fig. 288). The east side of the Sierra Nevada is a fault scarp several thousand feet high, which, however, is not vertical but has a slope of perhaps 20°. The west face of the Wasatch Mountains east of Salt Lake City contains the remnant of a great fault scarp. It too is not vertical but has a high dip. The question is often raised as to why most faults do not leave scarps. In the Appalachian Mountains there are many large faults but rarely any fault scarps. The explanation may be that the faults are old and that erosion has reduced the high side to the same level as the low one. The movement, even though large, took place so slowly that stream erosion reduced the high side as fast as it came up, preventing the formation of a fault scarp of any considerable size. Faults of 30 to 40 feet displacement, resulting in scarps 30 to 40 feet high, have formed during the present century and the results have been observed and recorded.

Many valleys have been formed by down-faulting of earth blocks between fissures that are roughly parallel. The Red Sea, Dead Sea, and

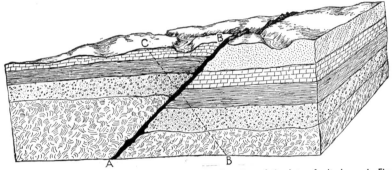

FIG. 289. A mineral vein along a fault. C-B is the location of the later fault shown in Fig. 290.

some of the great lakes of Central Africa are in faulted valleys, sometimes called *rifts*. The basin of the Great Salt Lake in Utah is due partly to faulting.

Kinds of Faults. The planes of some faults depart only a few degrees from horizontal, and the upper part may slide upward over the lower, bringing older rock on top of younger (Fig. 289). The moving of the part above the fault plane upward over the part below could be brought about only by pressure from the sides, and such faults give positive indication of the direction of forces that produced them. In low-angle faults the edges of the overlying beds commonly curve back (drag) toward the fault plane. Where the fault plane dips 45° or more, the upper part usually slips down over the lower, and this movement must be brought about by tension. Such faults are known as *normal*, as they are more numerous than those of the compression type, which are called *reverse*.

Ore Deposits along Faults. The fissure along which faulting takes place and the crushed rock in that zone allow relatively free circulation of water, and if the water bears minerals in solution they may be deposited in this zone. Many of the rich ore deposits of the world were formed along faults. The broken and cracked rocks in the "drag" portion are favorable for water circulation and for the deposition of ore materials to a considerable distance from the fault itself.

Faults Cause Loss of Ore Veins. Although faults are favorable as places for deposition of ore, they may be troublesome in mining operations. Suppose ore had been formed along a fault plane inclined at an angle of 45° (Fig. 290). It might be discovered at the surface and shafts or core-drill holes sunk to find the direction, size, and nature of the vein beneath the ground. The presence of sufficient ore having been proved, expensive machinery is installed and the mine put in operation. Five hundred feet down the vein stops abruptly against another

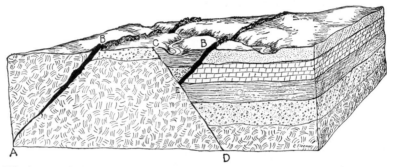

FIG. 290. A second fault cut that shown in Fig. 289 and offset the vein.   In mining down the vein from B, the vein is lost at E.

kind of rock. The mining engineer knows that he has encountered another fault that has cut the vein; he must determine whether the vein has gone up or down and how far it has been shifted. It may have gone down so far as to make mining unprofitable, or it may have gone up and been eroded away (Fig. 290). There are two ways to get at the problem: one, the expensive way of drilling to find the ore; the other, a geological investigation to see whether direction and amount of movement can be determined without the drill.

Fault Causes Loss of Coal Bed. Expensive prospecting where a small amount of geological investigation would have solved the problem was undertaken. A coal bed dipping steeply eastward was being mined on the side of a mountain. Down-dip it was found that the coal bed flattened out, and it was expected that the entire region to the east would be underlain by it at a workable depth. The coal was valuable, as it was high grade and the bed was about 5 feet thick. Companies leased all of the land thought to be underlain by the coal and started sinking shafts and drilling to see at what depth the coal would be found. However, no coal was found farther than ½ mile from the mines. A geological examination of the region showed that a fault paralleling the mountains cut the bed about ½ mile from the mine and that the part to the east had gone up some 12,000 feet (Fig. 291). As the surface to the east was at the same level as that to the west, there had been some 12,000 feet of erosion, and the coal had been carried away millions of years before mining was undertaken.

Faulted Oil Structures. Not many years ago, a faulted oil structure was considered worthless because it was believed that the oil would have escaped along the fault, but it is now known that faulting in oil structures is usually favorable.

Active Faults. Faults along which movement has taken place within recent times are called *active*. When the Panama Canal was being planned, extensive geological investigations were made to find whether

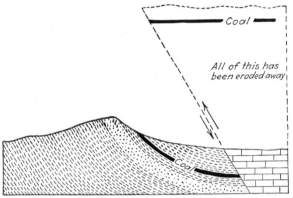

FIG. 291. A coal bed lost by faulting and subsequent erosion. The rocks on the east side were pushed up 12,000 feet in relation to those on the west, and all of the upthrown side above the limestone has been removed by erosion.

any active faults existed in the Canal Zone. Two dangers were to be anticipated from active faults: first, as earthquakes originate along faults, shocks might do great damage to buildings in the fault zone; second, a lock located on an active fault would be broken if movement occurred. A lock damaged by an earthquake might be repaired, but if the lock were located on an active fault it would eventually be ruined by fault movements.

One of the large cities in the United States had to take its entire water supply across an active fault and, therefore, provision was made for quick repairs in the event that the water mains should be broken.

Folds. One who has learned that beds of sediments form in nearly horizontal position is likely to be surprised to find folded sedimentary beds of steep inclination (Fig. 292), but such occur along nearly all mountain ranges and in some plains. The maximum amount of inclination of a bed from the horizontal is called the *dip*. Vertical dips, though not common, occur in many places, and overturned beds (those tilted beyond the vertical) are nearly as numerous as vertical beds. Dips

FIG. 292. Steeply dipping limestone beds near Monterrey, Mexico.   (*Photograph by Carl C. Branson.*)

FIG. 293. Beds dipping about 200 feet per mile.   (*Photograph by Lee, courtesy of U.S. Geological Survey.*)

ranging from a few feet to 200 feet per mile are much commoner than greater dips (Fig. 293).

The beds in any region may dip in various directions. From a given place the dip may be in opposite directions like the roof of a house, forming a fold known as an *anticline* (Fig. 294), *i.e.*, the beds are inclined away from each other. At another place in the same region the beds may be inclined toward one another so as to form a trough, called a *syncline*.

FIG. 294. A small anticline along the Pan-American Highway near Tamazunchale. (*Photograph by Carl C. Branson.*)

One may have a mental picture of anticlines and synclines and go into the field expecting to find the anticlines forming hills and the synclines forming valleys, but only rarely is that true. Such structures may not show in the topography owing to erosion. Erosion may have proceeded so far as to create synclinal hills and anticlinal valleys, as shown in Fig. 299, page 295. Ordinarily, the bend at the top of an anticline and the bottom of a syncline is not exposed. One may find beds dipping north and a short distance away the same beds dipping south. Between the two places the beds must curve over at the top of an anticline, but the higher beds of the arch have been eroded away and many of the lower beds are concealed by mantle rock. Rarely, one finds the top of the fold clearly exposed, as shown in Fig. 301, page 297. Rocks may dip in all directions away from a small area, making a structure *dome* or inverted basin; or they may dip in all directions toward a small area and make a *synclinal basin*. In many regions the rocks seem to be inclined in only one direction with no identifiable anticlines or synclines.

Anticlines were of interest to geologists chiefly as scientific phenomena until it was found that oil is trapped in some of them and that the main

FIG. 295. Conglomerate and sandstone resting unconformably upon hematite schist, Hartville, Wyoming. (*Photograph by Carl C. Branson.*)

supply of oil comes from them. Finding and mapping anticlines and investigating them in various ways became a serious economic problem on which a great many geologists were employed. However, only a small proportion of anticlines actually produce oil, as explained on page 360.

Folds as Engineering Hazards. Folded strata may be seriously considered in various excavations and constructions. A tunnel was driven through a mountain in such a way that its top followed the bottom of a syncline. The engineer in charge relied upon the arch at the top of the tunnel to hold up the overlying rock, but the down bending of the beds left inadequate support and the tunnel caved in.

Along one side of the Gaillard Cut in the Panama Canal, the beds dip steeply toward the canal. A slippery shale bed slides on the underlying rocks when they are wet, and this has caused the slides into the canal which have stopped traffic at some periods and kept steam shovels at work removing the slides ever since the canal was dug.

In the anthracite-coal region of Pennsylvania, the rocks are greatly folded and much of the mining is in steeply dipping beds. The mine roof is weak because of the presence of rock shattered during folding, and it is difficult to get adequate support by timbering. Waste rock is dumped back in the mines to fill up the excavations and aid in supporting the roof. Mining on steep slopes is expensive.

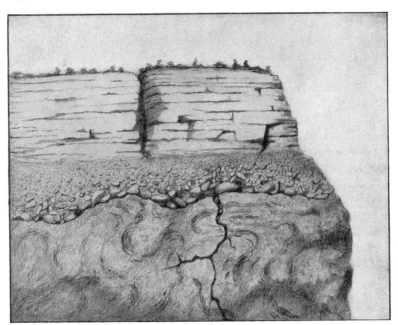

FIG. 296. Unconformity, with conglomerate resting upon gneiss.

Unconformity. After erosion of a land surface, seas may advance over the eroded area and deposit beds of sediments on the rocks. The relationship between the newly deposited sediments and the underlying rocks is called *unconformity* (Figs. 295 and 296). Any agent—wind, glaciers, rivers, organisms—might make the new deposits and the relationship would be unconformable. The essential of an unconformity is that an eroded surface mark the contact of the underlying and overlying rocks. The underlying rocks may be horizontal or dipping at an angle, or they may be igneous or metamorphic.

Unconformities are of great importance in geology as they record the conditions of the region during a time when sedimentary rocks were not forming at that place. They show that the area was land rather than sea, and the geologist may be able to determine something of the length of time that the area was above the sea by the thickness of rock eroded away.

DIASTROPHISM

Many of the structures considered in the preceding part of this chapter were produced by earth movements. The larger of these movements, those which involve great masses of the earth, are known as *diastrophism*. In Chap. 5, the rate at which the lands are being reduced by stream erosion was found to be, on the average, about 1 foot in 5,000 years in the Mississippi Valley, but the rate is 1 foot in 9,000 or 10,000 years for the entire North American continent. At that rate, the North American continent would be cut to sea level in about 22,000,000 years. Allowing for decreased rate with lower grade of streams as base level is approached, it might take 50,000,000 to 60,000,000 years, which is, however, only a small fraction of geologic time. In order to have kept lands available for erosion and for the continuity of land life, they must have risen sufficiently to compensate for the downcutting. Such land uplift has been observed in many places and evidences of uplift are almost universal. Two main types of diastrophic effects are recognized: *general uplift* without much differential movement, and *local uplift* with folding. General uplift produces plains and plateaus, and local uplift may produce mountains. Downward movements seem to have dominated in the ocean basins and to have been common on the continents.

Continental Movements. The movements that produced plains and plateaus may be designated as continental. During some periods half of the present lands of North America were under the sea, and during other periods the part of the continent out of water was 50 per cent larger than it is today. At times all of the lands were nearly at base level, and at other times they were high. At present, the lands of North America seem to be above their average elevation during former geologic time. Continental movements are, and have been, so slow that they would not be noticed by residents of a changing region, except by the advance or retreat of shore lines. Indiana, Nebraska, New Mexico—any region without a coast line—may be rising, stationary, or sinking, at the present time and the fact may not be known to the residents.

The presence of sedimentary rocks containing fossils of sea animals is considered as conclusive evidence that the seas once covered an area, and the 75 per cent of the land area that is made up of such sedimentary rocks bears witness to the former great extent of the seas over the land. Unconformities between rock formations are evidence of times when the area was land undergoing erosion. Over wide areas in North America the presence of marine beds more than 4,000 feet above sea level indicates an uplift of more than 4,000 feet. On the other hand, the presence of 40,000 feet of marine sedimentary rocks would suggest a sinking of more than 40,000 feet to keep the region beneath the sea while the sediments were being deposited.

In places, many unconformities are present; therefore, the land was above sea level and eroded, then sank below sea level and received sediments again, these movements being repeated many times. Some areas (such as Illinois, Indiana, and Iowa) that are now far from oceans alternated between land and sea during much of geologic history and were never affected by mountain-making movements but only by uplift and sinking, which left their records in slight dips of the rocks.

Mountain-making Movements. Mountain-making movements consist of faulting and decided warping of the earth's crust. Intense folding has affected some areas hundreds of miles long, and, in places, faulting accompanied the folding. The difference between the tops of the highest folds and the bottoms of the deepest troughs amounts to more than 50,000 feet in some mountains. Folded mountains seem to have been formed, in the main, by lateral pressure that forced the rocks to buckle up or break and fault.

Basins comparable in size to mountains and continents have been formed by diastrophism. The basin of Lake Superior, for example, and the much larger basin of the Mediterranean Sea were formed by differential downwarping.

Causes of Diastrophism. The causes of earth movements have been investigated by students from numerous points of view, but few consider that they have reached a satisfactory solution. It seems clear that sharp folds must have been caused by lateral pressure and that shrinking of the interior of the earth has been the source of the pressure. Shrinkage may have been caused by cooling, by pressure which caused rearrangement of atoms, and, possibly, by atoms' changing. All three may have been instrumental in causing shrinking, but their relative importance is not known.

Sediments have been deposited to such great thickness that their weight caused the sinking of the earth at that place. Such sinking would crowd the underlying rocks, causing lateral pressure and consequent upwarping of the margins of the sinking area.

Present Movements. At the present time, some lands are known to be rising slowly and others sinking. Northern Scandinavia seems to be rising at the rate of about 1 foot in 40 years. If erosion continues there at the average rate, the land should be about 24,900 feet high in 1,000,000 years, i.e., the land would have risen 25,000 feet and been cut down 100 feet. Part of the coast of South Greenland appears to be sinking. Stone huts built long ago by the inhabitants are now submerged, and the Greenlander has learned not to build his hut near the shore. Some old inhabitants of mountainous regions have thought that they were able to see fixed objects in the distance that were invisible from the same place during their youth on account of intervening hills. This would be evidence of downwarping of the intervening hills or rise of the land from which the observations were made or of the object seen in the distance. Such observations cannot be trusted, as they depend on the memory of a person through a long period of years. On page 283 differential movement of several feet along fault planes is mentioned.

In Chap. 8, drowned valleys were mentioned as indicators of sinking coasts; and raised beaches, barriers, and other coast-line structures well above sea level, as evidences of rising coasts.

MOUNTAINS

The most striking features of the landscape are mountains, and more people are attracted by them than by any other land form. A mountain has been defined as a hill with a relief above the surrounding land of 1,000 or more feet. Groups of mountains may have many peaks with small summit areas or may consist of ridges with few distinct peaks. On the basis of origin, mountains are classified as *volcanic, folded, faulted,* and *erosional.*

Volcanic Mountains. The simplest, and in some ways most spectacular, of all mountains are volcanoes. Volcanoes have always been a source of wonder and danger to man, and most of them are in volcanic mountains. Most volcanic mountains start with the issuing of lava or other volcanic products from an opening in level ground. Gradually, the extruded material accumulates around the opening and may finally form a great mountain. If the extruded material is thin lava, it spreads a long distance over the surrounding land and makes a gently sloping mountain of wide extent.

Mauna Loa. Mauna Loa in the Hawaiian Islands is one of the best-known lava cones of low slope. It covers an area of about 200 square miles and slopes in most directions so gently that a modern automobile could be driven up in high gear. At the top is the opening from which the lava flows. Though Mauna Loa has very gentle slopes for a mountain, it should not be understood that it has no steep slopes. Stream erosion attacks volcanic mountains vigorously in regions of heavy rainfall, and in some places Mauna Loa is dissected by deep, steep-walled canyons; it is the original slope that is gentle, not that superimposed by some other agent.

Shape of Volcanic Mountains. Viscous lava gives rise to mountains with much steeper slopes than does liquid lava, and some cones are really steep. The volcanic mountain is actually made up of a succession of lava flows, some of which may be only a few inches thick and others hundreds of feet thick. Lava cones are noted for their symmetry, though none is perfectly symmetrical.

Some volcanic mountains are made up of ash and cinders, and they too have good symmetry. They may be very steep and, being composed of loose materials, erode rapidly. Lava flows associated with the ash and cinders help to hold the shape of most ash mountains.

FIG. 297. Mt. Ranier, a volcanic mountain which has been eroded by streams and glaciers. (*Courtesy of Ranier National Park Company.*)

Well-known Volcanic Mountains. In the United States, volcanic mountains are few compared with those of other types; Lassen Peak in California is the only one that has been active within historical times. Great areas in the United States are covered with extrusive igneous rocks, but, in the main, the lavas that formed them come from fissure flows. East of the Rocky Mountains there is not a volcanic mound in the United States. The San Francisco Mountains in Arizona are lava cones, not greatly dissected by stream erosion. Mt. Shasta and Lassen Peak in California and Mt. Rainier (Fig. 297) and Mt. Hood in Oregon and Washington are well-known volcanic mountains.   Mt. Vesuvius and Mt. Etna are among the best-known mountains in the world because they are active volcanoes.   In Central America and South America many mountains are volcanic in origin, although most of the great mountains of South American are not of this type.

Mountains Caused by Folding.   The great mountain ranges of the world are, in the main, due to rock folding and subsequent erosion. Probably the Rocky Mountains are the best known of any mountains in North America, but most people who have traveled widely in them scarcely realize what they are.   They consist of a large number of independent or semi-independent ranges, so numerous that no one is able to tell exactly how many and no map shows all of them.   Nearly all of these ranges are of the folded type.

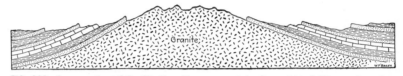
FIG. 298. Cross-section of the Big Horn Range, mountains formed by folding and erosion.

The Big Horn Mountains.   The Big Horn Mountains, which trend north-south through central Wyoming, are a good example of folded mountains (Fig. 298).   They consist of one great fold (the highest part of which must once have been about 28,000 feet above sea level) with minor folds and faults on the sides.   If this range had been shaped entirely by folding, its width (the distance between flanks where the dipping rocks give way to nearly horizontal strata) would have been about 30 miles and its length about 150 miles.   As soon as the central part reached a height great enough to cause water to flow from it, streams began cutting valleys into the fold.   As the range consists of valleys and hills between the valleys, every hill directly and definitely related to a valley, the main features of the mountains are due almost entirely to stream erosion.   Most of the valleys run nearly at right angles to the main trend of the range, and the streams have formed canyons that dissect the range from the middle to the margin on both sides.   Two highways cross the range through canyons on both sides of the mountains.

When the folding of the range started, some 13,000 feet of sediments lay horizontally upon igneous and metamorphic rocks, and the folding raised the igneous and metamorphic rocks to the same extent as the sedimentaries.   After 15,000 feet of rocks had been cut away from the top, the igneous and metamorphic rocks were laid bare in the middle of the range, and the flanks of the mountain were made up of dipping sandstones, shales, and limestones.   The softer layers of rock were eroded away along the trend of the mountains, and harder layers were left standing as ridges or hogbacks.   The canyons running from the heart of the mountains outward are in igneous or metamorphic rock near the center of the range and in sedimentaries on the flanks.   However, the complexity of the range does not end with this, for later all of the main valleys were glaciated and great numbers of cirques gave form to the highest peaks.   The main valleys have been scoured out so as to be more or less U-shaped, and in the canyons of the higher parts of the range many lakes are present.

One might suppose that the Big Horn Range is of volcanic origin if he thought only of the igneous core, but the granites that constitute the interior of the range are the result of an intrusion into other rocks long before the uplift of the range started.   The magma cooled and all of the rocks into which it was intruded were eroded away before the lowest

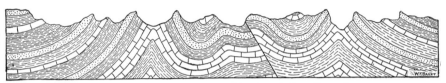

FIG. 299. A section across part of the Appalachian Mountains.

of the sedimentary rocks were laid down.   The range was forced up by great lateral pressure rather than by intrusion of lava into the core.

Most of the other ranges of the Rocky Mountains have histories much like the one reported for the Big Horn Mountains.   Most of them are made up of a core of igneous rocks, with dipping sedimentary rocks on the sides.   Stream erosion has laid bare the igneous rocks at the cores and created the ruggedness of the ranges, in many of which glaciation has been superimposed on stream work.   Only those ranges, however, that have an elevation of 11,000 to 12,000 or more feet above sea level have been glaciated; in all of the rest, stream erosion has been the sole shaping agent.

The Appalachian Mountains.   The Appalachian Mountains of eastern United States, although much lower and less picturesque than the Rockies, have had a longer and more varied history.   They too are of the folded type (Fig. 299), and the folding was much more intense than that described for the Big Horns.   Instead of one large arch the Appalachians are made up of numerous smaller ones.   In crossing the Big Horns one is impressed with the eastward dip of the rock on the east side and the westward dip on the west side, but in crossing the Appalachians one finds numerous changes in direction of dip and may cross many well-marked anticlines.   These intense folds were not raised so high as the folds of the Big Horns, and the greatest ones did not bring the igneous rocks high enough to be laid bare by erosion, so most of the mountains consist of ridges of sedimentary rocks.   If there had been no erosion, the Appalachians would have been a peculiar-looking compound ridge, like many sheets of paper compressed into hundreds of folds; but, as with the Rockies, erosion has been the agent that has created the mountain forms.   Erosion began as soon as folding brought the rocks above sea level; more than 50,000 feet of strata have been removed in some places, and more than 20,000 feet in most places.   One looks in vain in the mountains south of central Pennsylvania for any sign of glacial erosion. U-shaped valleys are not present.   No cirques, moraines, or glacial lakes appear.   It is stream erosion alone that has shaped the topography. North of central Pennsylvania, continental glaciers helped shape some of the lower hills and in places covered the entire range.

Striking features of the Appalachian Mountains are the nearly level tops of the main ridges with their summits in approximately the same plane.   If no rocks had been eroded from the ridges, these would be explained as the original tops of the great folds, but thousands of feet of strata have been eroded from the top of each ridge.   It does not seem possible that independent stream erosion could produce level-topped ridges of about the same elevation.   If all of the valleys between the high ridges were filled to the tops of the ridges, a nearly level plain would result.   There are only two ways in which such plains could be produced: one by the filling of a depression with sediments, which would make a plain of nearly horizontal layers, and the other by stream erosion carried to peneplanation.   The latter explanation fits the case and we conclude that the entire region was reduced nearly to a peneplain.   Later, this erosion surface was raised and much dissected by streams and the tops of the ridges are the only parts remaining of the peneplain.   There are other evidences that the old Appalachian folds were peneplaned after their original great uplift, some of which will be given in the summary of the history of the Appalachian Mountains.   As the southeastern part of these mountains is composed mainly of metamorphic rocks, the general appearance of the region is not of parallel ridges, like those in the region made up of sedimentary rocks, but of dendritic valleys and ridges.

Although the Appalachians are an intensely folded range, the Alps are much more complexly folded and have many overturned folds and complex faults.

Hogback Mountains.   Hogback mountains are ridges (Fig. 300), or a series of ridges caused by erosion of dipping strata.   The softer beds are cut much lower than the hard ones, and the latter form one slope of the ridges.   Such mountains form in regions where the beds have been tilted in one direction and eroded, as shown in Fig. 103, page 111. Hogback mountains isolated from others are rare, but an example of such a one is the Great Hogback in western Colorado.   Most of the

FIG. 300. A hogback mountain in western New Mexico. (*Photograph by Lee, courtesy of U.S. Geological Survey.*)

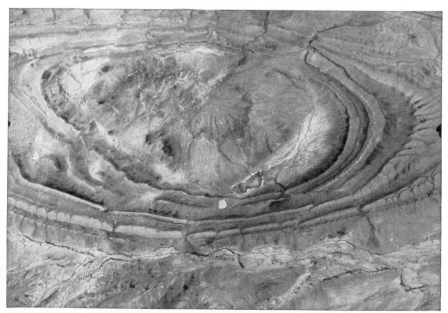

FIG. 301. Air view of Grenville Dome, Wyoming. The ridges are resistant layers dipping away from the center of the dome. (*Courtesy of Jack Ammann, Photogrammetric Engineer.*)

ridges of the Appalachian system are hogbacks, and most of the chains
of the Rocky Mountains are flanked by hogbacks.

  Domed Mountains. In some places strata are domed, *i.e.*, folded so
that they dip in all directions from a general center. If the doming

FIG. 302. Cross-section of a domed mountain.

FIG. 303. Fault-line valleys near the Wet Mountains, Colorado.   Straight lines are rare in nature,
and these straight valleys and linear patterns of vegetation indicate faults.   (*Photograph courtesy of
Production and Marketing Administration, U.S. Department of Agriculture.*)

is high and the dips are large, mountains may form from such structures.
The Black Hills of South Dakota are an example of domed mountains,
and Figs. 301 and 302 represent small, low-domed mountains.

  Mountains Caused by Faulting.   As stated in a previous paragraph,
some fault scarps are high and steep and form the sides of mountains.

FIG. 304. Guadalupe Mountains, Texas and New Mexico. Mountains formed by erosion of faulted bedded rocks and of reefs. (*Courtesy of Muldrow Aerial Surveys, Inc.*)

FIG. 305. Rugged mountain features in Alaska produced by streams, glaciation, and weathering. (*Official photograph, U.S. Navy Air Corps.*)

The most rugged mountains in the interior of the United States are the Tetons of western Wyoming. The east face of these mountains is a fault scarp, which has been greatly modified by erosion. Some mountains are uplifted blocks with faults on two or more sides. Many of the Great Basin ranges of the United States are tilted fault blocks. As with most mountains, the main topographic features of mountains caused by faulting are erosional (Fig. 303), and the older the range, the less conspicuous the fault scarps.

Most mountains are faulted to some extent. Some parts of the Appalachians are cut by many faults with thousands of feet of displacement, but other parts have few faults. Great folds may contain faults parallel to them or across them.

Mountains of Erosion. Many low mountains are remnants of horizontal strata that have been left by stream erosion. Where valleys are

FIG. 306. Glaciated granite core of the Wind River Mountains, Wyoming. (*Photograph by M. G. Mehl.*)

deep, like those of the Colorado and its tributaries in northern Arizona, the region becomes mountainous when it reaches a mature stage of topography. The top of Mesa Verde in southwestern Colorado has an area of several thousand square miles. Its sides are steep because the thick resistant sandstone that forms the top rests on soft shales (see Fig. 98, page 108). Streams have removed all of the sandstone and cut deeply into the shales over a large region on all sides of the mesa, leaving it a steep-sided, flat-topped mountain, some 2,000 feet high, flanked by low shale hills. A photograph taken from the butte shown in Fig. 101, page 110, shows the topography (Fig. 92, page 101) developed on the soft shales near the mesa. Some parts of Mesa Verde were dissected by stream erosion, leaving many buttes. Both mesas and buttes may be mountains if their relief is great enough.

The Catskills in eastern New York are mountains of erosion carved in nearly horizontal strata. Grand Mesa in western Colorado, another mountain of this class, has a relief of more than 3,000 feet.   If one could imagine the region of the Grand Canyon of the Colorado dissected by tributaries 50 miles long and as deep as the canyon itself, he would get a picture of mountains of erosion rising to heights of a mile or more and covering a great area.   Many mountains are a combination of stream and glacier erosion.   Yosemite Valley is one of the best examples of such features, but there are many such in Alaska (Fig. 305) and in the Rocky Mountains (Fig. 306).

CHAPTER 14

EARTHQUAKES

In preceding chapters we have shown that numerous physical forces are continually at work within the body of the earth and upon its surface. Those agents working on the surface are constantly changing the shape and size of the features that give it variety and beauty. Likewise, the physical forces beneath the surface are rearranging rock materials by shifting magmas about and altering the structure of solid rocks. The adjustments beneath the surface, however, involve various crustal movements, some of which, because of their suddenness and intensity, produce tremors in the rocks and thus are known as *earthquakes*.

No other demonstration of the mighty forces at work within the earth's body is so appalling to man as are earthquakes. They occur suddenly and swiftly, involve vast areas, and leave a trail of destruction behind them. Mountain making is an evidence of the tremendous forces that act upon portions of the earth's crust, but the growth of mountains is so slow that the span of man's life is much too short to enable him to detect the movements that take place. It is very different, however, with earthquakes. The solid land shakes; surface objects are injured or destroyed—and all in the space of a few seconds.

Volcanoes have been looked upon with awe and terror ever since primitive man's first encounter with their fiery floods, and within the historical period of the human race the toll of life taken during volcanic eruptions has amounted to many thousands. The destructiveness of volcanoes, however, does not compare with that of earthquakes, for usually there are signs of an approaching volcanic eruption and thus the inhabitants of nearby regions are able to escape. Earthquakes come without warning. Furthermore, volcanic areas are fewer and more sparsely inhabited than are the areas subject to earthquakes, and in the earthquake regions the shocks are just as apt to occur, of course, in the most densely populated areas, where their destruction of life and property is enormous, as in the regions of scattered population. Recent earthquakes in congested areas have been in Japan, in Messina, Sicily, and in San Francisco and Long Beach, California.

Science has, as yet, failed to safeguard man against earthquakes by devising a method of detecting them in advance. The late Dr. F. Omori, director of the Tokyo Seismic Observatory and one of the foremost authorities on earthquakes, predicted, in 1921, that within six years of that date a destructive earthquake would occur in Japan. Actually, it came within two years; but, in view of the fact that an earthquake may come and go in two minutes, any prediction in terms of years is of little value as a warning. Seismologists (students of earthquakes), however, are eagerly striving to invent instruments or devise methods by which warnings of an approaching earthquake may be given. So rapid are earthquake movements, however, that no means of communication yet devised by man is swift enough to enable those near the center of a disturbed area to warn the inhabitants of surrounding areas in time for them to escape.

Recorded descriptions of earthquakes go back nearly 2,500 years. Herodotus, Pliny, Livy, and many other historians mention their occurrence and destructiveness; hence man has long been accustomed to pay human toll to the earthquake. Much superstition has surrounded their occurrence; it was thought that they were imposed as a punishment for the misdeeds of the people living in the affected area.

An earnest effort to study the character of the movements, speed, source, and cause of earthquakes began about 1840. Though much has been learned in over 100 years of study, the appalling destructive power of the earthquake over man and his works is as great as ever. In fact, this power is greater than it was formerly, for man has aggregated millions of his kind into small areas, has housed himself in deathtraps, and thus has paved the way for nature's demonstration of the fact that she brooks no control of her forces by her own progeny. Man must work in conformity with nature's laws, for only by so doing can he hope to avoid paying the extreme penalty. The occurrence and force of earthquakes should prove of benefit in correcting the arrogance of man by showing him his own puniness and weakness and also in developing in him a fuller appreciation of nature's laws.

Earth movements may be fairly well classified in two groups: the small but rapid movements, and the great, slow movements. It is the rapid movements of earth masses that are called "earthquakes." These movements may be so small as to be barely capable of detection by the most delicate instruments, or they may be of such magnitude as to be noticeable to all at distances of several thousand miles. An earthquake is in reality a vibration of a rock mass that moves forward and then returns to essentially its former position. The total movement (save at the point where it originates) is small.

Methods of Detecting and Recording Earthquakes. The science of determining the size and character of earthquakes is called *seismometry* (*seismos* = "earthquake"; *metron* = "to measure"). The first instruments made were able to record only the fact that there had been an earthquake and so furnished no information as to its size or velocity. Such instruments are called *seismoscopes*. The first one was invented in A.D. 136 by a Chinese. Many curious devices have been invented since that time. Anyone can easily make a simple seismoscope by placing a small round rod of wood or metal in a vertical position on a horizontal plane that is covered with fine sand to keep the rod from rolling. A moderate earthquake shock will upset this rod, and it will fall in the direction the earthquake is moving.

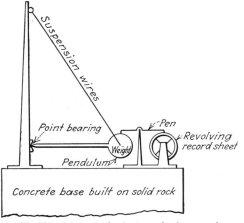

FIG. 307. Diagram of a horizontal seismograph.

The detailed record of an earthquake is made on an instrument called a *seismograph*, which was invented and first used in Italy about 1841. The fundamental requirement of a seismograph (Fig. 307) is that it have a delicately mounted heavy pendulum that remains essentially stationary as the earth moves beneath it. A long, slender rod rigidly attached to the pendulum supports a self-feeding pen which rests upon a surface of smoked paper—the record sheet. During an earthquake shock, the pendulum and the pen are stationary while the record sheet moves with the earth. The pen thus registers the movement on the paper; and, as the record sheet is wound on a drum run by clockwork, the exact time of the movement is also recorded. In the latest models of seismographs, the record of the vibration is photographed, and thus the friction of a pen is eliminated. The pendulum may be suspended vertically, horizontally (Fig. 307), or it may be inverted and rest upon a pivot. Some inverted pendulums weigh many tons.

An earthquake may involve movement in three directions: one vertical (usually small compared to the other two) and two horizontal.

Most modern instruments record the horizontal movements in a north and south and an east and west direction. The record of an earthquake shock is called a *seismogram* (Fig. 308), which is really the earth's autograph of its movements. The records show that the movements during an earthquake are very complex. The instruments are extremely sensitive, recording minute shocks. Strong winds, the firing of cannon, or the passing of loaded trucks all leave a record on the sheet.

Velocity of Earthquake Waves. A study of seismograms has shown that there are three types of earthquake waves. Two of the waves take a short course through the earth and the other one follows the surface.

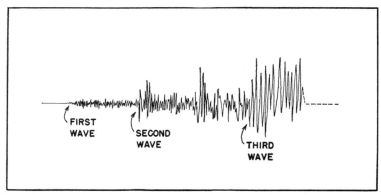

FIG. 308. Seismogram of the Assam earthquake of August, 1950, recorded at Aberdeen, Scotland, a quarter of the way around the world. Arrival of the first wave was followed, about 9 minutes later, by arrival of a second wave, which was followed in about 16 minutes by arrival of a third wave. (*Modified after Tillotson.*)

The first wave passing through the earth is much faster than the second one. The surface wave, though the slowest of all, is large and consequently does much damage. The relative size of the three waves is indicated in the seismogram of Fig. 308.

The first of the waves to reach an instrument are those that take the shorter route through the earth. These are the preliminary tremors. Some of these waves travel as fast as 6.75 miles per second (375 miles per minute). They could thus traverse the diameter of the earth in 20 minutes. The determination of the velocity of these waves has added much to our knowledge of the condition of the interior of the earth, which has been shown to be 1.5 times as rigid as steel. It is the study of the paths of these waves that has revealed the presence at the center of the earth of a core composed dominantly of metals (iron, nickel, and many others). The radius of this core is about 3,400 kilometers (2,110 miles) and waves in passing through this portion of the earth travel slower than through the outer portions.

The velocity of the slow surface wave rarely exceeds 2 miles per second

(120 miles per minute) and may be only 8 or 9 miles per minute. This large reduction in velocity is due to the great abundance of cracks and fissures in the rocks of the outer part of the earth.

Amplitude of Earthquake Waves. The actual distance that the ground moves, known as *the amplitude of the vibration*, is always small. A movement of ¾ inch is highly destructive; a movement of ⅜ inch is a severe quake; and one involving only ³⁄₁₆ inch will shatter a chimney. Rarely, the amplitude of waves is larger. In the Japan earthquake of 1923, the amplitude of the wave that caused the greatest destruction was 3.5 inches. In one of the later shocks the wave had an amplitude of 7.1 inches but it was less destructive because of a much slower velocity. Very probably, there have been earthquakes of larger movements which our seismographs were unable to record because the recording paper was too small.

Time Length of Earthquake Shocks. An earthquake rarely lasts more than 2 minutes and most of them only a few seconds. The California earthquake of 1906 was of less than a minute's duration, and the earthquake at Assam, India, in 1897, lasted 15 seconds. Messina, Sicily, was destroyed in 35 seconds. After the main earthquake shock, there are usually recurring shocks of less intensity.

Intensity of Shocks. An earthquake originates at a point or along a line usually called the *centrum*. The place on the surface over the centrum is called the *epicentrum*, from which the intensity of the shock decreases with the distance. Scales showing the variations in intensity have been devised and are generally used in describing the character of the shock. A scale suggested by McAdie is given in the following table:

SCALE OF EARTHQUAKE INTENSITY

Intensity	Description
1	Earthquake detectable only by instruments
2	Very feeble
3	Feeble
4	Noticeable by man, but no damage
5	Felt generally
6	Slight damage
7	Walls cracked
8	Badly built houses destroyed
9	Violent; much destruction and loss of life
10	Catastrophic

This scale is a convenient means of comparing shocks of different areas and also those of different parts of the same area.

Frequency of Shocks. Earthquakes are of frequent occurrence. The estimate has been made that, on the average, one occurs in some part of the earth every 2 hours and 27 minutes. Certain areas undergo a

vast number of shocks of varying intensities.   Japan and Italy are each
credited with about 1,500 shocks a year, which is an average of nearly
4 per day.   The records from 1875 to 1925 show a total of 27,500 shocks
for each of these two countries.   Other countries have had hundreds
or thousands of shocks during the last 50 years.   California has about
200 shocks of varying intensities per year.   During a period of 3 months
in the early part of the nineteenth century, there were 1,874 shocks in
the New Madrid area in southeastern Missouri and western Tennessee,
but only 8 of them were severe.

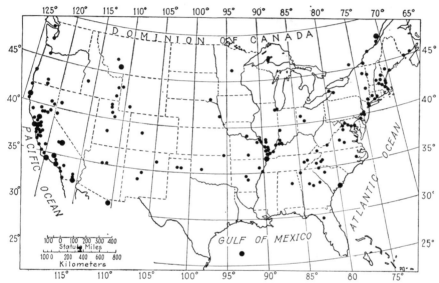

FIG. 309. Map showing location of earthquakes in the United States.   (*After N. H. Heck, Scientific
Monthly*, 1930.)

Earthquake Zones.   Earthquakes occur most abundantly in areas
containing mountains (especially the younger mountain ranges), which
shows that the stresses set up in the rocks during the formation of the
mountains were not all relieved but are still causing movements.   Though
earthquakes occur in regions of older mountains, such as the Appalachians, the stresses in such regions have been largely relieved during the
long interval since the folding took place.   Margins of the continents are
also weak zones and hence are the locations of many earthquakes.   It is
worth noting that about 53 per cent of all earthquakes occur along a belt
of younger mountain ranges (the Alps-Caucasus-Himalaya belt), and 41
per cent along the margins of the continents around the Pacific Ocean.
The other 6 per cent are scattered over the earth.   Figures 309 and 310
show the location of the earthquakes known to have occurred in the
United States and the world, respectively.

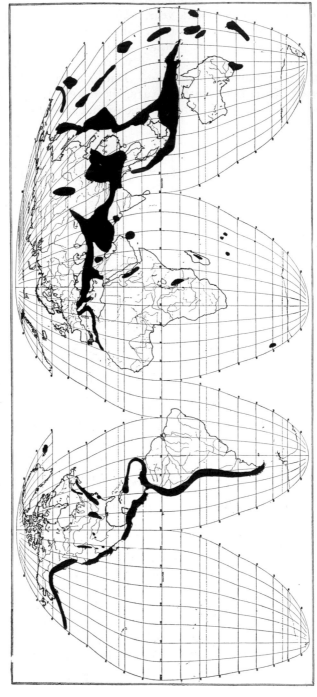

FIG. 310. Map of the world showing distribution of earthquake areas. (Based on No. 101 Hc of the Goode Series of Base Maps. By permission of the University of Chicago Press.)

Causes of Earthquakes. Earthquakes originate from various causes. These are, in the order of their importance: *faulting, volcanism, landslides,* and the *collapse of cavern roofs.* The last two causes are local in extent and relatively unimportant so will not be discussed here. The vast majority of earthquakes originate within 10 miles of the surface, though some may be due to causes acting at much greater depths.

Earthquake Waves due to Faulting. Most earthquakes are directly associated with earth movements along faults. It is this movement associated with faulting which sets up the elastic waves that produce an earthquake. An examination of Fig. 311 will help to make clear just what happens along a fault plane when movement occurs. A slow differential pull exists within the rock, the direction of which is shown by the two sets of arrows. As a result of this pull, a strain develops in the

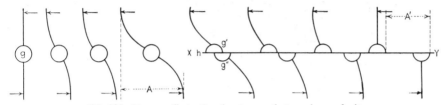

FIG. 311. Diagram illustrating the stresses that produce a fault.

particle *g*, tending to separate it into two parts *g'* and *g''*. If the strain gradually increases over a long period of time, the pull on both parts of the particle will increase until finally it amounts to that indicated by the distance at *A*. If the pull or strain exceeds this distance, the particle will separate, as has occurred at *h*. The earthquake shock starts the instant the rupture occurs. The parts *g'* and *g''* continue to move apart along the plane *xy* (the time required for the separation is measured in fractions of a second) and finally come to rest separated by the distance at *A'*, which is probably less than that at *A*. The sudden parting (called the *recoil*) and attendant moving of the particle (and, of course, those adjacent to it) start the vibrations that form the earthquake. The process can be illustrated by slowly stretching a rubber band until it breaks. The elastic property of the rubber causes the two parts of the band to snap back, just as the elastic property of the rocks causes the rebound following their break. Rocks are remarkably elastic within narrow limits.

The displacement along a fault plane is influenced by many factors, chief of which is the quantity of strain that has accumulated in the rocks. It depends also on the character of the fault plane, *i.e.*, whether it is an old or a new one. The displacement accompanying the movement thus varies widely. The slipping during the California earthquake of 1906 was dominantly horizontal (Figs. 312 and 313). The vertical

FIG. 312. Displacement of 8 ½ feet (shown by fence) due to faulting at time of California earthquake of 1906. (*Photograph by Gilbert, U.S. Geological Survey.*)

FIG. 313. Road offset 20 feet by a fault, Marin County, California, 1906. (*Photograph by Gilbert, U.S. Geological Survey.*)

slipping during an earthquake at Yakutat Bay, Alaska, in 1899, amounted to 48 feet; and in New Zealand, in 1929, to 20 feet.   In numerous minor shocks, however, the displacement is no more than a few inches.

After an earthquake has occurred, the rocks adjacent to the fault undergo adjustment for a considerable period of time.   This causes a large number of small shocks.   In the 24 hours following the Japanese earthquake of September 1, 1923, 237 shocks were felt, and during the month of September a total of 720. As these adjustments near completion, an affected area becomes free from shocks and there is a quiet period. Such a period in an area subject to earthquakes is known to be the forerunner of a severe shock, but we have no means of determining positively when it will occur.

Earthquakes Caused by Volcanism. The movement of magmas and gases within the earth's crust, especially the common spasmodic movement, is another means of starting an earthquake. It has long been known that earthquakes accompany the eruptions of volcanoes. Shocks may occur before an eruption and so are more or less of a warning of volcanic activity, but a greater number of shocks follow an eruption, evidently owing to readjustments within the magmas and the surrounding rocks below the surface. As a rule, shocks that accompany volcanism are less severe and destructive than those that are due to faulting.

Why Earthquakes Are So Destructive. A question often asked is why so small a vibration ($\frac{1}{2}$ inch or even 3 inches) as that usually accompanying an earthquake shock should cause so much damage. The answer is that the destructiveness of the earthquake is not due to the amplitude of the waves but to their great velocity. As the wave moves forward, objects upon the surface are set in motion. What happens to tall objects may be illustrated by considering the fate of a tall tree during an earthquake. The base of the tree moves forward with the wave, and this forward movement passes at a much slower rate up the tree. The forward movement of the ground, however, is immediately followed by the recoil or backward movement, and thus the direction in which the base of the tree was moving is instantly reversed and the backward movement starts up the tree. However, as the top of the tree had not traveled so far forward as the base, it may be snapped off by the quick reversal in direction of movement. Just so would the top of a tall chimney be snapped off. During the Japanese earthquake of 1923, 110 of the 240 chimneys over 45 feet high in the area affected were completely destroyed, and more than 40 of those not destroyed were seriously damaged.

Tall buildings, if rigidly built, sway or oscillate back and forth during an earthquake shock, and if poorly built are destroyed (Fig. 314). If a building can rock or slide upon its base, all of the movement will not be transmitted to the structure and the damage will be less. If a building is not too high and is well built, it will not be seriously damaged beyond the cracking of the walls, breaking of glass, and destruction of the chimneys. The greatest damage to buildings is inflicted upon those located on soft ground, such as that made by filling low places with earth. This ground moves and slips irregularly in various directions, and the build--

ings upon it, unless very rigidly built, are rocked to pieces.   The great loss of life in the earthquake at Messina, Sicily, was due in large part to the poor construction of the houses.

The greatest damage inflicted by earthquakes occurs where the wave reaches the surface at an angle of 30 to 50° and not directly over the epicentrum, as in that place the movement is usually up and down.

FIG. 314. Church in Santa Barbara, California, demolished by earthquake of 1925. (*Photograph by P. D. Tarr.*)

Aside from the damage due to the earth vibrations, fires cause great destruction of life and property, as do also the sea waves that are produced so commonly by submarine earthquakes or those occurring near the sea shore.   These waves are called *tsunamis*.

Fires that start in towns or cities during or following an earthquake shock cause such terrible destruction because the water mains have usually been severed by the earthquake and, thus there is no water for fighting fire.   At the time of the Tokyo earthquake, thousands of lives were lost in the accompanying fire, which burned over an area of 8,300 acres.   Fires covered an area of 2,300 acres in San Francisco during the earthquake of 1906.

Tsunamis are caused by the transmission of the movement of the solid rock to the mobile water above.   Such waves are of exceptional size and travel away from the epicentrum of the earthquake.   If the wave reaches the shore while still of considerable magnitude, it may cause great damage.   In a shore indentation having converging walls, tsunamis

commonly attain heights of 10 or 20 feet.   The one accompanying the
Lisbon earthquake reached a height of 60 feet owing to such a cause.   The
velocities of tsunamis have been estimated at 300 to 400 miles per hour.

Some Important Earthquakes.   The importance of earthquakes to
man is usually measured in the number of human lives lost and the
damage done to property, though seismologically the greatest earthquake
shocks are those of the highest intensity, whether great human losses are
involved or not.   Probably the most intense earthquake shock observed
since seismological measurements were established[1] occurred in Assam,
India, near the Tibet border, on August 15, 1950 (see Fig. 308, page 305).
The initial shock was followed, during the next 11 days, by 22 violent
aftershocks.   Relatively few (less than 1,500) lives were lost because no
large cities were in the area.

This earthquake is of special interest because an impressive first-hand
account of it was written by a man who observed it from the epicentral
area.   Captain F. Kingdon-Ward and his wife were camped on the bank
of the La Ti torrent in the village of Rima, Assam.   Describing the shock
on the night of August 15, 1950, Captain Kingdon-Ward[2] wrote:

. . . It was about 8 P.M. . . . on a hot, close night, the stars shining brightly up
and down the arid gorge. . . .

Suddenly, after the faintest tremor . . . there came an appalling noise and the
earth began to shudder violently.   I jumped up and looked out of the tent.   I
have a distinct recollection of seeing the outlines of the landscape, visible against
the starry sky, blurred—every ridge and tree fuzzy—as though it were rapidly
moving up and down; . . . solid-looking hills were in the grip of a force which
shook them as a terrier shakes a rat. . . .

. . . it felt as though a powerful ram were hitting against the earth beneath us
with the persistence of a kettle-drum.   I had exactly the sensation that a thin
crust at the bottom of the basin, . . . was breaking up like an ice floe. . . . The
din was terrible; but it was difficult to separate the noise made by the earthquake
itself from the roar of the rock avalanches pouring down on all sides into the
basin. . . .

Within two hours the air was so thick with dust that every star was hidden.
. . . Violent tremors continued all night. . . .

Of the results visible next day, and later, Captain Kingdon-Ward says:

Long fissures cut across the stony fields, running for the most part parallel with
the river bank, past or present.   In some places numerous fissures lay close
together; elsewhere far apart. . . . These cracks were rarely more than a few
inches wide and two to four feet deep. . . . Here and there a small block of land
had sunk bodily. . . .

[1] ERNEST TILLOTSON, "The Great Assam Earthquake of August 15, 1950," *Nature*,
vol. 167, p. 128, 1951.

[2] F. KINGDON-WARD, "Notes on the Assam Earthquake," *Nature*, vol. 167, pp.
130–131, 1951.

As for the mountains which enclose the basin, they had everywhere been badly mauled. Wide belts had been ripped off, carrying trees and rocks; whole cliffs had crashed down, deep wounds scored; and everywhere rocks continued to cascade down hundreds of gullies. The damage done in the main Lohit valley was bad enough; that done in the tributary valleys, where every stream had to break through a narrow gorge thousands of feet deep, was infinitely worse. The destruction extended to the very tops of the main ranges—15,000–16,000 ft. above sea-level. No wonder the mountain torrents began to flow intermittently as the gorges became blocked, followed later by the breaking of the dam; whereupon a wall of water 20 ft. high would roar down the gulley, carrying everything before it and leaving a trail of evil-smelling mud.

It is indeed fortunate that such an intense earthquake shock did not occur under a large city to cause the appalling disaster that would have been inevitable. The number of human lives that have been destroyed by earthquakes will never be known, but it must be several millions. The list of earthquakes known to have been destructive to human life is a long one, as the following table shows, but casualties will increase faster in the future than in the past, owing to the steady increase in the world's population and its growing congestion in earthquake areas.

Probably the most destructive earthquake that ever occurred was the one on February 2, 1556, in the provinces of Shansi, Shensi, and Honan in north central China (see Table). Nearly 200 years later, in 1731, another earthquake occurred in the same region—this time at Peking. China has since been visited by two terribly destructive shocks, both of which occurred in the same area but in the province of Kansu. As can be determined from the table, the total loss of life during these four earthquakes approximates 1,226,000.

The earthquakes in the Kansu province were in an area of loess, which was loosened and moved in such great quantities that the Chinese, lacking a word for "landslide," described what happened thus: "The mountains walked" (Shan tso-liao). The loosened loess moved down the hillsides into the valleys, burying houses, villages, and rivers. Great numbers of people lived in caves in the loess and in mud-brick houses. Their fate can easily be imagined.

Southern Japan was visited by a tremendous earthquake on September 1, 1923. The main shock center was only about 55 miles from Tokyo and 40 miles from Yokohama and, therefore, the destruction and loss of life were tremendous. The shock came at noon on Saturday when there was a vast number of people in the business districts. Block after block of houses went down, and the fire that broke out immediately burned those who were imprisoned in the falling structures. The cause of the earthquake is believed to lie in the fact that a fault zone has developed between Japan and the great ocean deep that lies 200 miles

High Mortality Caused by Earthquakes from 577 to 1951

Place	Year	Number killed
Constantinople, Turkey	577	10,000
India	893	180,000
Georgia (Caucasus)	894	20,000
Iraq, Arabia	1007	10,000
Tabriz, Persia	1050	50,000
Catania, Sicily	1137	15,000
Persia	1139	100,000
Syria	1158	20,000
Catania, Sicily	1169	14,000
Kiangsi, China	1333	10,000
Naples, Italy	1456	60,000
Lisbon, Portugal	1531	30,000
China (Shansi, Shensi, and Honan)	1556	830,000
Naples, Italy	1626	70,000
Calabria, Italy	1638	10,000
Sicily and Catania, Italy	1693	100,000
Yeddo (present city of Tokyo), Japan	1703	190,000
Algiers	1716	18,000
Peking, China	1731	96,000
Kashan, Persia	1755	40,000
Lisbon, Portugal	1755	60,000
Syria	1759	20,000
Calabria, Italy	1783	80,000
Central America	1797	40,000
Carácas, Venezuela	1812	12,000
Sumatra	1815	20,000
Aleppo, Syria	1822	20,000
Mt. Ararat, Armenia-Persia	1840	10,000
Naples, Italy	1857	12,300
Calabria, Italy	1857	10,000
Mendoza, Argentina	1860	12,000
Peru	1868	20,000
Khorasan, Persia	1871	30,000
San José de Cúcuta, Colombia	1875	16,000
Honshu, Japan	1891	20,000
Kangra, Punjab, India	1905	20,000
Messina, Sicily, and vicinity	1908	164,000
Central Italy	1914	12,000
Central Java	1919	10,000
Kansu, China	1920	200,000
Persia	1923	20,000
Japan	1923	250,000
Kansu, China	1927	100,000
Quetta, India	1935	60,000
Erzingan, Turkey	1939	23,000
Total	....	3,114,300

to the east.   The epicentrum of the earthquake was located in this zone
of weakness.

There have been several earthquakes in the United States within the
last 140 years, but fortunately none has been especially destructive of
life.   At New Madrid, Missouri, shocks began December 16, 1811, and
continued at intervals until March 16, 1812.   During that period, more
than 1,800 shocks of a wide range of intensity were noted.   The disturbance was on the flood plain of the Mississippi River and was accompanied by irregular and local settling of the land and the formation of
several lakes.   Cracks were formed and filled with material from below.

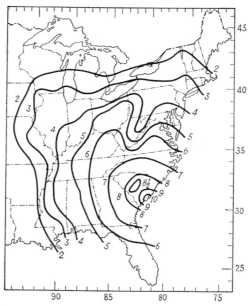

FIG. 315. Map showing immense area in United States affected by earthquake at Charleston, South
Carolina, in 1886.   Numbers indicate intensity of shock (see table, p. 306).

An earthquake occurred at Charleston, South Carolina, on August 31,
1886, the shock of which was felt over an area of 2,000,000 to 3,000,000
square miles (see Fig. 315).   Another earthquake, which was more
destructive of life and property occurred in San Francisco, California,
on April 18, 1906.   It was caused by a horizontal movement along a
fault plane more than 300 miles in length (Fig. 316).   The greatest
damage done was in San Francisco and this damage was primarily due to
fire, as the mains carrying the city's water were severed.

Geological Effects of Earthquakes.   The geological effects of faulting
are often ascribed to earthquakes, but it must be remembered that an
earthquake is only the vibration of the earth resulting from the faulting.

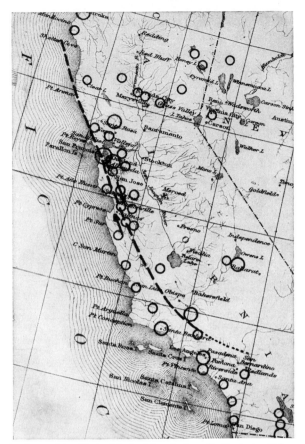

FIG. 316. Map showing position (dashed line) of San Andreas Fault, along which occurred the movement that caused the San Francisco earthquake of 1906. (*Data from various sources.*) Also, approxi-
mate location (circles) of the major earthquakes known to have occurred in California. (*Data from
N. H. Heck, Scientific Monthly, 1930.*)

FIG. 317. Small crater (two days after earthquake) from which sand and salt water were ejected
during earthquake at Great Salt Lake, March, 1934. (*Photograph furnished by Glenn Walter.*)

Some effects of the earth vibrations are that underground drainage is changed, springs being closed at one point and opened at another; and small craters are produced from which water, gases, mud, and sand may be ejected (Fig. 317) or into which sand and mud may be washed. A settling of the ground takes place, also, producing depressed areas, which may later become the sites of lakes, like Reelfoot Lake in Tennessee, formed after the New Madrid earthquake. Vibrations may also start landslides (like those in the loess in China) and so act further in reshaping the features on the surface of the earth.

As we have seen, the immediate results of earthquakes are destructive to man; but it may be that in the long run they are a protection to him, because, as the vibrations relieve stresses and strains in the rocks, the earthquake may be the safety valve that prevents even greater and unimaginable catastrophes.

PART II: HISTORICAL GEOLOGY

CHAPTER 15

HISTORICAL GEOLOGY

INTRODUCTION

In the first part of this volume we have studied the materials of the earth, the forces at work on the inside and outside of the earth, and the features resulting from these forces. These studies might well have been grouped under the headings Chemistry of the Earth and Physics of the Earth, the former including the study of the earth materials, the latter the study of earth forces.

For the most part the illustrations for these earlier studies have been of actual conditions and events that have existed or have taken place during times of recorded human history. Most of them could be duplicated at any time, and might be observed by anyone who would travel to places favorable for their study.

Historical geology, the succession of events through which the earth has passed, is deciphered by applying the facts and principles reached in the study of the chemistry and physics of the earth to the record which past events have left in the earth. It is only by constantly reviewing the present-day variety of conditions and their characteristic effects that the beginner can hope to penetrate the haze obscuring past events and conditions as recorded in the rocks. For instance, we have learned that glaciers are today breaking up rock in a distinctive way and are accumulating the debris in a characteristic manner. If glaciers have existed in past geological times, the deposits formed by them should indicate their glacial origin even though they have been consolidated into beds of rock and deeply buried.

Just as one may study any special phase of human history, various successions of earth events may claim our attention. For the beginner it is desirable to push historical inquiry over the entire field as far back as direct or even indirect evidence extends. No matter how meager this early evidence may be, it affords a background against which later and better-recorded events can be more fully appreciated. As a geologist one may legitimately inquire into earth events as far back as the earth was in any way comparable with the earth today, and attempt to interpret the records preserved in the rocks. Even so far back, there is history recorded: history of the birth and infant stages of the earth. We may never know this story with any degree of certainty but a logical beginning of the story can be set up, a beginning which, though incapable of proof, is entirely in keeping with the details of the part that follows. Every thinking person is interested in the origin of the earth and even in the origin of the universe, but science has no theory for the origin of the universe and the origin of the earth falls within the province of astronomers.

Fossils are the most useful instruments for deciphering earth history. They are remains or impressions of animals and plants preserved in the rocks. A typical way for a fossil to form is by an animal dying where his remains may become covered with mud. The soft parts decay and the hard parts are encased firmly in the mud. If the animal is a clam, the inside of the shell may also fill with mud. Animal remains that have been preserved in recent time are not called "fossils"; the remains must be buried for thousands of years before they become true fossils.

The hard parts of the animal may be replaced slowly by other materials, *i.e.*, become petrified (see page 145). The ordinary replacing materials are calcium carbonate, silica, and iron sulfide. Animals of Pleistocene time have been found frozen in the ice; many insects are preserved in amber (the fossilized gum of plants); and fossil footprints commonly occur in sandstone and shale.

Fossils enable one to classify animals and plants into species and to make differentiations among them on minute characters. Every formation that originated where animals or plants were living is likely to contain fossil remains of them, and they are the geologists' most trustworthy historical material.

CHAPTER 16

ORIGIN OF THE EARTH

Many hypotheses have been formulated to explain the origin of the earth, but only a few have been sufficiently elaborated or supported by broad knowledge of the earth and the heavenly bodies to warrant serious consideration. Of those that do deserve attention, two are outstanding, the nebular and the planetesimal, and they are directly opposed to each other at almost every point. In general these two hypotheses may be thought of as typifying the hot and cold origins, respectively.[1] Modifications and combinations of one or both of these have been elaborated and have ranked as independent hypotheses. Under any of the hypotheses of earth origin, geologic history would not be greatly different from that demanded by the nebular and planetesimal hypotheses.

The Nebular Hypothesis. The first reasonable hypothesis for the origin of the earth was proposed in 1755 by Immanuel Kant, professor at Königsberg. His attempt to account for the rings observed about Saturn led to the conception which, when amplified by others, became the nebular hypothesis. The astronomer Laplace brought to the support of the hypothesis the necessary background of scientific data and was really the first to state clearly the complete series of hypothetical steps leading up to our known solar system. For this reason the nebular is often designated the Laplacian hypothesis.

As the name indicates, the solar system—the earth and the other eight planets, the satellites, asteroids, and the sun itself—originated from a nebulous mass. The hypothesis, as modified to meet later scientific

---

[1] Recent work has greatly favored the theory of hot-earth origin, and it now appears that the geologist must consider that the original earth was a molten body. The more important hypotheses of recent years are:

Gaseous-tidal hypothesis of Jeans and Jeffries (tidal disruption with gaseous filaments)

Binary star hypothesis of Russell and Lyttleton (tidal disruption of a companion star to sun)

Nebular cloud hypothesis of Weizsäcker (sun passes into nebular cloud which condenses into planets)

Nova hypothesis of Hoyle (companion of sun explodes to provide material for planets)

developments, stipulates that originally all the material of the present solar system was combined into a single sphere, which was an extremely

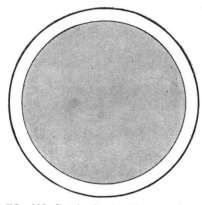

hot, highly tenuous, rotating mass of gases, expanded to a size even greater than the diameter of the orbit of Pluto. If these assumptions are granted, the sphere must have shrunk in size and increased in speed of rotation, and a stage must have followed in which the speed of its equatorial belt was so great that an equatorial ring was left behind as the main mass continued to shrink (Fig. 318). Shrinking and speeding up of the rotating sphere left behind nine rings (Fig. 319). Each of these collected into a rotating sphere, which revolved about the central body in the path of its ring, its present orbit. The remains of the original gaseous sphere is the sun; the rings, modified into nine

FIG. 318. Sketch showing the star from which the solar system originated, at a stage after the first ring had separated from the parent nebula and before the second ring separated. Diameter of the sum at this stage about 5,000,000,000 miles, the size of the orbit of Neptune.

spheres, are the planets. Each of the planets in turn shrank and some left one or more rings revolving about them, which remained, like the rings of Saturn, or consolidated and became satellites, like the moon.

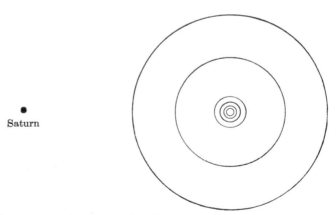

Saturn

FIG. 319. The parent nebula has shrunk from the size shown in Fig. 318 to the size of the orbit of Mercury, the innermost planet. The outer two rings have condensed to globes, Saturn and Pluto (Pluto not shown).

Planet evolution is typified by the changes the earth ring has undergone. In its first stage the earth was a hot gas; the gas condensed to a liquid; a solid crust formed on the outside; and pressure from the weight of the mass caused the center to become solid.   The earth, with a solid center, crust, and liquid or semiliquid zone between, was in the stage in which earliest geologic records might be preserved.   In later development most of the interior solidified.

FIG. 320. A spiral nebula, consisting of a central sun-like mass and spiral arms with knots.   A form similar to this one was postulated for the planetesimal hypothesis as an early stage in the evolution of the solar system.   (R. C. Moore, "Historical Geology," from a Lick Observatory photograph.)

The hypothesis is simple and its implications are clear and satisfying if not too carefully scrutinized.   So many things are now known about the earth and the heavens that were unknown in the days of Laplace that the task of bolstering and modifying the nebular hypothesis has become burdensome.   When modified to fit present knowledge it has lost nearly all of its distinctive features and really deserves an altogether new name.

The Planetesimal Hypothesis.   Astronomers have long been interested in spiral nebulae (Fig. 320) which are assemblages of stars and nebulous matter of unbelievably great size and thousands of light years distant from the earth.

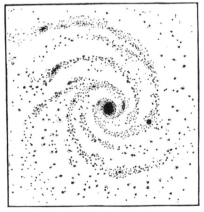

FIG. 321. A stage in the evolution of the solar system when many of the planetesimals have been gathered up by the larger nuclei and some of the nuclei have reached the size of planets.

Early in the twentieth century the geologist Chamberlin and the astronomer Moulton conceived the idea that a small nebula of this type gave origin to the solar system, and they worked out the hypothetical steps leading from a small spiral to a planetary system.

They assumed that spiral nebulae are made of gases and solids and that they formed from the partial wreckage resulting from the close approach of two great stars.   In this type of nebula there is a comparatively dense central mass about which curl two opposed spiral arms (Fig. 321).   Chamberlin and Moulton assumed that the central mass comprises the major portion of the wrecked star, and the arms the remainder.   They assumed also that each particle in the arm, no matter what size, has an individual orbit about the central mass and is following this path at tremendous speed.

If we conceive of the wreckage in the spiral arms as being made up of fragments varying greatly in size, with a few exceptionally large masses composed of either closely associated fragments or a single unit, it is evident that as each unit moves in its orbit it must cross and recross the paths of countless other units.   Where the paths cross there is opportunity for the larger units to grow by overtaking or being overtaken by smaller units.   Ultimately the wreckage would be cleared up and combined into a few bodies (planets chiefly) whose orbits would be too nearly circular to cross one another.   The satellites are details in the clearing-up process—bodies that have come so near a planet as to be controlled by it but retaining sufficient speed of revolution to prevent their being drawn into the planet.

Comparison of the Nebular and Planetesimal Hypotheses.   It is evident that the two hypotheses demand different explanations for the origin of the atmosphere, water, and heat of the earth.   Perhaps a modification of the planetesimal hypothesis made by Jeffries, that the original nuclei of the planets were of planet size in the beginning, should be accepted for some of the planets.[1]   Barrell thought that the infall

---

[1] H. Jeffries, who has been chiefly responsible for modifications of the planetesimal hypothesis, summarizes its 1939 status from his point of view as follows:

"It appears from various lines of investigation that the solar system some thousands of millions of years ago must have departed widely from its present state and that the earth cannot have existed as a separate body for more than about 3,000 million years at the outside.   The sun at that time must have been in nearly its present state. The smaller bodies in the system cannot have been formed by slow condensation from the gaseous state, and the present extension of the system implies a more violent disturbance than any we can suspect from the present state of the sun.   It appears that the breakup of the sun through the tidal action of a passing star can account for many of the features of the system but fails to account for the rotations of the planets.   If, however, the star actually collided with the sun, a cause of rotation is provided, and such a theory gives estimates of the total mass of the planets and the rates of rotation of the sun and planets which agree with the facts.   There is a further difficulty in the collision theory in accounting for the production of enough angular momentum, but this can apparently be avoided on the assumption that the sun was originally a double star and the encounter was not with the sun, but with the companion."

of units in the clearing-up process was sufficient to produce enough heat to fuse most of the infalling material, and that suggestion also seems reasonable.

The early history of the earth under the two hypotheses may be compared as follows:

NEBULAR	PLANETESIMAL
Earth began as a large globe of gas	Earth began as a small aggregate of solid rock, or (Jeffries' modification) as a great mass of sun material
Earth was originally very hot	Earth was cold but developed heat
Earth has always been a cooling body	Earth has usually been a heating body
Earth originally had a very large atmosphere	Earth originally had no atmosphere

The explanations of earth origin are called "hypotheses" because they are proposed explanations—they have not reached the class of "theories." The hypotheses are supported by many facts but may be abandoned with the growth of astronomical knowledge. The planetesimal hypothesis fits geological conditions much better than the nebular. Hypotheses of earth origin are not part of geological science, but they have had profound effects on it.

CHAPTER 17

DAWN OF EARTH HISTORY

As in the case of human history we must begin our study of geologic
history with our earliest evidence, *i.e.*, from the earliest known rocks.   In
order to make a beginning the geologist must determine which rocks are
the oldest.   After he has found ways of distinguishing older rocks from
younger, he should be able to explain the methods to the layman.   In
making the explanation, he would be fortunate could he stand on the brink
of the Grand Canyon of the Colorado River and examine the layers of rock
that make up the canyon walls (see Fig. 322).

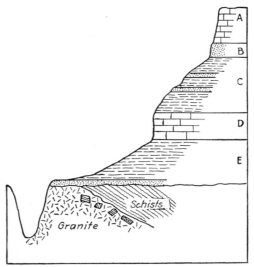

FIG. 322. A section of the mile-high wall of the Grand Canyon of the Colorado River.

Early History of the Rocks in Grand Canyon Wall.   The rocks at
A of Fig. 322, being at the top, must be younger than those at B below.
A must have been deposited on something and the present association
shows that the something was B.   B in turn must have been deposited
on C, which must have been present before B was deposited.   A is
400 feet thick, made up of more than 250 beds, and each higher bed of

A must be younger than the bed on which it rests. The canyon section comprises more than 4,000 feet of sedimentary rocks in which we are able to determine without question which are the older. The lowest sediments rest on an eroded granite surface. Not only had this surface been eroded, but several thousand feet of the granite had been removed by erosion before the sandstones resting on it were deposited.

One may compare the history of Grand Canyon beds and associated structures with that which one might discover by observing an old structure, like the Chinese Wall. That wall has been mended in places—a new wall has been built on the jagged remains of the old one. The method of laying this upper part of the wall is different and the rocks

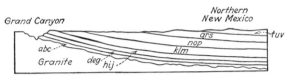

FIG. 323. Section of the rocks eastward for 400 miles from the Grand Canyon. The letters represent the sequence of fossils: a, b, c, the oldest; and t, u, v, the youngest.

used in it are of a different kind. It is evident that the new upper part of the wall is the younger—the old wall had to be there as a foundation of the new. History was in the making between the old and the new. What destroyed the upper part of the old wall? Was it merely the work of the elements or of man? If it were the work of the elements, the time was long, hundreds of years, and the wall itself tells nothing of the history of those hundreds of years. The same is true of the gap in the Grand Canyon wall. For the thousands of feet of granite that were eroded away, the only record is the gap itself.

In studying present-day erosion, it is evident that a rate of 1 foot in 5,000 years is rapid. If we apply the modern rate to the granite removed in the Grand Canyon district, we find that the history of millions of years is recorded only by effects of erosion.

Eastward from the canyon (Fig. 323) other rocks overlap those that form the rim of the canyon. These rocks must be younger than the rim rocks and they are, in turn, succeeded by still younger rocks. One may walk eastward on the bare rocks of the various formations and find that he proceeds constantly from older to younger rocks. They are no longer in one great canyon, but overlap, as one shingle overlaps another (Fig. 323). More than 10,000 feet of these beds appear above the rim rock of the canyon in a distance of 200 miles to the east. No history had been discovered in going over these rocks save that deposition was occurring when they were formed. With a possible average of 1 foot of rock deposited in 4,000 years, one may compute that he is on rocks

40,000,000 years younger than the rim rocks.   To the geologist the outline of the history is clear, but the study has just begun.

Our object being to find a record of earliest geologic history, we must
determine whether the granites in the bottom of the Grand Canyon
are the oldest rocks.   The Colorado River has cut down more than
1,000 feet into the granite since it cut through the overlying sediments.
As the granites were not exposed to weathering before the canyon was
cut in them, the younger rocks above have been exposed to weathering
in the canyon walls longer than the granite and may look older and more
extensively weathered than the granite.   However, we have established
the relative ages of the granite and the overlying rocks and we know that
the top of the granite that forms the eroded surface must be millions of
years older than the sandstones and conglomerates that lie on the eroded
surface.   Is the granite the oldest rock exposed to the observation of
man?   If we could take a trip such as Major Powell made through the
canyon, we might be able to find older rocks in the canyon itself.   Going
up the canyon from Bright Angel Trail, we find that the granite continues
for a hundred miles.   The granite itself furnishes nothing to indicate
age, but at one place we find great masses of gneisses and schists in the
canyon walls and blocks of those rocks in the granite (Fig. 322).   The
granite reached its present association as magma, and, in order to contain
within itself the blocks of schists and gneisses, the granite magma must
have passed through those rocks.   The gneisses and schists were not only
solid rock but were metamorphic rocks before the granite magma
appeared.   As they are much older than the granite, we have traced
geologic history to a time preceding the formation of the granite.

Oldest Rocks Known to Geologists.   The Grand Canyon furnishes
us no older rocks than the gneisses and schists, but if we go to the region
northwest of Lake Superior we shall find the same association of gneisses,
schists, and granites as is found in the Grand Canyon, and in addition
we can prove that some of the schists were derived from shales.   It is
apparent that, before the granites formed in the Lake Superior region,
there were present sedimentary rocks of great extent and thickness
composed of materials derived from the complete chemical weathering
of complex rocks.   Before the granites were intruded, the shales had
undergone regional metamorphism and become schists.   Geologic time,
as represented by the schists, thus goes back millions of years before the
granites were formed, and these schists derived from shales seem to
be the oldest rocks known to geologists.

Fossils in the Grand Canyon Rocks.   The evidences we have thus
far considered in earth history tell us very little of what took place during
early geologic time.   Perhaps we had better return to the Grand Canyon
and get more information.   An examination of the sandstones and con-

glomerates overlying the granite reveals remains of animals in the rocks. The remains are called *fossils*, and consist of shells and impressions of invertebrate animals. The man who knows invertebrates recognizes the shells as those of sea animals. Remains of sea animals have been found at hundreds of places in the Grand Canyon rocks, and no remains of land animals have been found with them. At some places shells of sea animals make up most of the rock. There is, therefore, no doubt that the sediments which formed the rocks were deposited in the sea. After the granites had been eroded for millions of years, ocean waters advanced over the eroded surface. The waters contained many kinds of animals, similar to those which now live in warm waters and unlike those of the colder climates.

In the rim rock of the canyon great numbers of fossils have been found. They, too, lived in warm marine waters, yet all are different from the animals of the lower and older rocks. A complete change in kinds of life had taken place from the time the older rocks were formed to the time the rim rocks were formed. However, there is a genetic relationship between the animals of the two periods and the animals of the higher rocks developed through many changes from those of the lower rocks. None of the animals in the higher rocks is like any modern animal.

Fossils from Younger Rock. In the rocks 200 miles east of the Grand Canyon, which we determined as being separated by 10,000 feet of rock from the canyon rim rock, many fossils occur, and all are different from the rim-rock fossils. All the rim-rock fossils are small, and nearly all are invertebrates. In the rocks to the east (in New Mexico) many of the forms are large, all are nonmarine and are forms that lived in a warm climate. None of them is like modern forms.

Extensive study of fossils has revealed many facts of geologic history and concerning evolution of life, but our present purpose is to examine the facts that help to determine the history of the earth. We can formulate from history preserved in the Grand Canyon region part of the geologic history of the world. Geologists have determined the history of the earth by visiting almost all accessible regions and by studying the geology of those regions in detail. The area in which you are at present has had years of study by geologists, and many articles have been written about its geology.

Eras. Geologic history is long, and in order to make it readily understandable geologists have divided the time into five great divisions (the eras) and into subdivisions of these (the periods). The eras are delimited by great breaks in physical history and great changes in animal and plant life. Each is terminated by broad uplifts of the land and by mountain making. The names of the eras are descriptive of the stage of development of the fossils in the rocks of each. The divisions of geologic time

Eras	Periods	Events	Life
Cenozoic	Cenozoic	Glaciation	Rise of man. Extinction of primitive types of mammals. Development of modern kinds of mammals
		Rocky Mts. and other Western mountains Great lava flows	Appearance of primitive man. Modern plants throughout the Cenozoic. Appearance of modern species of mollusks. Beginning of modern types of mammals
Mesozoic	Cretaceous	Rocky Mts.	Culmination of reptiles. Culmination of complex sutured cephalopods in America. Great abundance of clams, particularly of the oyster type. Appearance of flowering plants
	Jurassic	Sierra Nevada Mts.	Great development of many kinds of reptiles. First appearance of birds. Mammals small and rare. Culmination of complex sutured cephalopods in Europe
	Triassic	Aridity Volcanism	Appearance of dinosaurs, flying reptiles, swimming reptiles, and mammals. Rise of complex-sutured cephalopods
Paleozoic	Permian	Glaciation Appalachian Mts. Aridity	Development of many kinds of strange reptiles. Disappearance of trilobites. Great reduction in life in the later part of the period
	Pennsylvanian		The first reptiles and insects. Culmination of Paleozoic plants
	Mississippian		Great development of sharks and crinoids. Plants become abundant
	Devonian		Development of fishes with rise of all main groups. Development of paired limbs. First forests. First amphibians. Old-age characteristics in trilobites
	Silurian	Aridity	Appearance of scorpions, air breathers. Fishes rare. Crinoids important. First coral reefs
	Ordovician	Taconic Mts.	Rise of cephalopods. Appearance of fishes
	Cambrian		Trilobites and brachiopods dominant. First abundant fossils
Proterozoic		Glaciation Volcanism	Some fossils, but all poorly preserved and most of them nondeterminable. Algae the most common form of life
Archeozoic		Volcanism	No fossils, but some indications of life

FIG. 324. A table showing geological eras, periods, main physical events, and some of the more important life events.

are listed in order, the youngest at the top to the oldest at the bottom in Fig. 324.

PRE-CAMBRIAN ARCHEOZOIC AND PROTEROZOIC

The rocks of the older eras are much altered, and fossils are rare. Since their history is difficult to determine accurately, the Proterozoic and Archeozoic will be treated together and called *pre-Cambrian* as coming before the oldest period (Cambrian) of the Paleozoic.

Wherever the base of the sedimentary series of rocks is accessible, it rests on metamorphic or igneous rocks. We have studied such contacts near the bottom of the Grand Canyon and they have been studied in thousands of places. The old igneous and metamorphic rocks are at the surface over nearly one-fifth of the land. (Consult your geologic map for the areas of outcrop of pre-Cambrian rocks (Fig. 325).) The area of such rocks in the Great Lakes-Hudson Bay region is the largest in the world; the one east of the Appalachian Mountains is important in size. Nearly every chain of the Rocky Mountains has a core of pre-Cambrian igneous or metamorphic rock (Fig. 326). In several places in the Mississippi Valley, the metamorphic and igneous rocks protrude through the younger sedimentary rocks, for example, in the Ozark region of southeastern Missouri and in the Arbuckle Mountains of Oklahoma.

If you go to the top of Pikes Peak (probably the best-known peak in the United States) you will find it made up of pre-Cambrian igneous rocks, but if you go to Mount Rainier (probably the most imposing mountain in the United States) you will find igneous rocks of recent date. If you cross the United States from Boston to Los Angeles through Albany, Cleveland, Chicago, Kansas City, Pueblo, Albuquerque, and Needles, you will see no pre-Cambrian rocks west of Albany, except in three or four small areas in New Mexico and Arizona. Many of the great mountains of the other continents have pre-Cambrian rocks exposed at their summits.

Kinds of Pre-Cambrian Rocks. A collection of Archeozoic rocks from almost any large area would include hundreds of varieties of igneous and metamorphic rocks, but no limestones, shales, sandstones, or any other kinds of sedimentary rocks. In the Proterozoic, sedimentary rocks dominate but igneous rocks form a larger proportion of the whole than in any later era.

Economic Products of the Pre-Cambrian. In Chap. 3, the origin of several types of ore deposits is discussed and the importance of igneous intrusions in inducing them is mentioned. The pre-Cambrian is the most important part of the geologic column for metalliferous deposits.

Iron. Iron is the most important metal to man, and the pre-Cambrian rocks furnish more than half of the iron used in the world. The largest

FIG. 325. Pre-Cambrian outcrops (in black).   (*Outcrop areas modified from Willis.*)

deposits of iron ore in North America are in the Lake Superior region, and they are pre-Cambrian in age. The mines of Minnesota and Michigan furnish about 80 per cent of the yearly output of iron ore in the United States, and about 20 per cent of the yearly output of the world is mined in this country. The ore mineral is hematite (Fe_2O_3), consisting of 70 per cent iron and 30 per cent oxygen. The ore mined is about 70 per cent hematite and 30 per cent rock; the actual yield of metallic iron is about 51 per cent of the material mined. Some of the important Minnesota deposits are mined in open pits and steam shovels are used to take out the ore.

FIG. 326. Section of a mountain, showing pre-Cambrian rocks of the core at the summit.

As far as geologists have been able to determine, the deposits originated from hot waters coming from lavas. Highly charged with silica and iron, the waters entered interior seas that existed in the Lake Superior region, and the iron and silica were precipitated to form extensive siliceous beds rich in iron minerals. In later periods these beds were folded, and subsequent erosion created many hogbacks, which are designated as "ranges." The iron content of the original rock was not more than 25 per cent; but, after the folding, ground waters, in circulating through the rocks, dissolved silica and left iron until the hematite content was 40 to 70 per cent. The ore deposits left after the solution and removal of the silica are irregular in outline, with thick masses of ore in some places and little or none in others. The best of the deposits underlie only a few square miles.

The great iron-ore bodies of Brazil, probably larger than those of the Lake Superior region, are pre-Cambrian in age, as are also the iron ores of Sweden, New York, Labrador, and several other parts of the world.

Copper. The pre-Cambrian rocks of the Lake Superior region contain some of the richest copper ores in the world. For a long time the copper mines of the Lake Superior region of Michigan produced more copper than those of any other region in the world—nearly half of the world production. The districts of Butte, Montana, and Bingham, Utah, have surpassed it in recent years, and each of three districts in Arizona has produced more in some years. The ore mineral in the Lake Superior region is native copper; this is the only region in the world where native copper is present in large quantities.

The copper occurs in three ways. Most of it is in cavities in pre-

Cambrian basalt; some forms a cement in conglomerates; and a small portion occurs in veins.

Before the use of modern methods in mining, some of the largest masses of copper were mined with difficulty, as it cost more to break up such large pieces than to blast out masses of rock small enough to be handled.

Gold. In recent years much gold has been mined from pre-Cambrian rocks in the Porcupine and Kirkland Lake districts of Ontario. The greatest gold mines in the world are in pre-Cambrian rocks in the Rand, South Africa. Gold is mined from the pre-Cambrian of the Black Hills and many other places.

Other Products. Nickel and cobalt are important metals that are mined from the pre-Cambrian rocks of Ontario, and asbestos and granite are produced mainly from pre-Cambrian rocks.

Close of Archeozoic. The Archeozoic era was brought to a close by continental uplift and mountain making. Great batholithic intrusions invaded and uplifted the older sediments and igneous rocks, accentuating the metamorphism of many of them. The North American intrusions and mountains extended from the Great Lakes region northeastward. The Adirondacks were a small part of the mountainous area.

A period of erosion during which the uplands and mountains were peneplaned preceded the opening of the Proterozoic. This seems to have been the longest period of erosion of geologic history. The reduction to a peneplain of mountains 2 to 3 miles high composed of igneous and metamorphic rocks must have taken many millions of years. Where the Proterozoic seas came in over the peneplain, they deposited sediments on the truncated mountain cores.

Close of the Proterozoic. The Proterozoic closed with continental uplift and mountain making. Some of the mountains were in the Lake Superior region, and others in several regions of the world. Batholithic intrusions were on a much smaller scale than in the Archeozoic. In many places erosion reduced the lands to peneplains before the incoming of Paleozoic seas.

Metamorphic rocks that were derived from sediments are abundant in the pre-Cambrian, and sedimentation at that time was much as it is now. There is no evidence to show that the climate of the pre-Cambrian was greatly different from that of the present, but weathering may not have been so complete, owing to the absence of land plants. We know slates and schists that must have come from shales, and the shales from clays; quartzites that came from sandstones; and marbles that came from limestones.

It is clear that igneous activity was much greater during pre-Cambrian times than it has been since, and that earth movements, which, together with volcanism, produced the metamorphism, were on a larger scale. The pre-Cambrian was a time of dominant volcanism.

Life of the Pre-Cambrian. In late pre-Cambrian, impressions of simple types of plants (algae related to the pond scums that are common at present) are preserved in the rocks. Algae were abundant in some places, but their impressions are faint and obscure. Probably no plants existed on the lands.

Impressions and fragments of a few kinds of very primitive animals appear in late pre-Cambrian rocks. All of them lived in water, and they appear to have been rare. The highest type of life was much simpler than the modern crawfish, and probably most of the forms belonged to the Protozoa (one-celled animals). The ameba, which is widely distributed in pond waters, is the best modern example of primitive life. It consists of one cell and resembles a droplet of oil, but has the power of moving very slowly, taking in and assimilating food, and reproducing its kind. Animals like the ameba lack coherence enough to make any impression on soft muds and they could not leave fossil remains. Probably types of life like the ameba lived for millions of years before anything higher developed and no trace of them will ever be found in the rocks.

For a long time pre-Cambrian rocks were known as *Azoic* or "without life"; the first traces of life were found in them only a few years ago. Here are the oldest records of life (the beginnings of life history) that may be read. The amount of unmetamorphosed pre-Cambrian rocks is small, and metamorphic processes destroyed most evidences of life. Even in the unaltered rocks, however, fossils are so obscure and rare that few have been found.

Pre-Cambrian life seems to have existed in swampy areas near the sea margins. The strictly marine rocks rarely contain fossils, and it is scarcely conceivable that the primitive life could have existed on land.

Plants must have originated before animals, as animals depend entirely on plants for their food. Animals do not have the power to get their food directly from mineral matter as plants do.

Earth's Surface in the Pre-Cambrian. At the dawn of geologic history the earth must have been an uninviting place. The entire surface was made up of rocks unrelieved by colors of plants. The surface was more jagged than in recent times, for plants help to weather off the edges of rocks and their presence tends to soften the appearance of irregularity. The lands must have been strangely silent, with no animal present to make its own peculiar noise.

The presence of active volcanoes and other types of volcanism at many places gave to the earth an aspect out of keeping with present-day conditions. It should not be supposed that the earth was hot owing to the volcanism, or that volcanism was prevalent over the entire earth at

the same time.   Volcanism may have been absent from areas as large
as the United States for tens of millions of years.

Climate of Pre-Cambrian.   At some periods of the pre-Cambrian,
the climatic conditions were more rigorous than in recent times.   Late
in the pre-Cambrian a continental glacier had its southern margin not
far north of the Great Lakes region.   Its east-west extent was more
than 1,000 miles.   The deposits made by the glaciers are now solid rock,
in places hundreds of feet thick.   The deposits are very irregular in
thickness and are composed of boulders, pebbles, sand, silt, and clay.
Many of the boulders have flat surfaces and some of the flat surfaces
bear scratches.   These evidences of glacial origin are not so clear as
those in the late glacial deposits but they are convincing to geologists.

Duration of Pre-Cambrian.   The length of pre-Cambrian time seems
to have been nearly 1,500,000,000 years.   The best geological clock is the
one supplied by the chemist, who has been able to compute the rate of
change of atoms of radioactive minerals to atoms of lead.   In this way,
it has been determined that some Archeozoic rocks were formed more than
2,000,000,000 years ago, and these are by no means the oldest rocks
known.

CHAPTER 18

THE PALEOZOIC ERA

In sharp contrast to those of the pre-Cambrian, the rocks of the Paleozoic era are normally not metamorphosed and they contain abundant fossils. The era is divided into seven time units which are called periods. For convenience in our study of them, we shall divide the era into Lower, Middle, and Upper Paleozoic. The oldest part, the Lower Paleozoic, consists of the Cambrian and Ordovician periods.

Although we shall not study all the periods individually, we should know the principles upon which the period boundaries are based. Many times in geologic history seas have advanced over the continents, and as they advanced, the waters worked over the mantle rock, the sediments brought in by streams, and the material eroded from the shores. These materials were sorted and were deposited to form various kinds of sedimentary rock. The sea advance constituted the first event of the period, and the sediments deposited by the advancing sea became rocks which are the evidence of the new period.

Why Seas Advance. The seas would not advance if land and sea bottom remained unchanged. A large upwarping of the sea bottom without a corresponding downwarping of some other part of it would cause general sea advance over the lowlands. Such a major upwarping, following a time during which the shore line had been relatively stationary, would cause a significant physical change of the earth's surface.

Erosion is taking place on part of the land surface all of the time, and it tends to lower the surface and thus facilitates sea advances. In mature stages of erosion, sea advances would take place only in marginal valleys, but in old stages the advance would be general. If the lands had been peneplaned, monadnocks might stand out as islands in the advancing sea. The piling up of the eroded material in the sea would raise the sea level very slowly. As the general rate of erosion is, perhaps, 1 foot in 9,000 or 10,000 years, the rise of sea level would be about 1 foot in 30,000 years. This may seem too slow to be of any significance but the total effect from erosion and deposition would be 4 feet in 30,000 years, 3 feet of down-cutting and 1 foot of sea rise. Some of the periods are 50,000,000

or more years in length.   The general elevation of the North American
continent is about 2,200 feet.   At the ordinary rate of cutting down and
sea advance the entire continent would be covered in about 15,000,000
years.   However, such a rate could not be maintained.   We have only
to recall the principles on which the rate of downcutting by streams
depends to realize that the lower the land becomes the slower is the rate of
erosion.   As more land is covered by the sea, less material is furnished
to the sea by erosion, and, therefore, the rise of sea level is slower.   The
last few hundred feet of the downcutting of the continent would be almost
inconceivably slow and would take a great deal longer than all of the
other downcutting.

Probably the most significant factor in causing an advance of sea on
the land is the downwarping of the land itself.   Such downwarping is
generally slow, but not so slow as the rise of the sea due to sedimentation.
Where the sea advances and spreads out over large areas of land, the
cause of the sea advance must be land warping.

If it were not for upwarping of the land or downwarping of the sea
bottom, the land would long since have disappeared.   After the seas
had remained on the land millions of years, some of or all the physical
changes that caused the sea advance might be reversed, and, consequently, the seas would begin to retreat.   Their withdrawal might be
as slow as their advance or might be fairly rapid, geologically speaking.
(By "geologically speaking" we mean that the time units should be
considered in the light of geologic rather than human history.   A year
in human experience is comparable to a million years of geologic time.)

A period closed when the sea had withdrawn into the ocean basins.
Further deposition was in places that are now inaccessible to the geologist.   The rocks of a period are those laid down in the seas from the
beginning of one major advance to the end of the succeeding major
retreat.   Some quibbling and disagreement might arise as to what is
meant by "major advance" and "major retreat," but as elementary
students we are not concerned with closer discriminations than these.

Methods of Identifying Sea Advances.   Questions arise as to how
geologists can determine whether rocks belong to one major advance or
another, to one period or another, how they know when the sea retreated
or when it advanced.   Most of these subjects have already been treated
in the work on physical geology, but they will be emphasized as we proceed
with the historical part.   We have considered the nature of unconformities without considering their significance.   According to definition an
unconformity is a relationship between two rocks in which the underlying
rock had been eroded before the bed overlying it was laid down.   Of
course, the overlying sediments fit into the irregularities of those beneath,
and the line of demarcation between the two rocks is easily made out

if they are well exposed. If, then, in the field, you should find a decided unconformity between two series of rocks, both of which were marine in origin, you would consider that the lower rocks had been formed in a sea that withdrew and allowed streams or some other agents to erode the surface, and that the seas then advanced over the eroded surface and laid down sediments that formed new rocks on that surface. Would that be the line of boundary between two periods? Where students go into regions made up of pre-Paleozoic rocks, they find them largely composed of igneous and metamorphic types. Suppose you should go into such a region and on top of the pre-Paleozoic rocks find a conglomerate made up of boulders and pebbles of those rocks, the materials fairly well sorted into uniform sizes and into definite beds (Fig. 296). Suppose you should find in the conglomerates some fossil shells of sea animals. (Although fossils are not common in conglomerates they do occur in some places.) In order to get the boulders and pebbles of the underlying rock, that rock had to be eroded, and very little erosion occurs except above water. Erosion that involves weathering takes place only where the rocks are exposed to the atmosphere. The pre-Paleozoic rocks, therefore, had been eroded before the conglomerates were formed on top of them. Since the conglomerates consist of fairly well sorted materials, they must have been formed in a large body of water as glaciers cannot sort materials. As the rocks contain marine fossils, the large body of water must have been part of the sea. You have, therefore, evidence of erosion of the pre-Paleozoic, and a sea advance over that pre-Paleozoic. The conglomerate constitutes the oldest rock of a period.

LOWER PALEOZOIC, CAMBRIAN PERIOD

In early studies of the geology of eastern North America, investigators found that the oldest rocks of the Appalachian Mountain region are conglomerates of the type described as having been laid down on pre-Paleozoic metamorphic rocks. This indicated that, early in Paleozoic time, seas had advanced over the region that is now the Appalachian Mountains (Fig. 327). Above the conglomerates are sandstones, shales, and some limestones, in a series ranging from a few hundred to thousands of feet in thickness (Fig. 330b). Another great unconformity at the top of the series indicates withdrawal of the sea and erosion of the rocks of that series. The conglomerates, sandstones, and shales can be traced the entire length of the Appalachian Mountain region, but laterally their extent is small, about the width of the Appalachian Mountains. Their original position and relationship to the underlying rocks are shown in Fig. 329. It is evident that the underlying rocks were bowed down into a syncline and that the conglomerates, sandstones, and shales were deposited in the syncline. The syncline has now come to be known as the "Appalachian Geosyncline," more commonly as the "Appalachian Trough." At one time it was difficult to convince even students who knew something of geology that the Appalachian Mountain region had been the site of arms of the sea, but the outlines of the geosyncline have

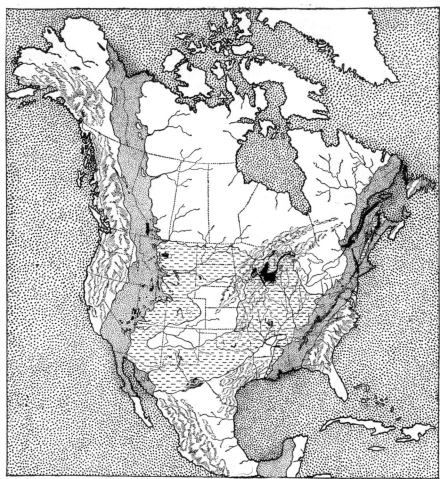

FIG. 327. Cambrian seas. Early Cambrian seas in Appalachian and Cordilleran geosynclines stippled. Upper Cambrian seas covered the dashed and stippled areas. Cambrian outcrops in black. The mountain areas shown were present in Lower Cambrian, but those in the interior had been eroded away by Upper Cambrian and the seas advanced over their eroded roots. (*Modified from Schuchert.*)

been traced in detail from Alabama to the Gulf of St. Lawrence and the events that led to the formation of the rocks described below have been interpreted as follows.

Sedimentation in Advancing Seas. In late pre-Cambrian time a long period of erosion was followed by the beginning of the downwarping of

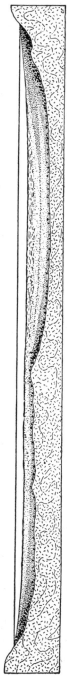

FIG. 328. Cross-section of the Appalachian Trough showing original position of early Cambrian sediments and their relationship to the pre-Cambrian rocks.

FIG. 329. The Upper Cambrian sea spread westward from the trough shown in Fig. 328 and the area of sedimentation increased. The coarse sediments and sands at the left are younger than those at the bottom of the original trough and higher layers of sediment are being deposited in the trough.

the Appalachian Trough.   As the area warped downward it came to be occupied by the major stream of the region, with minor streams coming from the sides, so that sediments from a very large area came into it.   At some period the ends were warped low enough so that the seas began to advance into the trough, and as they advanced they were furnished sediments by the great river that occupied the trough.   In addition their waves reworked the alluvial fans and flood-plain deposits that were already there.   In the shallow waters near shore, waves worked down to the solid rock; if the wave work was sufficiently vigorous sand, silt, and clay were carried away and pebbles and larger pieces of rock were left on the sea bottom.   As the seas advanced farther and the pebbles that had been deposited were in deeper water, sand was deposited over the pebbles.   Later, when the seas had advanced so that the shore line was hundreds of miles away and the sea was deep enough so that the storm waves did not strike the bottom, clays were deposited over the sands. In still later stages, with failure of even the finest of sediments to reach the region, limestones were deposited over the shales.

Alternation of Sediments.   We might say that in a normal section of rock formed in an advancing sea there should be conglomerates below, succeeded by sandstones, then by shales, and finally by limestones.   But such a succession rarely, if ever, occurs, for the progress of the sea is not uniform and during the general advance there are minor retreats.   Stream flow varies greatly, stages of low water are succeeded by floods, and the entering streams carrying sediments change their courses.   All of this has been treated in the chapter on Running Water, but we may consider a concrete example in the oldest Paleozoic sea.   The shore line had advanced far enough that sands were being deposited over the pebbles when a great storm with very strong waves rolled pebbles out over the sand and sand was again deposited over the pebbles as soon as the storm subsided.   The shore line kept moving away from this place, but after a few years another great storm brought pebbles.   This time, as the shore line was farther away, the pebbles were smaller.   The lower rocks formed in an advancing sea instead of consisting, then, entirely of pebbles are likely to be made up of alternating beds of sand and pebbles.

The same kind of variation took place when clays began to be deposited above sands.   Clays had been laid down to a thickness of 2 or 3 feet when a particularly great flood of some river entering the sea brought in much more sand with a much stronger current than usual, and a few inches of sand were deposited above the clay.   After the flood, when normal conditions returned, clay was again deposited above the sand.   Years later, an unusually great storm stirred up the bottom and moved sand beyond the ordinary limit, so that sand again, temporarily, succeeded clay.   Finally, when the shore line was far enough away, calcareous muds were deposited above the clays.

Once a great river changed its course and entered the sea near the place where the calcareous muds were being deposited. It carried a great deal of sediment, and clay was again deposited above the calcareous materials. The river again changed its course and entered the sea so far away that no clays reached the area of deposition.

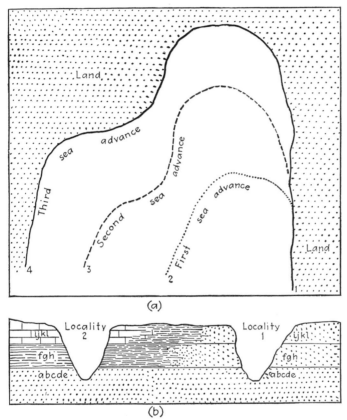

FIG. 330. (a) Map showing changing shore lines during part of the sea advance into the Appalachian Trough. (b) Section to show relationships of rocks and life near localities 1 and 2 of a. In the shallow water near 1 the deposits are sand and gravel. In the deeper water at 2 the sands grade into clays and the clays into lime as the seas advanced.

The above example merely shows possibilities. Unusual storms and floods may come in periods of a few years to a few thousand years, but the change in the river would be much less frequent. The change of the Hwang Ho River, as discussed on page 121, is an example of this. Alteration of different kinds of sediments is the rule rather than the exception in all changes from one type of sediment to another (Fig. 330).

To go back to these first deposits on the pre-Paleozoic rocks that were formed by the sea advancing in the geosyncline, we find that the lowest deposits were alternating conglomerates and sandstones, followed, in order, by sandstones, alternating shales and sandstones, shales, alternating limestones and shales, and, finally, limestone.

But even this succession is very much generalized and ideal rather than actual, as in some places the sedimentation did not go beyond the sandstone stage, and in others did not reach the limestone stage, before changes came that altered the entire order of deposition. In Fig. 330, let us assume that the point designated as "1" is a place where sand was being deposited near shore. The sea advanced up the trough so that the margin was finally hundreds of miles from 1 but the lateral margin of the sea stayed near this spot and sands were carried out to it as long as the sea remained over the area, or until the near-lying land was cut so low that it no longer furnished sand. Point 2 was far enough from shore to receive the normal succession, and though at point 1 sandstones formed all of the time after the first conglomerates, at 2, sandstones were succeeded by shales and shales, in turn, by limestones.

The limestones and shales at 2 might be of the same age as the sandstones at 1. How then could the geologist, by examining sections at 1 and 2 (of *b* in Fig. 330) where a stream had cut through, determine the relative ages of the rocks in the two places?

Use of Fossils. Suppose that while the first sandstone was forming at 1 of Fig. 330 species of animals lived that we may designate by the letters *a*, *b*, *c*, *d*, *e*, and that the same species lived in the sea at 2. By the time the sea had advanced to 3, however, life at 2, as well as at 1, and throughout all of the sea of that time in the trough, had changed decidedly. The species living in this sea were *f*, *g*, *h*. When the seas had advanced to 4, limestones became the dominant rock at 2, and life had again changed so that the main forms were *i*, *j*, *k*, *l*. This would be true also of 1 where sandstone was still forming, and the relative ages of the rocks could be readily determined by their fossils and the kind of rock would have no significance.

Source of Sediments. The sediments that were deposited in the trough were all derived from igneous and metamorphic rocks. The igneous rocks were granites, basalts, diorites, gabbros, and felsites, and the metamorphic rocks were mainly gneisses, schists, and slates. The weathering of these old rocks appears to have been rather complete, as the rocks forming from the weathered materials are mainly shales and limestones.

Further Spread of Cambrian Seas. The margins of the oldest Paleozoic rocks are on the east and west sides of the Appalachian Mountains, and it is inferred from this that the seas in eastern North America occupied only the Appalachian Trough (Fig. 327) during most of the oldest period of the Paleozoic. However, there were many minor oscillations of the sea in the trough and they even withdrew almost completely during one part of the Cambrian.   Before the close of this period the lands west of the trough became so low that the seas spread over them and a sandstone was deposited over wide areas in the central part of North America. The seas finally spread westward through the interior and the Rocky Mountain region and joined with another great geosynclinal sea near the Pacific (see upper Cambrian sea margins on Fig. 327).

The Cordilleran Geosyncline. At about the same time that the Appalachian Geosyncline was forming, an even larger geosyncline formed from the Arctic Ocean nearly to the Gulf of Lower California.   It was roughly parallel to the Pacific Coast.   The history of this geosyncline during the first period of the Paleozoic was much the same as that of the Appalachian Geosyncline, although the sediments deposited were thicker and more nearly continuous than those in the east.   At nearly the same time that the seas spread west from the Appalachian region, they spread east from the western geosyncline and finally covered nearly half of the North American continent.   In the early stages of this widespread sea, the sediments were mainly sands, silts, and clays, but in the later stages so little land was exposed that only a small amount of clastic material came into the seas and the deposits were formed mainly from material in solution.

The Close of the Cambrian. The earliest Paleozoic period represents a time of little movement of the continental masses.   After the seas had remained over the continent for perhaps 40,000,000 or 50,000,000 years, they withdrew from the western area, the Appalachian Trough, and the interior, leaving only minor epicontinental seas on the land.   This withdrawal constituted the close of the period.   There was no mountain making of importance and no igneous activity.

LOWER PALEOZOIC, ORDOVICIAN PERIOD

During the second period of the Paleozoic, the seas advanced again through the Appalachian Trough (as in their first invasion of the continent), but they soon spread with many minor oscillations into the interior and to the Cordilleran Trough.   Finally, they covered about 60 per cent of the continent, constituting the widest spread of continental seas during all geologic time in North America (Fig. 331).   At their maximum extent, they were still oscillatory and retreated widely, only to advance again over about the same area.   The period closed with a widespread withdrawal and extensive mountain folding in western New England and eastern New York, usually designated as the "Taconic uplift."   The time of formation of the mountains is fixed, because rocks of the second period are greatly folded and eroded and those of the next period were deposited horizontally over the tilted beds (Fig. 332).

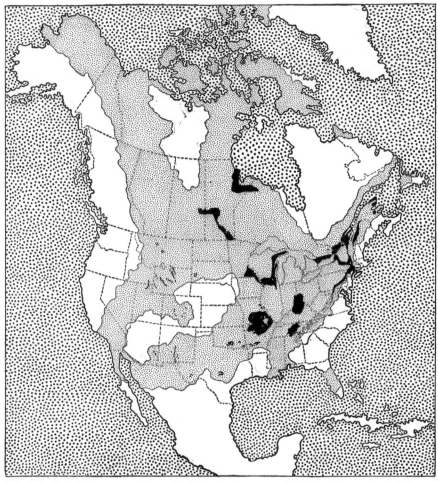

FIG. 331. Ordovician seas and outcrops. Fine stipple represents Middle Ordovician epicontinental seas. Ordovician outcrops in black. (*Seas modified from Schuchert.*)

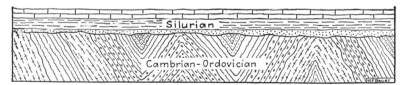

FIG. 332. Relationship of Cambrian and Ordovician rocks to Silurian rocks where the older beds were folded and peneplaned before the Silurian sea advanced.

LIFE OF CAMBRIAN

Records of life before the Paleozoic are very scarce, although as stated before, several kinds of fossils have been found. The rocks of the first Paleozoic period are sometimes characterized as the oldest rocks bearing fossils in abundance. As the seas came into the Appalachian and Cordilleran troughs, they brought with them many kinds of animals that had developed since the time of formation of the youngest known pre-Paleozoic rocks. The life that came in was unlike the life of the present. The most striking absentees were the animals that now dominate the earth, *i.e.*, the vertebrates or backboned animals. This is the group to which fishes, crocodiles, birds, horses, elephants, man, and nearly all of the large animals belong. Notwithstanding the absence of the vertebrates, the animals, as a whole, were well on their way toward the highest organization. Probably nine-tenths of all basic organic structures in animals had appeared by the beginning of the Paleozoic period.

Trilobites and Brachiopods. Two types of animals, trilobites and brachiopods (Figs. 333, 334, and 335), which were abundant throughout most of the Paleozoic, dominated the oldest Paleozoic seas. The trilobites were remotely related to the modern lobsters and crawfishes. Brachiopods had two shells, roughly resembling clam shells, although the two animals are not closely related. About 73 per cent of the animals in the first Paleozoic sea were brachiopods and trilobites. If you should find a rock in which brachiopods and trilobites are the main fossils and other fossils are rare, you might, with a considerable degree of confidence, but not with certainty, identify this piece of rock as having come from the oldest Paleozoic period.

Lower Paleozoic Stage of Development. Although evolution was far advanced in the early Cambrian, the life forms were young and almost all of the orders were still to be evolved. One of the laws of evolution that is probably invariable is that youthful forms change rapidly, whereas old-age forms change slowly. No old-age form, moreover, seems ever to have given rise to anything radically different from itself. The Cambrian forms were youthful, and changes went on rapidly. For example, with the first seas there seem to have come in not more than 25 species of trilobites, but more than 1,000 species had appeared before the close of the period. On an average, each species produced 40 new ones. You may visualize this by imagining 40 kinds of birds, such as crows, hawks, ducks, geese, and sparrows, developing from one kind of bird. It might be assumed that this is very rapid evolution, but the matter deserves a little further consideration. How long was the Cambrian period? If we say 50,000,000 years, the evolution takes on quite a different aspect, and the changes may have been very slow, even imperceptible, through periods many times as long as historical time.

FIG. 333. Brachiopods, trilobites, and a jellyfish in a Cambrian sea.

By studying Fig. 336, we may trace the evolution of one species into the many that it produced. One species came in with the first seas of the period and minute changes gradually accumulated until the original species was no longer recognizable, but two species, both slightly different from the original and from each other, had arisen. At this stage, at the end of 10,000,000 years, three species had existed. In the next 10,000,000 years, each of the two new species formed two others, so that four species were living at the end of 20,000,000 years and three had died out. In the next 10,000,000 years, each of the four gave rise to two more, so that at the end of 30,000,000 years eight species were living and seven had died out. At this rate of evolution 63 species would have evolved in 50,000,000 years,

FIG. 334. Cambrian trilobites. (After Walcott.)

of which 32 species would be living and 31 would have died out. No such regularity of evolution or results could be expected or would ever occur,

FIG. 335. Cambrian brachiopods. (After Walcott.)

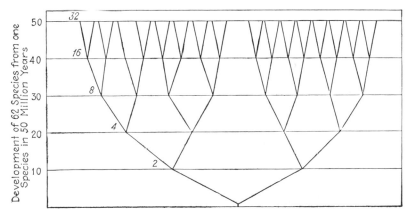

FIG. 336. Development of 61 species from one species in 50,000,000 years. The diagram represents a possible pattern in a case where two species develop from one each 10,000,000 years.

as chance plays a very large part in evolution, and though some species might give rise to many, others gave rise to none. The emphasis here is on the slowness of the process.

Students unfamiliar with the various proofs of the length of geologic time are likely to think that investigators of living animals should be able to notice permanent evolutionary changes, but the geologist does not consider that likely, as all changes that he has been able to trace in the geologic past have been exceedingly slow in terms of historical time.

Effects of Change of Environment. The youthful forms coming into the early Paleozoic seas had other factors than youth in favor of rapid evolution. As the seas spread over the continents, opportunities for rapid changes in environment were created. The animals had been living in shallow water near the shore, and the spreading seas may have forced them into water that was deeper or shallower, muddier or clearer, fresher or saltier, quieter or more agitated, cooler or warmer. Any one of these changes might favor individuals with some particular modification, or it might destroy the animal. The spreading, at any time, or even the shrinking of the seas forces modification of habitat and, consequently, favors certain characteristics of the animal at the expense of others.

The withdrawal of the seas at the close of the first period probably caused the extermination of many species that, having become accustomed to certain living conditions, could not adjust themselves rapidly enough to the new ones forced upon them. A graphic example may serve to illustrate this. Suppose the waters should begin to rise on the present North American continent until all lands lower than 8,000 feet were submerged. You may well imagine what would happen to many species of animals now living on the continent. The land above 8,000 feet high is all in the Rocky Mountain region and the high mountains near the Pacific Coast. All of the land animals would be forced into an area no larger than the state of California. That area could not produce enough food for the 190,000,000 people of North America, and unless food could be brought in from the outside the human population would have to decrease. Those species of animals that could not be used for food probably would be exterminated and those species of plants that were not in some way directly useful to man would be killed off. In the process of change, animals not infrequently adopt a new habitat as distinctly different as are air and water. This time would be particularly favorable for such adjustment, and some species would be likely to adapt themselves to living in the sea. No rapid adjustments would be required but very great changes would be necessary before the adaptations were complete, and the animals' regular habitat became water.

Absence of Land Life in Cambrian. No land life of the earliest Paleozoic period is known, or, if there were such, it did not leave fossils. With no plants or animals present, the land was just barren rock. Without the protection from eroding agents afforded by a covering of plants, the details of erosion must have been somewhat different from now.

Absence of Vertebrates. In the rocks of the Cambrian period no bone has been found, and if animals with bones had been present geologists would almost certainly have discovered their remains. The internal skeleton remained, then, as a great organic structure still to be developed.

LIFE OF THE ORDOVICIAN

In the second period, which is the upper part of the Lower Paleozoic, some forms of life were decidedly different from those in the first period. The restriction of the areas of shallow seas had caused great modifications

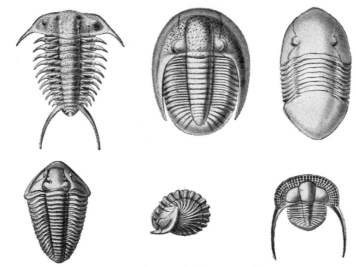

FIG. 337. Ordovician trilobites. (*From Cleland, courtesy of American Book Company.*)

FIG. 338. Ordovician brachiopods. (*From Paleontology of New York.*)

in animals and the disappearance of great numbers of species. The readvance of the sea gave opportunity for remaining forms to develop and expand and for new species to originate. Not only did new species in great numbers come in (probably more than 6,000 being known from the second period) but not more than 10 or 15 of the more than 2,000 species of the Cambrian lived over into Ordovician. New classes of animals appeared and some of these became as abundant as the brachiopods and trilobites, in spite of the fact that trilobites and brachiopods (Figs. 337 and 338) were more numerous than they had been in the Cambrian.

Cephalopods.   We need pay attention to only a few of the new classes. One of these is the cephalopods, of which the pearly nautilus and the octopus are modern forms.   This class was represented only by small individuals in the first part of the period, but in the second part the class included the largest and most powerful of the earth's inhabitants.   The earliest cephalopods had small conelike shells; and, as they developed, the cone increased in length and became a long, slender, straight shell. As the animal grew, it added to the length of the shell and left the older part unoccupied.   This was accomplished by the addition of a cross

FIG. 339. Ordovician marine life.   Cephalopods, trilobites, corals, bryozoans, and brachiopods. (*Courtesy of the Royal Ontario Museum of Palaeontology.*)

partition behind the animal each time it moved forward in the shell (Fig. 339).   Some such shells, more than 1 foot in diameter and 15 feet long, have been found; but, with the very beginning of the evolution of this class, before the close of the second period of the Paleozoic, its members assumed a great variety of forms.   Straight shells were the most common, but some were slightly curved, strongly curved, or loosely coiled, and still others were tightly coiled.   All had partitions in the shell and the entire group may be recognized by them.   If it were not for the partitions, many of the shells would greatly resemble snail shells.

Snails, Clams, and Bryozoa.   Snails and clams (Fig. 340) of many kinds have been found in Ordovician rock.   Bryozoa (moss animals) were possibly the most abundant creatures in the Ordovician seas. They were extremely small and lived in colonies.   The colony pictured in Fig. 340 shows about 50 animals on the side exposed and there were as many on the opposite side. The colony is shown natural size. Some Ordovician beds are composed largely of bryozoans.

Fishes. The other important class that appeared was the fishes (Fig. 341), the first of the vertebrates. One should not, however, expect to find fossil fishes in Ordovician rocks, as probably not one geologist in a hundred has ever collected any fish remains from this period. The

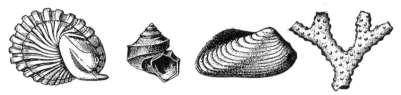

FIG. 340. Ordovician trilobite (enrolled), snail, clam, and bryozoan. *(After Goldring, courtesy of the New York State Museum of Natural History.)*

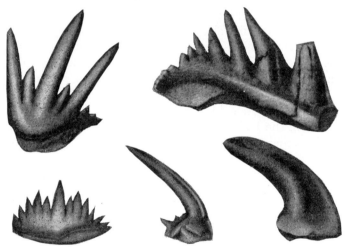

FIG. 341. Ordovician fish (conodont) jaw elements. Five species from the Middle Ordovician, enlarged about 25 diameters. *(After Branson and Mehl.)*

other classes that possessed hard skeletons had them on the outside of the body as shells. Forms like the modern crawfish and grasshopper represented in the early Paleozoic by trilobites, periodically break open the outer covering, escape from it, and form a new covering. This is highly wasteful and comparable to a man's having to burn down his old house before he can have a new one. The development of the internal skeleton made possible organic changes that the external skeleton had prevented, and paved the way for the evolution of the highest types of animals.

Absence of Land Life. Although no fossils of land animals or plants have been found in Ordovician rocks, there can be no doubt that the more primitive plants lived in great numbers, as animals depend indirectly at least upon plants for their food. No animal has the power within itself of taking chemicals directly from the air, the water, or the rocks and transforming them into animal food. Plants perform this function and animals must either eat the plants or eat other animals. Undoubtedly, the first living matter to originate was one of the lowest types of plants.

ECONOMIC PRODUCTS OF THE LOWER PALEOZOIC

Cambrian. The economic products from the Cambrian are not of great importance. Some of the gold from the Black Hills is found in the sandstones and conglomerates that were formed at the time of the very widespread sea near the close of the period. This gold was a placer deposit formed with the conglomerate. Such deposits originate, upon the weathering of gold veins, by streams' transporting the pebbles and finer fragments of rock and particles of gold and redepositing them. Most of the gold is of dust size but flakes and nuggets occur. Gold is about six or seven times as heavy as ordinary rock, and, therefore, is concentrated by the running water that deposits the gravel. A considerable amount of the gold that has been mined in the world was recovered merely by washing gravel. When such gravel becomes cemented, it forms a consolidated placer. Such Cambrian placers are not uncommon in the United States, but the Black Hills seems to be the only place where they were mined, and even there they did not constitute the main source of the gold.

The greatest lead deposits in the United States are in Cambrian rock in southeast Missouri. They occur in a dolomite that was formed at the time of the greatest extent of Cambrian seas. The ore mineral is galena, which consists of lead and sulfur. The galena particles are disseminated through the dolomite and were deposited there subsequent to the time of formation of the rock, probably, by warm or hot water that moved upward through the rock carrying the lead in solution. The lead ore was one of the reasons for the early exploration and settlements of southeast Missouri. However, the French were hunting for silver and mined the lead only incidentally. The oldest mines in the Mississippi Valley are here and have been worked since 1720. For many years the area has yielded more lead than any other in the world, and there is sufficient ore for long continued production.

Ordovician. The economic products of the Ordovician are of much greater value than those of the Cambrian, and the oldest important petroleum and natural gas fields are among them. Ordovician rocks yielded important quantities of petroleum and natural gas from older fields in Ohio, Indiana, and Ontario. This production was from limestones called "Trenton" but is now of relatively little importance. Rocks of the same age, but with sandstone reservoirs, yield much oil in Oklahoma and Texas. Thick sequences of limestone and dolomite of Lower Ordovician age occur in Oklahoma (the Arbuckle limestone) and in Texas and New Mexico (the Ellenburger dolomite). The upper part of these thick formations is porous at many places because of solution along and below an unconformity. They are the source of an ever-increasing amount of high-grade petroleum.

Lead and zinc are produced from Ordovician rocks in the Tri-State area of Iowa, Illinois, and Wisconsin.

An Ordovician sandstone bed called the St. Peter sandstone is widespread in the upper Mississippi River Valley and is an important source of artesian water. It is an almost pure quartz sand containing less than $\frac{1}{10}$ of 1 per cent of iron compounds, and it is therefore used extensively in the manufacture of glass (iron makes glass green).

CHAPTER 19

PETROLEUM GEOLOGY AND PETROLEUM
OF THE PALEOZOIC

The most important use now made of geologic knowledge in the world's economic system is in the finding of petroleum and natural gas. Three-fourths of all the geologists in the United States are engaged in that search.

The first oil found in the United States was in Pennsylvania in 1859. This and most early fields of the world were discovered by drilling near seeps of oil at the surface. No geologic data were used, and discoveries were made largely by accident and good fortune. Until 1920 little use was made of geologic advice, but since that time all companies have acquired a geologic staff and statistics show that a relatively small expenditure has repaid them richly. It is still part of folklore to attribute wisdom to such "wildcatters" as those who found Spindletop Dome and the East Texas Field, but for each such success there are thousands of failures.

The Anticlinal Theory. Even as the first fields were being found, some geologists noted that the accumulations were on anticlines. In general one still searches for structurally "high" areas, or for areas of porous rock elevated relative to surrounding porous rock.

Geologic Methods of Locating Oil. The petroleum geologist in searching for oil accumulations does not look for the tops of hills. Your study of anticlines has shown you that stream valleys are likely to form at the crests of such structures. The anticline shown in Fig. 342 is a producing oil field; yet the wells are on the floor of a valley. Another field in the same area lies on a hill, which by the process of erosion has been formed by a hard layer at the center of the anticline (Fig. 344).

A geologist starting his search in a new region first studies the geologic section exposed at the surface. He examines and measures the beds in order to determine what kinds of rock and what thicknesses of beds are to be expected where those rocks are beneath the surface.

A field geologist entering the region shown in Fig. 344 readily sees that an anticline is present. He wishes to know if potentially oil-bearing

FIG. 342. Anticlinal oil field near Lander, Wyoming.   This is the north end of the structure.   (Courtesy of Production and Marketing Administration, U.S. Department of Agriculture.)

FIG. 343. A stream valley in the top of an anticline.   The beds at the right of the picture dip to the right; at the left they dip in the opposite direction.   (Photograph by E. B. Branson.)

rocks underlie the structure.   If igneous rock is near the surface, or if only nonmarine rocks or beds lacking in porosity are beneath, it cannot yield oil.   Nine miles away a valley is cut across the beds, and the older layers are exposed.   The geologist studies this section and finds that

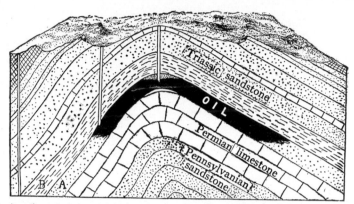

FIG. 344. An oil-producing anticline in Wyoming with two producing wells and a dry hole.   (A) Reservoir sand; (B) shale which forms an impervious cap.   Above the oil-saturated sandstone (shown in black), the sandstone is filled by natural gas; below the oil it is filled by water.

below the nonfossiliferous red siltstones and the nonporous Triassic dolomite exposed at the surface in the anticline there is shale overlying porous sandstone.   Beneath the sandstone is a highly fossiliferous limestone of Permian age.   The fossils are hard parts of animals, and the decaying flesh of those animals may have become petroleum.   The

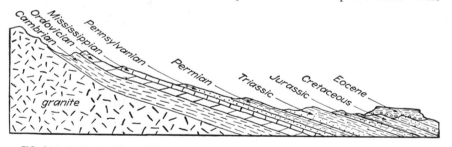

FIG. 345. Geologic section exposed in a canyon 10 miles south of the area shown in Fig. 344.

petroleum of the limestone may have moved upward into the porous sandstone and have accumulated there.   The shale above would serve as an impermeable cap to prevent escape of the oil.   This sequence of rocks is a favorable one for oil accumulation, and the anticline is worth testing by drilling a hole.

Figure 344 illustrates the conditions found in the anticline by the drill. Well 1 produced natural gas from the apex of the structure.   Well 2 is a good oil well.   Well 3 is in a low structural position and yields a small amount of oil.   Well 4 found only salt water which fills the pores of the reservoir on the flanks of the structure.

Age of Oil-bearing Strata.   The geologist is careful to determine the age of the rocks drilled into.   Some fields produce only from rocks of one age; others from rocks of more than one period, as do many of those in Texas, Oklahoma, and Wyoming.

The states that lead in production from Paleozoic rocks are, in order of their present production from that era, Oklahoma, Kansas, Texas, and

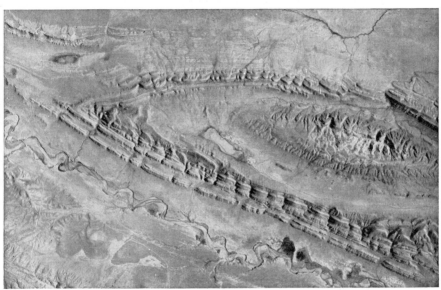

FIG. 346. An oil-producing anticline in western Wyoming. (*Courtesy of Production and Marketing Administration, U.S. Department of Agriculture.*)

New Mexico.   Most of the earlier production from these areas came from Pennsylvanian rocks, and until 15 years ago it was believed that there was no deeper oil in the region.   In recent years deeper wells to older rocks have provided much of the new oil.

If the geologist investigating the area shown in Fig. 344 had found that the rocks underlying the surface rocks were Cambrian in age, he would have given an unfavorable report.   Rocks of Cambrian age have been found productive at only one place in the world.   Geologists do not insist that no oil will be found in Cambrian rocks, but they do say that experience has demonstrated that the chances are too poor to warrant the expense of drilling to rocks of that period.   If it had been found that the rocks immediately underlying the structure are granite or other igneous rock, the geologist would have reported that it was impossible for oil to be present.

Petroleum Reserves.   In 1950, the United States produced 52 per cent of world oil.   This does not mean that the United States has more than half of the world's oil but that this country has found and is using more of its oil than most other countries.   As yet, more oil is found each year than is produced within the United States, but the date is not far off when production will exceed rate of discovery.   We shall then have to pay a higher price in order to produce from deeper zones and more expensive wells, we shall have to import more oil, we shall have to use oil shale resources, and we shall have to find substitute fuels.   There is steady improvement in efficiency of production and in elimination of waste, a fact that makes the present outlook brighter than it would otherwise be.

Natural Gas.   Natural gas is the cheapest and best fuel now being used.   It generally occurs with petroleum, but there are many gas fields which yield no oil and some oil fields with no gas.   Until the last 10 years much gas produced with petroleum was burned or vented into the air, but state controls now prevent such waste.   With increasing price of coal, more and more natural gas is being used as fuel, and pipe lines now carry gas from the southwestern states into California, Illinois, and New York and will presently reach New England.   Some natural gas is rich in carbon dioxide, and this material is compressed and sold as a refrigerant.   Helium occurs in sufficient quantities in some gases to be extracted and used in dirigibles.   Butane and propane are separated from gas and are compressed, bottled, and used as fuel at houses not serviced by pipe lines.

ORIGIN OF PETROLEUM

The manner of origin of petroleum is still not completely understood, but geologists agree that it formed from animals and plants which lived in the sea at the time the sediments were being deposited.   The evidence for this origin is overwhelming.   First, petroleum is related to organic matter chemically and in its optical properties.   Second, all extensive occurrences of petroleum are associated with sedimentary rocks.   Third, large amounts of petroleum are never found except in association with rocks with numerous marine fossils.

As the sediments were deposited, oil was formed by partial decay of animal and plant tissue and was buried in the accumulating sediment. This organic material remained in the sediment as it was altered to rock. Dark shales are likely to be high bituminous, and oil can be extracted from them, but the present cost is uneconomic.   The petroleum in most cases has moved out of the original sediment and has entered porous layers.   In these porous layers, it moved upward and accumulated in traps, *i.e.*, in places where impervious material prevented further movement.

The original accumulation of organically rich sediments occurred in widespread, shallow seas well out from the shore.   Sediment accumulated at a rate of about 1 foot in 10,000 years, and in each cubic foot of this sediment there was about enough organic matter to make 1 pint of petroleum.   No doubt such deposits are being laid down today, but the rate of formation is exceedingly slow, and we are using petroleum much faster than it can be formed.

CHAPTER 20

MIDDLE PALEOZOIC; SILURIAN AND DEVONIAN PERIODS

The periods that we shall consider as Middle Paleozoic are the Silurian and Devonian of the standard section.   The Middle Paleozoic is strikingly different from Lower Paleozoic in several respects.   The periods are based on the sedimentary rocks laid down during a great advance of the sea, as was true in the Lower Paleozoic.   In the third period, the Silurian, the seas were quite different from those of the other periods (Fig. 347).   The western margin of the sea was a little west of the Mississippi River, but in all of the other periods far western regions had been under water.   Most of the Rocky Mountain region is entirely free from Silurian deposits.   The Devonian seas (Fig. 348) were not so extensive as those of some other periods, but their rocks occur in both eastern and western areas and through the interior.   In both periods the Appalachian Trough was one of the early places to be invaded, and served as a depository through most of their duration.   The rocks of both periods are shales, limestones, and sandstones, with limestones forming a larger proportion than would be expected from the proportion of calcium carbonate to clays, silts, and sands derived from normal weathering.   The earliest known occurrence of salt and gypsum is in the Silurian, but they occur in small quantities compared to limestone.   The largest deposits of salt and gypsum occur in New York, Ohio, and Ontario.

The relationship and extent of the formations show that the seas oscillated a great deal, and they did not always cover the same areas on readvancing.   Salt and gypsum are present in the rocks of only a few periods, although, as the materials forming them are common in sea water, they should be present in most marine deposits if special conditions were not required for their formation.   Clearly, special conditions did exist.   Late in the Silurian period the seas withdrew from most of the North American continent, and isolated bodies of salt water were left in New York, Ohio, and Ontario.   Most of these bodies of water were merely shut off by bars from larger bodies of salt water.   The climate must have been arid so as to make evaporation equal or exceed the inflow from streams.   Apparently many of the isolated bodies of water com-

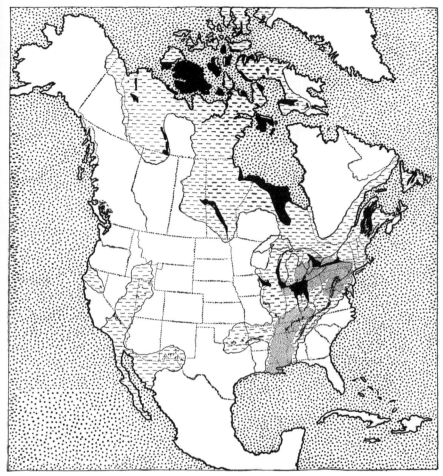

FIG. 347. Silurian seas.   Area of middle Silurian seas dashed; of late Silurian seas in fine stipple. Outcrops shown in black. (*Modified from Schuchert.*)

pletely evaporated and all of their salt and gypsum were precipitated on the sea floor.   The sea water contains a little more than 1 part in 100 by volume of salt.   As some of the salt deposits are 200 feet thick, more than 20,000 feet of water must have evaporated in order to deposit that much. However, one should not assume that there was a basin 20,000 feet deep, for other facts show that the water was comparatively shallow at all times (see page 379).

LIFE OF MIDDLE PALEOZOIC

The life of the Middle Paleozoic in its general aspects was not greatly different from that of the Lower Paleozoic.   In the seas the brachiopods, clams, (Fig. 349), trilobites, and cephalopods were dominant forms.

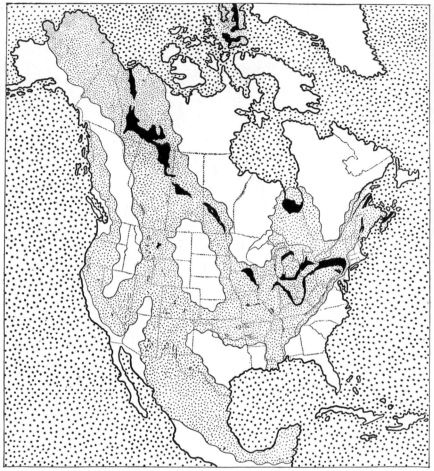

FIG. 348. Devonian seas. Epicontinental seas in fine stipple; outcrops in black. (*Modified from Schuchert.*)

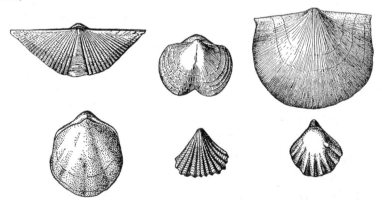

FIG. 349. Silurian and Devonian brachiopods. (*From Paleontology of New York.*)

Trilobites. Trilobites were showing old-age characteristics before the close of the Devonian. In the earlier Paleozoic they had been young and subject to great numbers of variations. In the Silurian they became less and less varied and in the Devonian the old-age characteristics showed plainly.

Of animals and plants in general, it may be said that one of the most conspicuous indications of a group's entering "old age" is the development of useless structures commonly designated as "ornaments." With the trilobites these were in the nature of spines and nodes on various parts of the body (Fig. 350). They had ceased to evolve changes that would fit them to their environment, or to develop many new species. One familiar with the development of life in the geologic past might predict, after examining the Devonian trilobites, that they were near the end of their course.

FIG. 350. An ornate Devonian trilobite. (Restoration by Irving G. Reimann.)

Cephalopods. Among the cephalopods a new type of structure appeared that was later to become the dominant feature of that group.

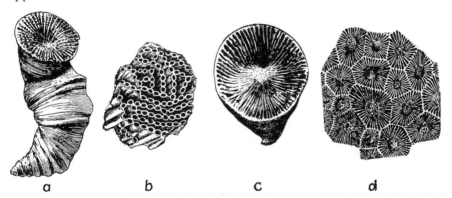

a   b   c   d

FIG. 351. Devonian and Silurian corals. (*From Pirsson and Schuchert, courtesy of John Wiley & Sons, Inc.*)

The partitions in the shells had been simple, gently curved plates heretofore, but in the Devonian a form appeared that had strong flexures in the edges of the partition, producing complex sutures.

Corals and Crinoids. Corals were present in late Cambrian seas and increased in numbers and kinds in Ordovician seas; and reef-building forms were abundant in Silurian and Devonian seas (Fig. 351). Crinoids appeared in the Ordovician and were abundant in some Silurian and Devonian seas. As one member of the Echinoderma, crinoids are related to modern starfishes and sea urchins. They consist of a cup or head,

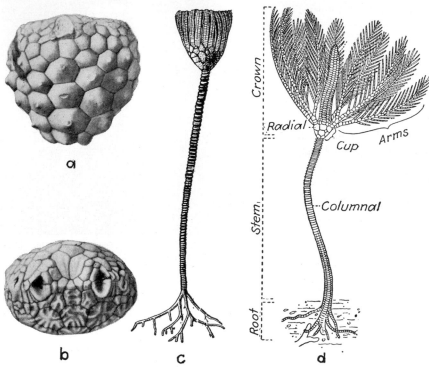

FIG. 352. (a and b) Crinoid heads from the Devonian (*from Branson*); (c and d) Silurian crinoids. (*Courtesy of the New York State Museum of Natural History.*)

with radiating arms, that contains the vital organs (Fig. 352). The root was attached to the sea bottom and stalk and body floated in the sea water (Fig. 353).

Fishes Develop Paired Fins. Fishes, which had appeared in the Ordovician period, were still rare and small in the Silurian. They came to the time of great evolutional vigor and great changes in the Devonian, which is known as the "Age of Fishes" (Fig. 354). By the middle of the period they had branched out into four main lines of development. One of these was the sharks, which appeared here for the first time and which in some respects constituted a great advance among fishes. Some of these sharks show the development of paired limbs, which up to this time had not been present. The fish fins had been long folds of skin along the sides of the body; now, the bone supports of these folds became segregated into four groups, two on each side of the body, and folds of skin were restricted to the four groups of bone to form the paired limbs. Bony fishes, which are today, and long have been, the dominant group of fishes, had their ancestral forms in the Devonian.   All of them were small, and there were few species.

Armored Joint-necked Fishes.   One specialized group, the "jointed necks," assumed some striking peculiarities and at some places were

FIG. 353. Middle Devonian marine life.   Corals, trilobites, cephalopods, and a crinoid.   (*Restoration by George and Paul Marchand under the direction of Irving G. Reimann, courtesy of the Rochester Museum.*)

the dominant form of fishes and the largest animals in the Devonian. In the joint-necks the lower jaw and the teeth of the lower jaw consist of just one unit; all other fishes have separated bones in the lower jaw and the teeth are separate pieces.   They are called the "joint-necked" fishes on account of two ball-and-socket joints between the skull and some armor plates on the back of the fish (Fig. 355).   These armor plates were a new type of development.   On the middle of the back was a heavy shield-shaped piece of bone and on either side of this piece were other bony plates.   Two of the latter, one on each side, articulated with the base of the skull by means of the ball-and-socket joints.   Here was the first heavily armored animal that had come into existence, and it furnishes us with another lesson in the economy of evolutionary development, which is that heavy armoring, though it may protect the animal temporarily, finally leads to extinction.   Some of these fishes reached a

FIG. 354. Restoration of a group of Devonian fishes. (From a painting by C. R. Knight, courtesy of American Museum of Natural History.)

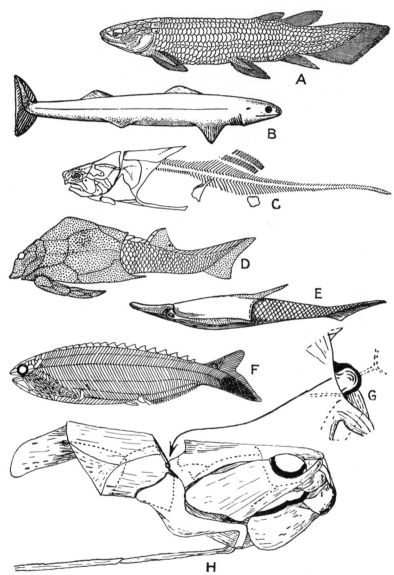

FIG. 355. Some of the better known Devonian fishes.   (a) Lungfish; (b) shark; (c) joint-neck armored fish; (d and e) armored fishes; (f) late Silurian fish; (g) joint between the head and armor of a joint-neck fish; (h) head and body armor of a joint-neck fish.   (a–e, *from Pirsson and Schuchert, courtesy of John Wiley & Sons, Inc.; f, from Kiaer; g and h, from Branson.*)

length of 25 feet or more and may be considered as giants among all animals of that time. Although they appeared first in early Devonian, they did not outlast that period. This is our first record of the dying out of an entire race. Another law of evolution that is illustrated here is that gigantism leads to extinction. The two laws may be stated in other ways: very large animals belong to short-lived species; heavily armored species soon become extinct. The joint-neck fishes are found in the Devonian of Ohio and New York, and in various other regions of the world. The black Devonian shales of northern Ohio are the best collecting ground for them in the world.

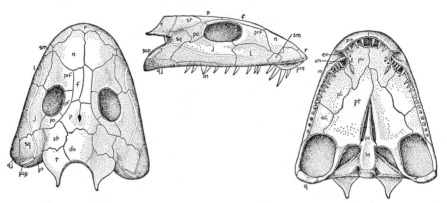

FIG. 356. Devonian amphibian skulls from East Greenland. (After Romer, "Vertebrate Paleontology.")

Lungfishes. Another peculiar type of fish was one that developed lungs and was able to breath air and live on land. These are known as the "lungfishes," and they were the first vertebrates that could live out of water. Their lungs were probably a mistake in development, as gills are more efficient breathing agents than such lungs. These fishes developed another inefficient structure: the paired fins became elongated and changed into a sort of legs without feet, enabling the animal to move about clumsily over the earth's surface. Here were two unsuccessful types of evolution toward higher forms, but the structures were not conducive to greater efficiency and the animals never progressed beyond the stage found in the Devonian. Although there are three types of lungfishes existing, the time of their greatest abundance was the Devonian. No other form seems to have developed from them, and they should not be confused with the Amphibia, next to be discussed.

Amphibia. A principle of evolution, emphasized in the chapter on the Lower Paleozoic, is that at times of rapid evolution in young groups, when they are giving rise to a great variety of new forms, some large changes develop that may lead to significant upward trends in evolution. Fishes were evolving rapidly and producing great numbers of radically

different types.   They had developed paired fins (almost paired legs in
the lungfishes) and had evolved a primitive type of lung.   It is not
surprising, therefore, that along another line
of evolution an efficient lung should develop
and that paired legs with walking feet should
appear.   This next higher group in the evolution of the vertebrates was the amphibians,
which left evidences of their presence in the
late Devonian rocks (Fig. 356).   The evidences are not extensive, just a track in the
Upper Devonian of Pennsylvania, a few bones
in Latvia, and some skulls in East Greenland.
There is a possibility that lung development
lagged behind the development of the feet.
Amphibians are cold-blooded animals that
breathe by means of gills in the early stage
and by means of lungs in the later stage.

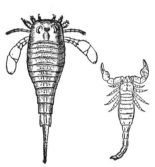

FIG. 357. Silurian land animals;
scorpion on the right, eurypterid
on the left. (From Pirsson and
Schuchert, courtesy of John Wiley
& Sons, Inc.)

They differ from fishes not only in having legs, feet, and lungs but in
having developed a three-chambered heart rather than the two-chambered
heart of the fishes.

FiG. 358. A Devonian forest.   (R. C. Moore, "Historical Geology," from a painting by C. R. Knight in
Chicago Museum of Natural History.)

Scorpions, the First Air Breathers.   While the seas were drying up
in New York, Ohio, and Ontario, the conditions forced various life adjustments to changing environment.   Sea animals that lived in these inland

bodies of water would surely have died off had the seas dried up rapidly or dried up within a few thousand years, but due to the slowness of the drying there was opportunity for adjustment to new conditions. The animals might start living part of the time in water and part of the time on land and finally develop the ability to live on land all of the time and to breathe air. Whether this was the cause or whether something else forced the change, the first of the air-breathing animals, scorpions (Fig.

FIG. 359. A Devonian seed fern (about 20 feet high). *(From the restoration by Winifred Goldring, courtesy of New York State Museum of Natural History.)*

357), appeared on the shores of the Silurian seas. Of course, the air-breathing vertebrates, like the lungfishes and the amphibians, did not develop from the scorpions. The ability to breathe air was an independent development in all three types.

The Oldest Forests. At some time during the Middle Paleozoic, plants of large size grew on land, and a record of the first forests (Fig. 358) has been found in the Devonian of New York state. The fossil trees were uncovered at the time the excavations were being made for the Croton aqueduct, part of the water system of New York City; stumps of trees and trunks 2 or 3 feet in diameter were found there in abundance. The trees belong to the fern group of plants (Fig. 359) and not to the higher group to which most trees of the present belong.   There are fossil fronds among them that look so much like fern fronds that anyone at all familiar with ferns could recognize them.   Before this time, all of the main groups of plants had appeared, with the exception of the highest.[1]

Thin coal seams occur in various parts of the world and many of the Devonian shales are highly carbonaceous.   Some of those in northern Ohio have so much plant material in them that they will burn.   However, much of the carbonaceous material in the rocks came from plants that grew in the seas rather than from land plants, and these had no connection with the Devonian forests.

ECONOMIC PRODUCTS

Salt.   As we have already considered the salt and gypsum as unusual rocks of the Middle Paleozoic, we shall discuss them first among the economic products.   The salt supply for the entire United States used to come largely from the Silurian of New York and Ohio, but the development of salt mines in other parts of the country has restricted the use of this salt to eastern and east central United States.   The salt is not actually mined.   Most of the material is dissolved and brought to the surface as a brine, and then the solution is evaporated to separate the sodium chloride from other salts as, when the seas in which the deposit was formed were in the late stages of evaporation, salts more soluble than sodium chloride had also been deposited.   Thus in evaporation of the brines brought to the surface, sodium chloride is precipitated first, and the remaining solution is drawn off.   Potash is among the most valuable of the very soluble salts remaining in the solution.

Gypsum and Other Quarry Products.   Gypsum is quarried, calcined, and used mainly as an interior plaster for houses.   It is also used for modeling purposes and for making plaster of Paris and cements.   Most of the gypsum from the Middle Paleozoic is quarried in Ohio and New York.

For the manufacture of natural cement, which was once a thriving industry, much of the raw material was derived from Middle Paleozoic rocks.   Portland cement has taken the place of natural cement and is a better material on account of being more uniform.   The natural cement was made by burning to clinker stage a limestone that contained about 20 per cent clay.   As limestones vary greatly in composition, even within short distances and between different beds in the same quarry, much of

---

[1] Botanists divide plants into four great groups, which they call "thallophytes," "bryophytes," "pteridophytes," and "spermatophytes."   The first includes one-celled forms and others of very low organization.   The bryophytes are the moss group, the pteridophytes the fern group, and the spermatophytes include all of the seed-bearing plants.

the quarried product had to be rejected because it contained either too much or too little clay. For Portland cement the materials are analyzed chemically; just the right proportion of the right shale or clay is mixed with the limestone, and the resulting product from any particular plant is quite uniform. Flagstones from the Devonian were formerly used in making sidewalks and roads, but their use has been largely discontinued with the development of cement; the use of Devonian limestones and shales in the manufacture of Portland cement is extensive. Limestones and shales of almost any period may be used in this manufacture; the ones selected for use depend largely on the location of their outcrops in the vicinity where it is desired to locate the cement plant.

Oil and Gas. Oil and gas are produced from both Silurian and Devonian rocks in West Virginia, Pennsylvania, Ohio, Texas, and Kentucky. The Marine pool in Illinois is an oil trap in a Silurian coral reef, and the recently discovered large oil fields of Alberta are mainly in Devonian coral reefs.

Iron. Much of the iron produced in the United States previous to about 1854 came from the Silurian of the Appalachian Mountains, from Pennsylvania southward to Alabama. An arm of the Silurian seas extended through the Appalachian Trough and the waters coming to it were highly charged with iron in solution. This iron was precipitated on the sea bottom, in some places with calcium carbonate, in some with clay, and in others with sand. Some parts of the ore are made up of little grains resembling flaxseed and it was named "flaxseed ore" on that account. Some of the rock has an iron content high enough to make it an iron ore, but most of it has not. When iron smelting was done by charcoal burned in the region and the amount of iron produced in any furnace was small and for local consumption, hundreds of furnaces were located near the mines. When the Lake Superior iron began to be produced, the small mines along the Appalachians were gradually abandoned and nearly all mining of this ore centered about Birmingham, Alabama, which now has the largest iron production outside the Lake Superior region. The Birmingham district has some advantages over the northern region in that it has an abundance of coal and limestone, used in smelting. Although the Alabama ore is of lower grade than that of the Lake Superior region, pig iron can be produced as cheaply there as it is from the better ores.

CLIMATE OF MIDDLE PALEOZOIC

Conclusions concerning climate of the Middle Paleozoic are based largely on the distribution of sea animals. Corals live almost altogether in tropical waters, particularly the reef-building corals, and these are widely distributed in latitude in both of the Middle Paleozoic periods.

During the Silurian, there seems to have been a path of migration for animals from North America to Europe directly through the polar regions, as the same species are found in central North America in the vicinity of Chicago, in the northernmost part of North America, in Spitzbergen, and in Sweden, and these species are not found generally distributed in the Silurian rocks. The presence of the same marine invertebrates in the warm temperate regions and in what today are the polar regions indicates a rather uniform temperature of water at that time. There are no positive evidences of seasonal variation in the fossil plants, but those variations might not have been present in the type of plants that grew at that time.

CHAPTER 21

UPPER PALEOZOIC; MISSISSIPPIAN, PENNSYLVANIAN, AND PERMIAN PERIODS

The Upper Paleozoic rocks are considered by many geologists to be the deposits of but one period, which they call the Carboniferous and which they divide into Mississippian, Pennsylvanian, and Permian. Other geologists consider that each one of these divisions is deserving of period rank. The names of all the Paleozoic periods preceding the Upper were derived from the British Isles. The term "Carboniferous" is descriptive of the extensive coal deposits that occur in the Pennsylvanian. "Mississippian" was adopted because of the great development of rocks of this age in the Mississippi Valley, "Pennsylvanian" because rocks of Middle Carboniferous age are so well developed in Pennsylvania, and "Permian" was so called from the province of Perm, Russia (this being the only departure from western European or American terms among the names of the periods).

Geography of the Upper Paleozoic. During the Mississippian period the extent of seas on the North American continent (Fig. 360) was not greatly different from that of other Paleozoic periods. The Appalachian Trough formed an early seaway, as usual, and seas were widespread in the interior and in the Rocky Mountain regions.

Pennsylvanian geography departed widely (Fig. 361) from that of other periods. Seas advanced and retreated many times over the same region; as many as 60 advances and retreats are known. The retreats were rapid, and the lands were at all times so low that swamps covered most of them. From the Appalachian region to eastern Kansas and Nebraska, half of the area above sea was in swamps during several of the land stages. The marine deposits are recognized by the fossils of marine animals they contain, and the swamp deposits were mainly plant remains that later became coal and at present constitute the great coal reserve of the United States from Kansas to Pennsylvania. The rocks associated with the coal are mainly shales, but sandstones are common, and thin limestones made up part of the marine formations. Erosion was vigorous during some of the sea withdrawals, and river channels were formed that were filled with sands when seas advanced again over the region.

In the province of Perm, Russia, much of the Permian consists of red sandstone, and in the Rocky Mountain region and Oklahoma red sandstones of Permian age occur at many places. These rocks are usually called "red beds," although all of them have been given formation names.

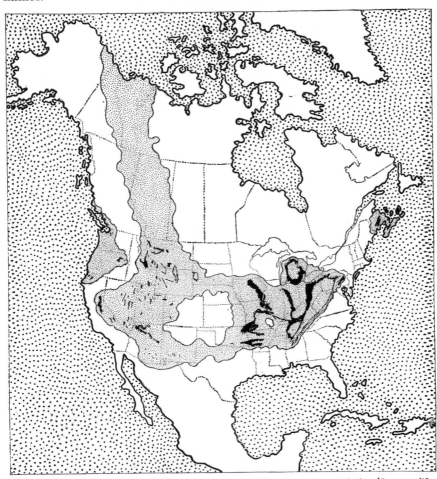

FIG. 360. Mississippian seas. Epicontinental seas in fine stipple; outcrops in black. (*Seas modified from Schuchert.*)

Shallow-water Deposits. A striking peculiarity of the Appalachian Trough sediments is that most of them show evidences of having been deposited in shallow water. Ripple marking is common in the rocks of every period, and rapid alternation of coarse to fine sediments is present in every period. Shallow-water fossils occur in nearly every formation, and mud cracks are present in hundreds of members.

In order to have 40,000 feet of sediments deposited in shallow water, the bottom of the trough must have been sinking at about the same rate that sediments were being deposited. At some times sedimentation

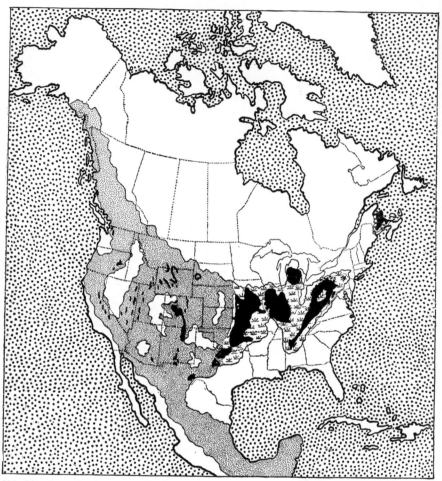

FIG. 361. Pennsylvanian seas. Outcrops in black; epicontinental seas in fine stipple; swamp areas shown by tufted lines. Seas covered the swamp areas during part of the period. (*Seas modified from Schuchert.*)

was the more rapid, and widespread top beds of deltas and alluvial fans were formed.

End of the Appalachian Trough and Close of the Paleozoic Era. With the close of the Mississippian, the Appalachian Trough ceased to be a permanent seaway and from an area of deposition became one of erosion. During the Pennsylvanian, the region was above water most of the time; and, in the Permian, the rocks were folded and faulted into the Appa-

lachian Mountains.   The sides of the trough were pushed 40 to 50 miles
closer together, and many sharp folds of large size developed that involved
strata several miles in thickness.   During the Paleozoic, some 40,000
feet of sediments were deposited in the trough.   As few unconformities

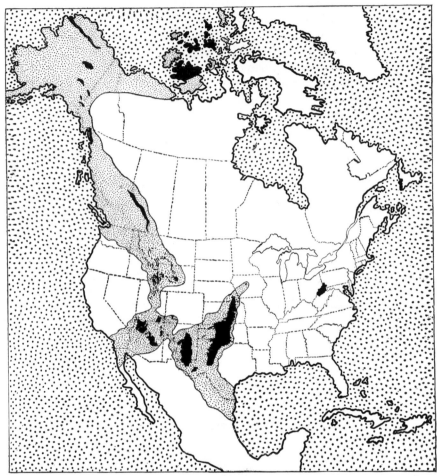

FIG. 362. Permian seas.   Area of epicontinental seas in fine stipple; outcrops in black.   (*Seas modified from Schuchert.*)

representing any considerable lapse of time are present in the section,
it appears that the trough area was above sea only a few times during
the Paleozoic.

Before the close of the Pennsylvanian, the seas withdrew to a Gulf of
Mexico extension that reached as far north as Nebraska and as far west
as Arizona.   This sea continued into the Permian, and the boundary
between the two periods is uncertain.   During the Permian the seas

advanced irregularly, became more and more restricted (Fig. 362), and finally withdrew to the ocean basins. Rock salt and potash were deposited in some of the restricted basins. The great Guadalupe reefs were formed at the margin of basins in West Texas and New Mexico.

Emergence of the Lands. The folding of the Appalachian Mountains changed geographic conditions so much that the later history of the region and of the adjacent territory was radically different from that of earlier times. Seas never again occupied the Appalachian Trough, although they overlapped parts of it.

At the end of the Permian all of North America emerged; no place is known where Paleozoic sediments grade into Mesozoic without unconformity, although in some places no unconformity can be identified positively. Not only did a period of erosion of the entire continent set in but it lasted well into the Triassic (the first period of the next era) over most of the continent.

LIFE OF THE UPPER PALEOZOIC

Inasmuch as Middle passed into Upper Paleozoic with no conspicuous geographic changes, striking life changes were not to be expected. There was a rather gradual evolution of the forms already present.

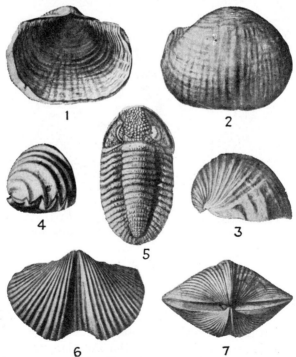

FIG. 363. Mississippian fossils. (1, 2, 3) Productids; (4) a common brachiopod; (5) a trilobite; (6 and 7) spirifers.

Trilobites. Old-age characteristics of the Devonian trilobites faithfully foretold the coming results; few trilobites were left in the Mississippian, and they were small and most of them with simple ornamentation (Fig. 363). From some 200 species in the Devonian, they dropped to

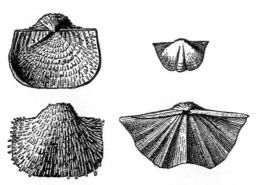

FIG. 364. Pennsylvanian brachiopods of the dominant types: productid at the left, spiriferid at the lower right, chonetid at the upper right. (*After Beede, University of Kansas Geological Survey.*)

about 20 in the Mississippian, and even where other fossils are abundant one rarely finds a trilobite. In the Pennsylvanian they are still rarer, and few species are known from the Permian of any region.

Brachiopods. Brachiopods retained their leadership in numbers of species and individuals and displayed no marked signs of old age. Two types, known as "spirifers" and "productids," dominated and made up nearly half of the 5,000 species known from the Upper Paleozoic (Figs. 363, 364, and 365). Productids were degenerate forms in some respects. They had lost their pedicle, a fleshy stalk by means of which most brachiopods were attached, and had developed spines. Productids had one convex shell and one that was concave (Fig. 363).

FIG. 365. Permian brachiopods: Spiriferina at the left, Hustedia above, Aulosteges at the right. (*After Carl C. Branson.*)

Crinoids. Another group of invertebrates, the crinoids, became abundant (Fig. 366). The joints of the stems have a hole in the middle, and some Indians, in localities where crinoid stems are common fossils, used them as beads. Some Mississippian rocks are composed almost entirely of these stems, which do not show conspicuously on freshly broken surfaces but weather out in relief. Over wide areas of the Mississippian sea bottom, the crinoids must have lived close enough together to appear like fields of waving grains as their heads moved back and forth with the movement of the water.   Crinoids occur for the most part in limestone because they were chiefly clear-water dwellers.   They decreased in numbers in Pennsylvanian and Permian times.

Insects.   Insects of considerable variety were present.   They first appeared in the Pennsylvanian and some kinds became abundant. Permian rocks contain remains of cockroaches several inches long. Dragonflies, with a wing spread of nearly 2 feet (Fig. 371, page 387), were

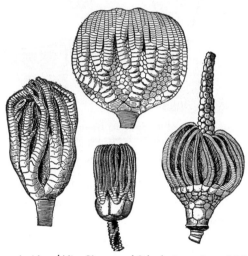

FIG. 366. Mississippian crinoids.   (After Pirsson and Schuchert, courtesy of John Wiley & Sons, Inc.)

the largest of the insects.   Other insects were comparable in size to those of the present, but many of the highest types of insects, such as bees and butterflies, had not appeared.

Sharks.   In the Devonian, sharks had appeared as inconspicuous members of the class of fishes.   In the Mississippian, they developed rapidly, and in one of the formations more than 400 species are known. They developed along two lines that were strikingly different.   One type had sharp, tearing teeth, like those of most modern sharks; the other type had flat, crushing teeth, some of them 2 or 3 inches in diameter. Shark skeletons are made of cartilage, never having had calcium compounds laid down in them to make them hard like ordinary bone.   On that account they are rarely preserved as fossils, and the remains of sharks found in the rocks are mainly teeth and spines, which are made of calcium compounds.   In the Pennsylvanian, sharks decreased rapidly, and few lived over into the Permian.

Amphibians.   Amphibians appeared first in the Devonian, and their remains are very rare in the Mississippian.   Land and water conditions in the Pennsylvanian were exceedingly favorable for the amphibians, and they increased rapidly (Fig. 367). All were small, but some of the swamps must have fairly swarmed with them. The development of Amphibia continued in the Permian, during which time some reached a length of 7 or 8 feet. They were broad and short-legged (Fig. 368).

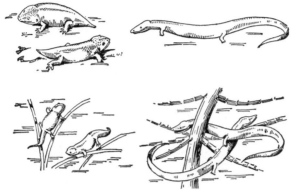

FIG. 367. Small larval amphibians from Pennsylvanian swamps. *(After Osborn, "The Origin and Evolution of Life.")*

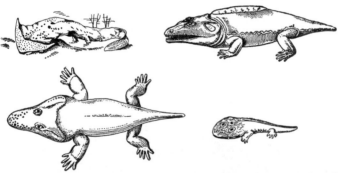

FIG. 368. Permian amphibians (those on the left about 5 feet long, upper right about 2 feet long, lower right a hypothetical form about 8 inches long). *(Upper left after Osborn, the others after Williston.)*

Reptiles.   While numerous changes were taking place in the amphibians, the reptiles branched off from them. The oldest remains of reptiles known are from the Pennsylvanian (about the time when amphibians were evolving so rapidly), but only a few specimens are known from the period. In the Permian the development of reptiles came with a rush and many strange forms have been collected (Fig. 369). None of them, except one lizard-like form, belongs to any of the modern types. Most of the Permian reptiles of North America have been collected from Texas, where continental deposits favorable for the preservation of their skeletons were formed. The most remarkable of these reptiles had long,

slender spines extending upward from the arches of the vertebrae, giving
to the top of the body a peculiar sail-like appearance with the sail extending lengthwise of the body (Fig. 370).   A specialized form had crosspieces
on the bony spines, making each appear like the mast of a ship with cross
arms.

FIG. 369. Permian reptiles (left, about 7 feet long; right, about 4 feet long).   (After Williston.)

FIG. 370. A Permian fin-backed reptile about 8 feet long eating a large amphibian.   (From M. G.
Mehl.)

Changes from Amphibians to Reptiles.   The differences between
reptiles and amphibians are not great as they appear in the skeleton,
the only part preserved as fossils.   The real distinguishing characteristic
is that in the early life of the amphibians they breathe by means of gills,
and reptiles never breathe with gills.   The difference is not so large as it
seems, because the gills are also present in the reptiles but only in the
embryonic stage.   In the process of evolution of reptiles the lung-breath-
ing stage developed earlier and earlier in the life of the individual until

FIG. 371. Pennsylvanian swamp life.   (From M. G. Mehl.)

the change to lungs came in the embryo.   In some ways this proved an advantage and was perpetuated, giving rise to the reptiles.   When changes start in a particular direction, they may go past the most advantageous stage if the changes are rapid and vigorous and may give rise to animals unfitted for any environment except the one into which they are born.   This did not happen with the reptiles in the early stages in the Pennsylvanian, but in the Permian almost any sort of monstrosity might be expected on account of the rapidity of the changes that were taking place (Fig. 370).

The vertebrate land life of the latest Paleozoic consisted of reptiles and amphibians, with possibly a minor development of lungfish. No birds or mammals were present. The Permian reptiles were probably no more abundant than reptiles at the present time, and the land was poorly supplied with life. There were no forms so big as the modern crocodile, and none of the modern forms was present.

Extinction of Many Reptile Groups. A striking thing about the Permian reptile groups was their complete disappearance. To say "complete disappearance" probably conveys the wrong impression, although the several groups seem to have left no descendants. Most forms disappear by changing gradually so that the old kind by which they were known is no longer present. The changes in 100,000-year periods would not be great enough to obscure the relationships, but the lost time between Permian and the next period, when preservation of reptiles was such as to enable investigators to study their anatomy, was in tens of millions of years. For most forms it is impossible to determine the ancestral form. It is not known from what Permian group modern turtles, lizards, snakes, or crocodiles came.

FIG. 372. Fusulinids. Special one-celled animals abundant in the Pennsylvanian and Permian. (*From Dunbar and Skinner, photographs courtesy of C. O. Dunbar.*)

Plants. The Mississippian contained no plants that need special mention. In places, plants were very abundant; and in some places coal was formed. The reason for the small amount of coal was probably the absence of swampy conditions rather than scarcity of plants.

In the Pennsylvanian came the great time of plant growth of the Paleozoic. The swamp conditions of the period have been mentioned in another paragraph, and the swamp vegetation will now be described. Apparently in the lowlands water plants grew in such profusion as actually to fill the swamps with dead plant remains. In places the spores of the fern group of plants accumulated in such quantities as to form beds of coal. In parts of the Mississippi Valley, sink holes had formed in the older rocks during early Pennsylvanian time and these were a favorable place for the lodging of spores. Cannel coal (a coal made up of spores) developed in the sink holes; in some to a thickness of more than 50 feet.

Scouring rushes and club mosses reached the greatest size of any of the trees, some more than 100 feet tall and 6 feet in diameter (Fig. 371). The modern representatives of these groups are small herbs. Tree ferns were abundant and smaller-sized ferns grew in great profusion. The most significant of all of the plants was one that seemed half way between the ferns and the seed-bearing plants. It had leaves like a fern but bore seeds. This was the beginning of the highest type of plants, the spermatophytes or seed-bearers, which now dominate the plant life of the world.

Decline of Plants. The most remarkable thing about the plant life of the late Paleozoic was its decline toward the close. From thousands of species in the Pennsylvanian, it was reduced to a few hundred in the late Permian, and not one of these passed over into the Mesozoic. The failure to pass over is not of high significance as the time between the latest fossiliferous Paleozoic and oldest Mesozoic may have been more than 10,000,000 years. (For the sparse vegetation of the Permian see Fig. 370.)

Permian Climate Unfavorable to Plants. Permian conditions were much more trying for plants than for animals, but the lack of plant fossils may be somewhat misleading. At the present time about one-third of the land surface is desert, and, although plants of many kinds may grow in deserts, few of them could be preserved as fossils because they contain too little woody tissue. Another reason is that they are unlikely to fall into water and get covered with mud so that the minerals in solution in the water may penetrate the tissues and change them to solid rock.[1] Probably more of the earth's surface was arid in the Permian than at present and smaller areas were favorable for plant preservation. Still another factor entered into the plant problem of the Permian. The increasing cold brought on glaciation over large areas and subjected plants to rigorous conditions. With continental glaciers extending into the tropics in Africa, Asia, and Australia, conditions for abundant plant growth were present during part of the time in only limited areas of those regions.

The question may be raised as to why, with glaciers in the tropics in other parts of the world, reptiles could live in such abundance in Texas and marine life flourish in the seas nearly as far north as the Arctic Circle. As glaciers develop only in regions of abundant snowfall,

[1] Plants fossilized in other ways than being petrified. A plant may fall into mud and become completely covered with it. After the mud becomes solid the plant tissue may decay and be removed and the cavity be filled with sand, silt, or clay. This creates a cast of the original trunk, just as a cast is made of iron in an iron foundry. Fossils formed in this way contain none of the cell structure such as is preserved in petrified plants, but their shape and exterior markings are reproduced in great perfection.

they could not form in Texas where the climate was arid. That does not fully answer the question, however, for reptiles do not live in cold climates, and Texas could be just as cold without glaciers as with them. Glacial deposits are numerous in the Permian but that does not mean that the Permian was cold during the entire period in those places where the glaciers formed. The period must have lasted at least 30,000,000 years, and 1,000,000 years was long enough for the glaciation. Pleistocene glaciation may not have lasted more than 1,000,000 years and that gave time enough for five advances and five retreats of the ice and for tropical plants to grow 500 miles north of the extreme southern boundary of the ice during an interglacial period. It is possible, then, to have boreal and tropical plants growing within the same area within a small part of one period and to have a continental glacier cover an area, and tropical plants grow in the same area within 1,000,000 years. The climate of Texas may have been cold enough for glaciers to form there during the same time that they were present in India, but the Texas Permian history that we have been considering may have long been over. The same consideration may have been true for aridity as for glaciation. A region that was arid during part of a period may have been well watered during another part. The region that was arid during the last part of the Silurian was under the sea during much of the earlier part of the period.

In India, Australia, and Africa a flora developed under the influence of glaciation during late Paleozoic and finally spread over most of the world. It is called the "Gondwana flora" from its supposed spreading across Gondwana land. The flora was made up largely of ferns and related forms and contained no tropical elements.

Permian and Its Life. The landscape in northern Texas during the period was, perhaps, typical. The area was low, something like the delta of the Mississippi at the present time. Vegetation may have been fairly abundant but not so plentiful as it is in the moist tropics today or as it had been in the Pennsylvanian. It was more like that at the mouth of a great river in a semiarid region. No flowering plants were present, the plants being mainly of the fern group, bearing no seeds and reproducing by spores only.

The streams in this region were bringing in mainly red sands, silts, and clays and depositing them as red beds on the lowlands, which were part of an old basin that had been laid bare by the drying up or withdrawal of the seas. Parts of the deposits were alluvial fans and parts were the top beds of deltas. Here and there, the wind piled up loess, adobe, and sand. Northwest and west lay the enclosed seas in which gypsum and salt were being deposited.

Most of the animals lived near the stream courses, but in the lowlands water was abundant enough for favorable habitat. On these lowlands the reptiles and amphibians lived (Fig. 371), but their remains were preserved as fossils only under exceptional conditions. The oxbow lakes formed by cutoff meanders were favorite drinking places for animals, and the muds there were finer and buried animals more efficiently than the ordinary flood-plain deposits. The chance for bones to be covered with water and mud was better there than elsewhere and, therefore, the chance for fossilization was better.

Animals as large as most vertebrates were not apt to die without other animals' eating the flesh and scattering the bones. If the carcass was covered with mud soon after the animal died so that other animals found it difficult to disturb it, the chance for fossilization was greatly increased. If the animals were preserved mainly in oxbows, their remains would be found only in an extremely small part of the total area. Such is the case with the Texas reptiles; one may search for days over these deposits without finding a bone and then find remains of several individuals near together.

Highlands should be included in the picture, as well as lowlands. The uplift of the Arbuckle and Wichita mountains in Oklahoma and the extension of that line of folding through Arkansas to the main Appalachian Mountains were taking place during the Permian. Streams were rejuvenated and became vigorous near their headwaters and were sluggish only where they came to the old sea flats.

The rivers contained lungfishes and primitive bony fishes as well as small clams. The highly saline seas had no life in them, but the open seas were separated from the inclosed parts only by sand bars in many places. On one side of the bar there were no animals while on the other side life was abundant. The fisherman drawing his nets through the inhabited sea would have brought out mainly brachiopods, among which the concavo-convex shelled productids would have been dominant. He would have worked for a long time before securing a trilobite or a crinoid. In some places cephalopods would have been the main catch. If he had used a very fine-meshed net, he might have secured great numbers of shells of one-celled animals of the type that made up a great deal of rock in the Pennsylvanian and was very abundant in some parts of the Permian (Fig. 372).

Permian Reef Life. If the fisherman had crossed over the divide from the Kansas seas into the western margins of the Permian basin of West Texas and New Mexico, he would have found different types of life in abundance. These organisms lived on the edge of the shelf at the margin of the deeper basin, and their remains piled up into great reefs similar to the present Great Barrier Reef of Australia. Most of the reef material consists of the remains of calcareous algae. At the reef margins are myriads of fusulinids.   Brachiopods are abundant, particularly the spiny types, and some of these were greatly modified in that they had long spines and a cup-like shell and that they lived in colonies.[2]

ECONOMIC PRODUCTS OF THE UPPER PALEOZOIC

The economic products so far produced from Upper Paleozoic rocks are of greater total value than are those of any other rocks representing a similar length of geologic time.

Mississippian.   *Oil, Gas, and Coal.*   Mississippian rocks contain much oil and gas in Pennsylvania, Ohio, West Virginia, and Illinois.   The oldest workable coal in North America is in the Mississippian of Virginia, but the available tonnage is small.   A delta was built into the Appalachian Trough and in its swamps this Mississippian coal was formed.

Building Stone.   Building stones (and limestone for making cement) are quarried in many places in the United States.   The limestone quarries of Bedford, Indiana, are the largest in the country in Mississippian rocks.   The stone is fine grained and is the oldest rock in North America made up mainly of the shells of one-celled animals (Protozoa).   Nearly every large city east of the Mississippi River has many buildings constructed of this stone.   The Berea sandstone (Mississippian) of northern Ohio is another well-known stone which is widely used.   It is quarried and sawed into blocks or left rough according to the use wanted.   The bedding is even and in many parts of the quarries the stone splits into the right thickness for building.   The stone in slabs 2 or 3 inches thick, was formerly used extensively for sidewalks; but, the formation being extensively ripple marked, the sidewalk surfaces became too rough with wear when the ripples appeared upon them.   Some layers in the quarries are used extensively for abrasives, particularly for grindstones.   Most of the grindstones used in the United States are made in northern Ohio from these rocks.

There are many quarries in the Burlington limestone (Mississippian) of Iowa and Missouri.   One of the best known is at Carthage, Missouri, where the rock is so compact and even grained that it takes a good polish and is used as marble.   The formation is peculiar in being made up very largely of the stems and other parts of crinoids.   More crinoids have come from it than from any other formation in America, and fine collections of them are in many museums.

Zinc and Lead.   In southwestern Missouri and adjacent parts of Oklahoma and Kansas, great numbers of caves and sink holes formed in

---

[2] Dr. G. A. Cooper of the United States National Museum and other geologists working with him have recovered literally millions of fossil shells from the Permian reefs of the Glass Mountains.   The shells have been replaced by silica, and Dr. Cooper has freed them from the rocks by dissolving more than 12 tons of the rock in acid.

Mississippian limestone before Pennsylvanian time; and, when the Pennsylvanian seas came over the region, they washed the residual chert from the hills into the sink holes and later covered the entire region with clay that now forms extensive shale deposits.

Circulating warm waters carrying lead, zinc, calcium, silicon, iron, and sulfur in solution deposited minerals of these metals between the pieces of chert that filled the sinks and buried caves. The resulting zinc-lead deposits were thus a heterogeneous mixture of galena, sphalerite, dolomite, calcite, quartz, pyrite, and chert. Crystals of calcite 6 inches in diameter are not rare, and masses of galena and sphalerite weighing several hundred pounds have been found. This is the most important zinc-producing region of the world, and lead valued at about one-fourth the worth of the zinc comes from the same region. It was formerly known as the "Joplin district," as Joplin was the main city of the region, but as most of the mining is now in Oklahoma and Kansas it is known at present as the "Tri-State" district.

Pennsylvanian. *Coal.* The Pennsylvanian is the great mineral producer, as the two mineral products (coal and oil) most important in amount and value come from it. About 90 per cent of the coal mined in North America comes from rocks of Pennsylvanian age. All of the coal of the United States east of eastern Kansas is of this age, except small deposits in Virginia and North Carolina. Pennsylvania is the chief coal-producing state and contains large deposits of both anthracite and bituminous coal. The anthracite deposits are in the northeastern part of the state. They are the only large anthracite deposits in the United States, and they underlie only a small area. The rocks in which they occur were intensely folded and the change from bituminous to anthracite probably took place during the folding (page 380). Since the folding, erosion has removed most of the coal-bearing strata and many times as much anthracite has been carried away by streams as has been left behind.

The finest deposit of bituminous coal in the United States is the Pittsburgh bed known as the "black diamond coal"; it was largely responsible for the growth of various manufactories in Pittsburgh. It cokes readily and is valuable for smelting iron. Many of the early iron mines were near enough to Pittsburgh to cause the smelting industry to grow up there, and, when the richer iron deposits of the Lake Superior region were discovered, it was cheaper to bring the ore to Pittsburgh than to ship the coal to the ore. The Pittsburgh bed underlay an area of 2,100 square miles, averaged about 7 feet thick, and is of very high quality. In spite of its thickness and extent, it is nearly exhausted and coal will be shipped from distant fields to Pittsburgh within a few years. For the accumulation of the Pittsburgh bed of coal, a swamp with an area of possibly 3,000 square miles must have existed for many thousands of years.

In some places in Pennsylvania and West Virginia, more than 50 beds of coal are present in the same section, and beds of marine origin alternate with most of the beds. There must have been more than 50 advances and retreats of the sea in such a region.

The total coal reserve in Pennsylvanian rocks is vast, but it is not inexhaustible and the more easily obtainable coal is being rapidly mined. About 545,000,000 tons of coal per year are mined from Pennsylvanian rocks. In general, the bituminous coal from the western part of the area is poorer than that from the eastern; the change to poorer coal is fairly gradual and constant westward.

For the century ending with 1935, coal was the most valuable mineral product of the world, and no nation reached industrial supremacy without access to large supplies of it. Most nations have guarded their supplies with great care, but the United States has always been prodigal of all of its natural resources and not until within the last few years has it made any effort to conserve them. Coal was mined in such a manner as to leave quantities underground that can never be recovered, and a great deal of that mined was wasted. Many mining restrictions have been enacted into law in some coal-producing states and more are needed. Such restrictions necessarily increase the price of the product, but the increase is not large, and the people of a nation should be glad to help in conservation to prevent deterioration and conserve for posterity. Conservation could be attained by the use of more efficient coal-burning engines. The average engine that uses coal for fuel gets only about 20 per cent of the power that might be obtained from the coal; 60 per cent would reduce the consumption of coal to less than half what it is today, as about three-fourths of the coal consumed is used in engines of various kinds. The United States produces more than half of the coal of the world, but exports little.

The question is often raised whether coal is forming at the present time. The answer is in the affirmative, but it is forming in only small areas and in small amounts. If one considers that the Pennsylvanian coal was at least 10,000,000 years in forming, with one-fourth of the United States under swamps, he will see that the rate was very slow. Vegetation is not accumulating today under conditions that would permit its formation into coal fast enough to keep one big factory running.

Oil and Gas. Since the invention of the internal-combustion engine such as is used in the automobile, petroleum has come to compete with coal as a producer of power, and many industries are directly dependent on petroleum or natural gas for their existence. Within the last 25 years world production of petroleum has increased from about 300,000,000 to nearly 4,000,000,000 barrels per year. This has raised the production and refining of petroleum to one of the big industries. The value of the annual petroleum production in the United States is greater than that of coal.

The Oklahoma-Kansas oil field has long been a large producer of petroleum for the manufacture of gasoline, and until 1927 almost the entire production came from Pennsylvanian rocks. While the areas east of Oklahoma were swampy land, a sea extended northward from Texas through Oklahoma and Kansas into Nebraska. The sea was shallow and abounded in animal life, and petroleum formed in it in great quantities. The rocks consisted of limestone, sandstones, and shales in alternating beds. Oil formed in shales and limestones and migrated into the sandstones. During the Permian, low folds formed in the rocks of Oklahoma and Kansas (at about the same time that the Appalachian Mountains were forming), and the oil migrated into the anticlines, from which it is obtained today.

Almost incredible amounts of oil are obtained from some wells and from some areas. The largest well ever brought in, in the Midcontinent province, made about 140,000 barrels per day, but most wells make a few to 5,000 barrels per day. A vast number of anticlines have been drilled in Oklahoma and Kansas and hundreds of them produced oil. This is a high average, as not more than about one-fifth of the anticlines of the United States have produced even where all conditions seemed favorable. The Pennsylvanian produces from many beds and that accounts for the production in so many individual pools.

The production from the oil fields of Oklahoma and Kansas has averaged about 300,000,000 barrels per year for the last 10 years. The oil is of high grade, although not so high as the oils from Pennsylvania and West Virginia that come from older rocks. The age of the rocks that produce petroleum seems to have little to do with the grade of oil produced. In some places high-grade oil is produced from younger strata and deeper drilling gets low-grade oil from the older rocks, and in other fields the reverse is the case.

There is a general idea that oil is in some way associated with coal and occurs only where coal beds are present, but oil and coal have no necessary relationship. Some of the largest oil fields have no coal and many of the largest coal fields have no oil. The two are formed under radically different conditions, oil always associated with bodies of still water, usually the sea, and coal, with swampy conditions. Oil is not always associated with salt water in the wells, although some people not familiar with oil production think that the finding of salt water in a well indicates that oil will be found and that the absence of salt water presages absence of oil.

Most of the more recent discoveries in Oklahoma and Kansas are in Ordovician and other early Paleozoic rocks. The shallow Pennsylvanian pools are becoming depleted, but deeper Pennsylvanian fields are being found in the Anadarko basin of western Oklahoma. The largest single oil area discovered in the last few years is the Pennsylvanian reef area of Texas, centering about Scurry County. The oil is trapped in thick limestone reef ridges surrounded by shale. The area has about the same amount of oil as has the Alberta fields in the somewhat different coral reefs of the Devonian.

Clay. Clay for the manufacture of brick, tile, and pottery comes in large part from Pennsylvanian shales, and fire clay, which is used in making brick for furnace linings and for other objects which must withstand great heat, occurs at many places in association with coal.

Iron. Extensive deposits of iron minerals were formed in Pennsylvanian swamps. Most of this ore is of low grade and in small deposits, and will not be mined until the cheaper high-grade ores of other periods are exhausted.

Permian. Economic deposits are numerous in Permian rocks but have been extensively utilized only in the last 20 years. Captain Bonneville, whose biography was written by Washington Irving, camped near an oil seep along the Oregon Trail and recorded its presence in his journal. A well drilled there in 1883 obtained black oil from the Permian rocks, and the well is still producing. There are several good Permian oil fields in Wyoming, but the most important ones are in West Texas and southeastern New Mexico. Yates pool in West Texas has yielded more then 300,000,000 barrels of oil from solution pores in Permian limestone, and single wells there have yielded up to 50,000 barrels per day. Many large and important oil fields in the area produce from sandstones, limestones, and dolomites from various levels in the thick Permian sedimentary section.

The largest known gypsum deposits of North America are in the Permian of southeastern New Mexico, but they are not being utilized. Rock salt in thick beds has a total thickness of more than a thousand feet at places under West Texas and New Mexico. Potash was deposited in the late stages of evaporation of the Permian basins and large quantities of this substance are now being produced from deep mines near Carlsbad, New Mexico, for fertilizer, munitions, and chemical uses.

In Wyoming, Montana, Utah, Idaho, and Colorado there are extensive beds of rock phosphate which are an important potential source of fertilizers. Fertilizers must come to be used more extensively in the United States as soils wear out. The phosphate of this region is being mined at few places at the present time and in small quantity. The government has withdrawn most of the phosphate areas from homestead entry and the deposits will finally be leased to producers.

Although, potentially, the Permian contains mineral deposits of great value, at present its production is small.

RECAPITULATION OF PALEOZOIC LIFE

In the Cambrian period, the seas brought in the first abundant life, which consisted mainly of brachiopods and trilobites. In the Ordovician many new groups of animals originated, most significant of which were the cephalopods and fishes. The trilobites and brachiopods increased in numbers over those of the first period, but they no longer dominated. In the Silurian, scorpions—the first air breathers—are known from the shores of the lakes which dried up late in the period. In this period coral reefs appear for the first time. The Devonian period is known as the "Age of Fishes" owing to the great expansion and development of the group during this time. During the same period, the amphibians (next higher group of vertebrates) appeared, and the trilobites began to take on old-age characteristics, which preceded their disappearance. In the Devonian, also, the first forests appeared.

The remarkable developments in the life of the Mississippian were the great abundance of crinoids and the number and variety of sharks. In the Pennsylvanian the amphibians gave rise to great numbers of highly varied forms and the reptiles evolved from them. Insects appeared for the first time. The expansion of plant life was significant, particularly the formation of coal from the plants.

The last period saw the remarkable evolution of strange reptiles, the development of large amphibians, the final dominance of the brachiopods, and, finally, the beginning of great reduction in all types of life and the disappearance of the trilobites and blastoids and of many of the reptiles.

CHAPTER 22

THE MESOZOIC ERA

The word "Mesozoic" means "middle life" and suggests life midway from its origin to its present condition. The term is only relative as the era is far later than the middle of geologic history, and animals and plants had progressed much beyond the middle in the evolutionary scale. However, the term is a good one as, in general, it connotes the situation correctly. The Mesozoic was not nearly so long as the Paleozoic, possibly 150,000,000 years in all. It is divided into only three periods: Triassic, Jurassic, and Cretaceous, and the same principles apply in the division into periods as are used for the Paleozoic.

When the Paleozoic closed with the uplift of the North American continent and the formation of the Appalachian Mountains, there seems to have been no sea left over any part of North America. All of the continent was exposed to erosion and was deeply dissected in many areas before the readvance of seas.

Causes of Sea Advances. It may be well to repeat the causes for advancing of the seas before taking up the physical history of the Mesozoic. First in order is the downwarping of the land or the upwarping of the sea basin. Downwarping of the land allows the seas to come in locally over the areas affected, and upwarping of the sea basin causes general sea advance. The second cause is the downcutting of the land by streams and other agents, which may bring it low enough to allow the seas to advance with very little rise of sea level. The third cause, the filling of seas by piling up sediments in them as streams carry materials from the lands, goes along with the downcutting. Both the cutting down of the land and the piling up of the materials in the seas make the differences between the depth of sea bottom and height of land smaller than they were before.

The Mesozoic-Paleozoic Boundary. As the Mesozoic-Paleozoic boundary is one of the most important in the geologic column, one would expect to find a plainly evident physical break there. In order to get first hand information about the boundary, geologists go to a place where it is exposed, the rocks of the Mesozoic resting directly on those of the Paleozoic. In eastern North America there is no place where oldest

Mesozoic rocks rest on youngest Paleozoic. No rocks of the first part of the Mesozoic, and none of latest Paleozoic, are present in or east of the Appalachian Mountains. One must go as far west as the Wasatch Mountains in Utah to find the contact of oldest Mesozoic and youngest Paleozoic beds (Fig. 373).

From what we have learned of geologic history and of Paleozoic rocks, have we anything definite to anticipate about the contact? We know that the Paleozoic closed with the folding of the Appalachian Mountain

FIG. 373. Contact between Paleozoic and Mesozoic rocks where the Paleozoic rocks are horizontal.

region and general uplift of the entire continent. Erosion was in progress on the entire continent for some time before seas came in again over the land. The first of the Mesozoic sediments would be deposited on rock surfaces produced by erosion, but on what kinds of rocks? Are the Paleozoic rocks different from the Mesozoic? In anticipating the appearance of the contact we should remember that the Mesozoic rocks were deposited millions of years ago and all have been subject to pressure and cementation, some to deformation and metamorphism.

The contact in the Wasatch Mountains shows nothing very striking, and expert geologists might pass it many times without finding it. Both Paleozoic and Mesozoic formations consist of shale, sandstone, and limestone, and the kind of rock gives no clue to the place of contact. In this region there was no deformation of the Paleozoic beds before the

Mesozoic seas came in and so the Mesozoic beds are parallel with the Paleozoic (Fig. 373).   Pre-Mesozoic erosion had not greatly roughened the surface of the Paleozoic rocks, and thus the slightly irregular surface on which the oldest Mesozoic sediments were deposited is not apparent in most places, even where recent erosion has exposed the contact.

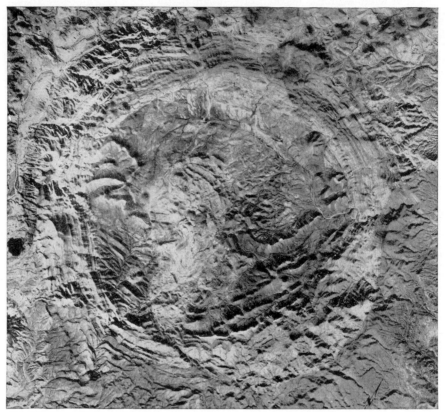

FIG. 374. The Solitario.   Mesozoic rocks in a truncated dome unconformable on steeply dipping Paleozoic rocks which make ridges within the inner circle.   The hill in the center is a Cenozoic volcanic neck, the third ridge of the rim is a sill, and the dark patch at the left is a lava flow.   (*Courtesy of Edgar Tobin Aerial Surveys.*)

Fossils in the rocks are, therefore, the only means of determining the contact, and the Wasatch Mountains section fails the geologist in that the lowest Mesozoic rocks are nonfossiliferous.

In many places in the Rocky Mountains, a red sandstone overlies limestone that contains Permian fossils.   Near the bottom of the sandstone one bed contains Mesozoic fossils, and on that account the line of contact is drawn at the base of the red sandstone.   The fossils are indicative of the age of the rock, and the change from limestone to red sandstone shows marked differences in physical conditions under which the rocks formed. After long investigations in this field, an unconformity was detected at the base of the red sandstone, and it helps to fix the place of contact.

If one could find a place where the latest Paleozoic rocks had been folded and eroded before the early Mesozoic rocks were deposited, the contact would appear definite and unmistakable, although it could not be identified as the Paleozoic-Mesozoic boundary without determining, by the fossils, the age of the rocks both above and below the unconformity (Fig. 374). Such a contact would suggest larger changes than those separating most periods and, therefore, might be an era boundary.

The changes in animals and plants from late Paleozoic to early Mesozoic were the largest recorded in geologic history from one period to the next succeeding, and the differences in fossils first gave rise to the era division. Geologists are accustomed to finding fossils of one period definitely related to those of the preceding, but early Mesozoic forms are so different from those of the late Paleozoic that they might almost belong on another planet. In order to bring about such marked changes in life, there must have been events as revolutionary in other parts of the earth as the elevation and folding of the Appalachian area that took place in eastern North America.

CHAPTER 23

LOWER MESOZOIC; TRIASSIC PERIOD

The Triassic (the oldest period of the Mesozoic) was named from its threefold development in the Alps. No such development occurs in America, where the history of the period was strikingly different from that in Europe and its record far less complete.

First Advance of Seas. The highlands at the close of the Paleozoic were of sufficient extent to keep the seas from advancing over any considerable area of the continent for a long period of time, and to prevent large invasions except where marked downwarping had taken place. It is not surprising that the first sea invasions were small, and, as the Appalachian Mountains had formed near the Atlantic Coast, we should not expect the earliest sea advance to have been on that coast. During the first period of the Mesozoic, the seas did not advance on either the Atlantic or Gulf Coasts, but all invasions were from the Pacific. At first the seas spread over a very narrow margin of land near the present Pacific Coast, and gradually crept in farther and farther. Although there were no mountains in the Pacific region, there were low ranges of hills and highland areas that caused irregular distribution of the seas. Near eastern California, a range of hills restricted the sea advance, but valleys through the hills, or gaps between them, allowed the seas to spread eastward into the area of the present Rocky Mountains and Great Basin (Fig. 375).[1]

Formation of Red Beds. From some source this eastern sea was supplied with red sand, and the sandstones, generally designated as the "red beds," were deposited over an area stretching from central Montana to central New Mexico and from eastern Colorado to Nevada. The red sandstones are the most noticeable, though not the most widespread, of the Mesozoic formations of North America. Along with the sandstones, red shales and siltstones were formed, and in many places gypsum was deposited. The gypsum indicates aridity while it was forming. Red sediments may also indicate aridity, but it should not be inferred on the basis of red color alone. West of the hills that restricted the

---

[1] Geologists are not in agreement on the extent of Triassic seas.

Triassic seas no red beds were formed, although the area seems to have been under the sea during most of the Triassic.   In California and western Nevada the deposits were mainly limestones.   Near-shore phases were conglomerates and sandstones, and offshore deposits included much shale.

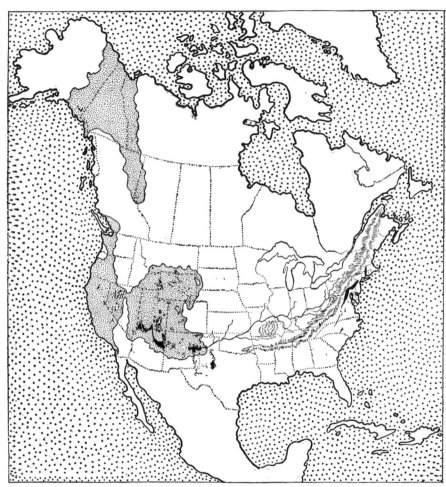

FIG. 375. Triassic seas.   Epicontinental seas in fine stipple; outcrops in black.

No Triassic rocks are exposed between the Rocky and Appalachian Mountains except in the Black Hills region, and it is probable that none was formed except in the vicinity of the front ranges of the Rockies.

Brown Sandstones.   In the late Paleozoic, synclines, anticlines, and faults, originating at the same time as the Appalachians and running parallel to them, formed eastward as far as the present coast line.   There is no evidence that any of the synclines was below sea level during the

Triassic, but they were the sites of rivers and lakes in which there formed alluvial fans and flood-plain deposits similar to those now forming in the Great Valley of California. In some places the intervening hills were high, and coarse materials were washed from them into the valleys. The streams were vigorous and deposited sand and gravel more extensively than the finer materials. Brown shale, siltstone, sandstone, and coarser-grained rocks were formed in the old synclines from northern Massachusetts to North Carolina (Fig. 375).

Many buildings in New York, New Haven, and other cities near or on the Triassic deposits were built of what was called the "Connecticut brownstone" before brick became cheaper and the fashion in stone changed. The brownstone fronts were once among the finest dwellings of New York City, and great rows of brownstone buildings may still be seen, although they have now become poor class and are rapidly being replaced by more modern brick buildings.

The eastern Triassic rocks are red or brown, but no gypsum is associated with them and the climate was not arid. Moist climate is indicated by coal deposits of Virginia and North Carolina. Coal from these beds was the first to be mined and used in the United States.

Volcanism. In New York, Massachusetts, Connecticut, and New Jersey, the Triassic was a period of great igneous activity. In the Connecticut Valley, lavas were extruded into a large syncline, were covered later by sediments and, in turn, by more lava. Magma rose through fissures and spread out laterally as sills, but most of the flat-lying basalts represent lava flows rather than sills or other magma intrusions. Much faulting took place in the synclines, producing many conduits through which the lavas issued.

The Hudson River, in its lower course, cuts through one of the old sills where they are columnar in structure. The Palisades consist of vertical prisms of basalt, which may be clearly seen for long distances. The Triassic igneous rocks are basalt and were extruded or intruded near the close of the period.

North American Seas and Outcrops. By examining the map (Fig. 375) of the Triassic seas and outcrops, you will see that they cover only small areas compared to those of most periods that we have studied and that the general distribution is greatly different from that of Paleozoic periods.

LIFE OF THE TRIASSIC

The greatest known break (or perhaps it would be more accurate to say the greatest known changes) in the life of the world as indicated by fossils is that from late Paleozoic to early Mesozoic, often spoken of as coming between Paleozoic and Mesozoic.

Invertebrates. In general, invertebrates were the dominant animals of the Paleozoic and vertebrates of the Mesozoic. Four classes of Paleozoic invertebrates were considered particularly because they were highly characteristic. Trilobites were abundant in early Paleozoic, but no specimen has ever been found in a Mesozoic rock. Brachiopods, although abundant to the close of the Paleozoic, became so rare that one may collect in highly fossiliferous Triassic rocks for many days without finding a specimen. Fossiliferous Paleozoic rocks are characterized by the presence of either trilobites or brachiopods or both; whereas fossiliferous Mesozoic rocks are characterized by the absence of trilobites and the rarity of brachiopods. Paleozoic and Mesozoic rocks may be distinguished also by cephalopods, a group of invertebrates that is common in the Paleozoic from the Ordovician onward and abundant in the Mesozoic. The cephalopod has a chambered shell, but the partitions between the chambers of most Paleozoic cephalopods were

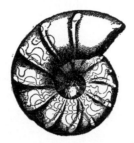

FIG. 376. A Triassic cephalopod with complex sutures at the left (*from Texas Geological Survey*), compared with a Paleozoic cephalopod with simple sutures (*from J. P. Smith*).

simple, whereas in the Mesozoic they were exceedingly complex (Fig. 376). The presence of very complex partitions, which are indicated on the outer side of the shell by sutures, is sufficient to determine that a rock is Mesozoic rather than Paleozoic.

In the earliest Triassic seas of California, Nevada, and Utah, many complex-sutured cephalopods lived. Some of the rocks are almost entirely made up of them, and throughout the period cephalopods were the most abundant animals. However, east of California and Nevada they did not last beyond the lower part of the Triassic. When the red sandstone and gypsum of the Rocky Mountain and Great Basin regions began to form, the cephalopods must have either emigrated or perished, and in the major part of the great series of red beds no cephalopods have been found. Few other marine invertebrates were present.[2]

Crinoids constitute another group of invertebrates that are very abun-

[2] The absence of marine invertebrates from the red beds has led many geologists to believe that the formations are continental in origin rather than marine, in spite of the extensive gypsum deposits in them; and, although geologists agree that large parts of the red beds are marine, some contend that considerable parts are continental. All believe that the parts that bear fossils of land vertebrates are mainly continental.

dant in some Paleozoic rocks.   The crinoids became very rare in the
Mesozoic and their fossils are practically absent from Triassic rocks.

The clam group (pelecypods) was abundant from Ordovician to the
end of the Paleozoic.   They were abundant in part of other Mesozoic
faunas but were rare in most of the Triassic.

Vertebrates.   Although it may not be possible for us to arrive at any
appreciation of the real differences between Paleozoic and Mesozoic
invertebrates, we can see the differences between the vertebrates, because
we are more familiar with them.   The oldest vertebrates, the fishes,
first appeared in the Ordovician period of the Paleozoic.   In the Devonian came the amphibians, which were capable of breathing air and had

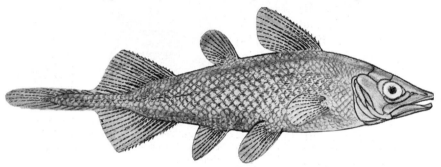

FIG. 377. A Triassic bony fish found in the library excavation at Princeton University and restored from
x-ray photographs. (*Courtesy of Glenn L. Jepson.*)

developed walking legs and a higher organization than fishes.   In the
Pennsylvanian, reptiles appeared, and in the Permian they became
rather abundant in some areas although most of them were of groups
that did not survive the Paleozoic.   The Mesozoic is known as the
"Age of Reptiles," and properly so, although the history of the reptiles
of the Mesozoic is still imperfectly known.

Reptiles of Western North America.   The oldest reptiles known from
the continental deposits of the Mesozoic of North America were found
in the red beds of the Rocky Mountain region and are about Middle
Triassic in age.   The number of kinds of these reptiles is small compared
to the number present in the Permian, and nearly all belong to a crocodile-
like group (Fig. 378).   In form they resemble the long-snouted crocodiles
that now inhabit the rivers of southern Asia.   Several different kinds
that lived during Middle and Upper Triassic left their remains in the
western red beds and they were probably rather numerous in the rivers.
Some fossils of other kinds of reptiles (one, a small dinosaur) have been
found in the red beds, but they make up a small part of the total and
need not be considered at this place.

Amphibians of Western North America.   Large amphibians were
rivals of the reptiles for the supremacy of the lands and rivers near the

western seas. Some of them were nearly 10 feet long, and skulls 30
inches long by 18 inches wide have been found (Fig. 379). These amphibians were the largest of their kind that ever lived in America. They
were the last of the old type of amphibian, and, in later periods, their
place was taken by the toad and salamander types. These amphibians
were clumsy, slow-moving creatures, and their bulk alone enabled them
to compete with the reptiles. They were heavily armored on the ventral
surface of the body, but the armor was of little use as a protection from
the reptiles because they were unprotected on the back. Perhaps the

FIG. 378. A Triassic crocodile-like reptile chasing a small dinosaur. (*From M. G. Mehl.*)

faunas of the Triassic rivers of the West may be compared with those of
the upper reaches of the Congo River—the crocodiles there representing
the reptiles; the hippopotamuses representing the amphibians. Such a
comparison is for numbers and sizes only as the amphibians are not
related to the hippopotamuses. However, one who has seen pictures of
the life of the upper Congo might replace the huge clumsy mammals with
amphibians of much the same weight, though not so tall, and thus get a
living picture. The crocodilians were smaller than those of the Congo
and were not of such predatory habits. The resemblance ends with the
two kinds of animals, as other kinds were very rare.

Faunas of Eastern North America. The best representation of Triassic
land life in any part of North America is from the deposits in the old
synclines in Connecticut. The same type of crocodile-like animals (Fig.
380) as those in the west was present here, but not as the most numerous
forms. Another **group**, destined to become the most abundant and

largest of the Mesozoic animals, the dinosaurs, had made its appearance. Tracks (Fig. 381) of the dinosaurs in the Connecticut Valley first attracted attention. Some of the sandstone surfaces there are marked with a complete network of tracks of various sizes and kinds. These were called "bird tracks," or more specifically, "turkey tracks," when they were first found, and a book was written on the bird tracks of the Connecticut Valley. The tracks look like those made by birds, and many of them were made by three-toed animals that walked on only two legs.

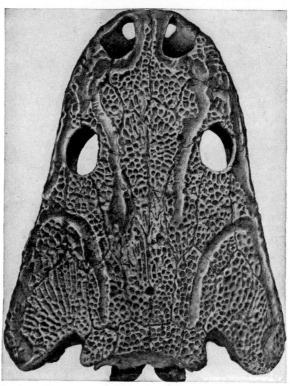

FIG. 379. Skull of a large Triassic amphibian. The animal was probably more than 10 feet long.

The number of kinds of tracks is much greater than the number of kinds of bones that has been discovered, but a few kinds of dinosaur bones have been collected and the peculiarities of the animals worked out. The rarity of the bones was such that at first they were collected no matter what the difficulty. It is told of Professor O. C. Marsh of Yale College that on finding dinosaur bones in the rocks of a bridge he succeeded in having the bridge torn down so that he might get the bones.

Although some of the Triassic dinosaurs were larger than horses, none of them reached such a size as to suggest that their descendants were to be the largest of all land animals. At this early stage they had begun

FIG. 380. A crocodile-like reptile from the Triassic of the Connecticut Valley. (*An unpublished drawing by Williston.*)

FIG. 381. Dinosaur tracks from the Triassic of the Connecticut Valley. (*After Moore.*)

to show varied and striking characteristics. Some were carnivorous, with long, strong teeth and others were strictly herbivorous. Some were quadrupedal and others had the forefeet reduced to small size, walked on strongly developed hind legs, and dragged a heavy tail that balanced the body. Some had solid, heavy bones and others had hollow, light bones and were agile jumpers. If one could have observed the life in the Connecticut lowlands, he would have been struck by the great variety in kinds of land animals of large size.

Amphibians similar to those of the West, but smaller, were present in the Connecticut Valley.

Swimming Reptiles. It seems that the occurrence of great variations in reptiles had two climaxes: the first coming in the late Paleozoic, the second in the first period of the Mesozoic. In central Europe and far-western North America, the developing reptiles lived near the sea margins, and it is not strange that some of them became good swimmers and finally took up their habitat in the seas. This was true of two large orders of reptiles that originated during Triassic time. Both developed paddles instead of feet and were good swimmers, but in other respects the orders were decidedly different. Reptiles of one order, the ichthyo-

FIG. 382. A peculiar small reptile from the Triassic of Europe. (*After A. S. Romer, "Vertebrate Paleontology."*)

saurs, had a very short neck and a long tail, which was the main swimming appendage; those of the other order, the plesiosaurs, had a very long neck and short tail.

Flying and Other Reptiles. Though the water afforded one habitat in which great specialization could take place, the air furnished another, and flying reptiles in primitive, poorly developed form appeared during the Triassic. (Flying reptiles will be described more fully in Jurassic and Cretaceous faunas.) Primitive forms of such modern reptiles as lizards and turtles also made their first appearance in the Triassic. Several other orders, which are not important enough for us to consider here, also appeared. This was a time of great variety of specialization and the appearance of numerous new forms. At such times the origin of strikingly different forms may be expected, and it was here that the culmination of animal life, the mammals, made its appearance.

Appearance of Mammals. The change from some highly specialized reptiles to lower types of mammals was not very large. Differences between the two as to the skeletal framework, *i.e.*, the bones, are small, and experts disagree as to what these differences really are. One rather pronounced difference between mammals and reptiles is in the teeth, which are differentiated into incisors, canines, and molars in mammals but not in reptiles. The lower jaw of reptiles articulates with a bone in the skull called the "quadrate" (Fig. 383). No quadrate is present in mammals, and their jaw articulation is quite different. The reduction and disappearance of the quadrate bone and the differentiation of the teeth into incisors, canines, and molars may be considered as transitional stages from reptiles to mammals. Both of these changes were taking place in one group of reptiles that lived in Triassic time in South Africa.

We readily tell the difference between mammals and reptiles by the hair on the bodies of the one and scales on the bodies of the other and

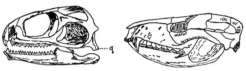

FIG. 383. Skull of a reptile on the left, of an early mammal on the right. The quadrate bone (q) present in the reptile skull is not seen in the mammal skull.

FIG. 384. Mammal-like reptiles from the Triassic of South Africa. (From a painting by C. R. Knight. Courtesy of Chicago Museum of Natural History.)

by the fact that mammals suckle their young and reptiles feed theirs in other ways. There are several anatomical differences in the soft parts of the bodies of mammals and reptiles, and there are embryological differences, but geologists can find no evidence on the time of origin of hair, the suckling of the young, or the embryological differences, as none of the soft parts is preserved in the fossil state. Fossils furnish direct evidence only of changes of the skeletal parts.

The appearance of mammals would have seemed to be of little importance if one could have observed this appearance and known the details.

Throughout the Mesozoic, mammals were small, rare, weak, and seemed to have little chance in competition with the reptiles. One might as readily predict that the descendant of some small form of the present, say the mouse, would finally become ruler of the earth, as to have said in Mesozoic times that mammals were the coming rulers.

FIG. 385. Fossil tree trunk in Petrified Trees National Monument, Arizona, weathered out to form a natural bridge. (*Photograph by W. T. Lee, courtesy of U.S. Geological Survey.*)

Plants. Among the striking curiosities for tourists who travel through western United States are the numerous petrified forests. Those of Arizona are well known and most of them are in Triassic red beds. Large trees are preserved in great numbers. The trunks are silicified (Figs. 141, 142, 385), and the silica is of many colors, giving a striking appearance to the petrified wood. In the main petrified forest, thousands of the trees have weathered out of the rock and lie scattered over the clays and sands of the red rocks. As they are much harder than the rest of the rock they remain behind after it has been eroded away. Trunks of trees 3 feet in diameter and 100 feet long have been found. Petrified forests in the Triassic are also rather common in New Mexico, Colorado, and Utah, and petrified wood is abundant in Wyoming. A peculiarity of some of the petrified forests is that the trees have no bark. They seem to have been transported for long distances and to have had the bark worn off in transit. Modern flowering plants had not appeared but conifers were abundant and, with the fern group, made up most of the Triassic flora.

MISCELLANEOUS

Climate. The cold climates of late Paleozoic gave place to warmer ones, and, before Middle Triassic, warm climates prevailed over most of the earth. Lower Mesozoic rocks are not known in many places in high latitudes, but in Spitzbergen, at 75° north latitude, the animal and plant life was much like that described for the Connecticut Valley. Reptiles and amphibians flourished there, and they cannot survive in very cold climates, as they are cold blooded (*i.e.*, their blood takes on the temperature of the surrounding medium). Rings of growth were not present in the Triassic trees, indicating absence of seasonal changes of climate. Gypsum deposits point to aridity in parts of the Rocky Mountain region, but arid conditions were local. The presence of large petrified trees points to abundant rainfall, but the trees may have grown in higher, more moist regions and been transported to the lower, arid places.

Economic Products.   The Triassic furnishes the least value in economic products of any period thus far considered.   The brownstones of the eastern deposits, some of the coal of North Carolina and Virginia, road metal from the igneous rocks, and the gypsum of the Rocky Mountain region constitute the small list.   Although gypsum occurs in great quantities, little is used.

Close of the Triassic.   No large continental movements took place to bring the Triassic to a close.   The seas gradually withdrew until none was left on the continent of North America.

CHAPTER 24

MIDDLE MESOZOIC; JURASSIC PERIOD

The term "Jurassic" was derived from the Jura Mountains located between Switzerland and France, where rocks of the period are well exposed. In North America, the seas advanced only from the Pacific Ocean during the early part of the period and spread eastward to eastern California (Fig. 386). Later, a sea advanced from the Gulf of Mexico through Mexico and Texas. Still later, an Arctic sea transgressed southward through western Canada into Montana and Wyoming and as far south as central Colorado. There were no Jurassic seas in the eastern part of the continent; this is the only period of geologic history in which no deposits are known east of the middle of the continent.

All Jurassic seas, except those near the Pacific Coast, were short lived, and the deposits in them were thin, not being more than 400 feet thick in most places. It is evident that a thin deposit, formed in a sea such as advanced from the Arctic, must consist quite largely of sediments formed as the sea was advancing and retreating. Such deposits would be made up largely of granules, sands, silts, and clays. Also, if the seas were shallow, sediments would not be well sorted, as materials after settling to the bottom might be disturbed by storm waves and mixed up with other materials, sands with clays, and pebbles with sands. Limestones would have little chance to form where the storm waves struck the bottom, and, although calcium carbonate might be deposited on the bottom, large storms would create waves that would mix it with sand, silt, and clay. In some places in Montana, Wyoming, Utah, Colorado, Idaho, and British Columbia, the seas were deep enough to permit limestones 40 to 50 feet thick to form over large areas.

Morrison Formation. In the Rocky Mountain region the formation called "Morrison" has long been under discussion as to whether it is Jurassic or Cretaceous. Although the authors recognize the controversial nature of the subject, the formation will be called "Jurassic" in this text. The Morrison overlaps the marine deposits formed by the sea that came in from the north and lies unconformably on them. The extent of the Morrison is great and it is worthy of consideration because of the fossils it contains. The presence of land fossils (in large numbers), poor bedding, poor sorting of materials, and loess and dune deposits indicate that it was continental in origin. Great variety of coloring, ranging through blues, greens, yellows, and reds; colors not confined to particular

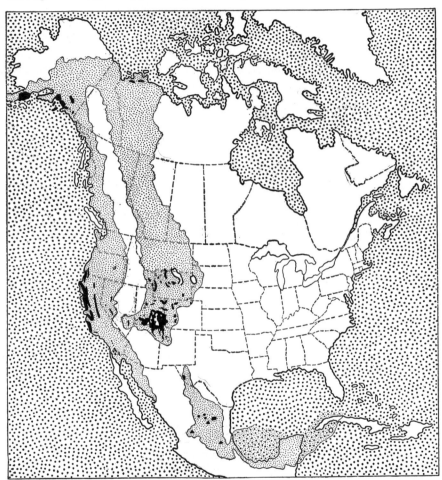

FIG. 386. Jurassic seas. Epicontinental seas in fine stipple; outcrops in black. (*Seas modified from Schuchert.*)

beds but crossing from one to another; and many pieces of wood in various beds are contributing evidences concerning origin.

LIFE OF THE JURASSIC

Marine Invertebrates. Life in the Jurassic seas shows general development from that of the Triassic. In North America, the seas were not so dominated by cephalopods as in the preceding period.

Fewer fossils are known from the Jurassic of America than from any other period; this is directly opposite to the condition in Europe, where Jurassic fossils are very abundant. Oysters and other pelecypods and a new type of cephalopod, with an internal shell, that looks like a slender cigar were common in the North American seas (Fig. 387).

Dinosaurs. The main interest in Jurassic life in America is in the land vertebrates, and most of these are contained in the Morrison formation. The most abundant fossils in the Morrison are dinosaurs, more of which have been collected from it than from all other formations in America, and more than from any other formation in the world. In March of 1878, three men independently discovered dinosaur remains in Colorado and Wyoming, the first reported from America. Professor O. C. Marsh of Yale College and Professor E. D. Cope of the Philadelphia Academy of Sciences became particularly interested in the dinosaur remains and soon had collecting parties in the field. The main areas from which collections have been made are near Morrison, Colorado, Wyoming, and Utah. The earlier collectors labored under great difficulties, for example, hostile Indians, and lack of roads, transportation, and money. Collecting vertebrate fossils requires a great deal of money; invertebrates may be collected without such great expenditure.

FIG. 387. Jurassic invertebrate fossils. Upper left, an oyster; lower right, a clam; upper right, a cephalopod with part of the shell removed to show one suture; lower left, internal shell of a new kind of cephalopod called Belemnite (Jove's thunderbolt). All about ⅓ natural size.

It was not until early in the twentieth century that systematic collecting of dinosaurs was undertaken. The older collectors picked up bones that lay on the surface and dug out those that could be easily obtained or were not too deeply covered. The modern collector of dinosaurs on finding bones scattered over the surface locates the place where the bones are in the solid rock by tracing the fragments of bone up-slope to their highest occurrence and then starts digging and quarrying the overlying rock. If he finds that the larger part of one animal or several animals are likely to be present, he puts a force of men to work removing the rock above the bones. The men may use scrapers and steam shovels to take the materials away and may loosen the solid rock by blasting. As the workers come close to the bone, they carefully chisel and cut away the rock near the bone itself and finally lay bare all of the skeleton (Fig. 388) present in the rock.   The fossils are then removed in blocks of rock as large as can be handled conveniently, and shipped to the museum to be prepared.   The enclosing rock may be cut away to leave the bones in relief, or the bones may be completely freed and mounted as skeletons.

The lands must have swarmed with dinosaurs in the Jurassic, comparable in numbers to those of the wild animals of present-day Africa. They were probably more numerous than modern African elephants but not so numerous as the bison once were in North America.   Orig-

FIG. 388. Several feet of rock have been removed from above this dinosaur, and the man is preparing the bones so that they can be transported.   (*After Matthew, courtesy of American Museum of Natural History.*)

inating in the Triassic, the dinosaur group progressed to greatest size and variety in Morrison time.   Morrison fossils furnish a splendid picture in comparison with which other dinosaur assemblages seem meager.   This picture would have been one of many had conditions been favorable for the preservation of fossils during all of the Mesozoic— actually it is comparable to one chapter out of a book of one hundred or more chapters.   We must, then, make the most of this fragmentary record.

On collecting specimens from the Morrison, or examining those already collected, one is impressed first by the huge size of some of them.   Dinosaur means "terrible reptile" and the name was given more on account of the size of the animals than their ferocity, although some of the species look sufficiently ferocious to warrant the appellation.   When one finds a single vertebra too large for him to lift or a leg bone 6 feet long and 8 inches in diameter, he is likely to wonder what sort of creatures lived in those days. Some of the dinosaurs of this time were the largest land animals that have ever lived (Fig. 389). Specimens more than 70 feet long have been collected, and fragments of considerably larger specimens are known. Some of the largest dinosaur bones of the same age as those of the Morrison have been found in South Africa. Some Jurassic dinosaurs may have reached a length of 100 feet.

Dinosaur Park. The best-known dinosaur quarry in the United States is near Vernal, Utah. This was first discovered by a party from the Carnegie Museum. After it had been worked extensively and many skeletons removed, it was finally established as a national park known as "Dinosaur Park." A sign along the highway leading east from Vernal directs travelers to it. Remains of many dinosaurs have been uncovered in the rocks and are exposed there for travelers to examine.

Dinosaurs in Museums. Some of the best of the dinosaurs from the various quarries have been mounted in the National Museum in Washington, the American Museum in New York City, the Carnegie Museum at Pittsburgh, the Museum of Natural History in Chicago, and the Peabody Museum at Yale University. Each of these museums contains several mounted skeletons of different kinds of dinosaurs. Many specimens of dinosaurs from America are in museums in Europe.

Brontosaurus. The largest type of dinosaur, the Brontosaurus (Fig. 389), had a very long neck and tail, a small head with a very small mouth, a huge body, and great columnar legs with solid bones. The animal was herbivorous and may have found it difficult, with such a small mouth, to eat food enough to keep alive, but reptiles are not so active as mammals and do not require so much food. These creatures were egg-laying and the eggs were hatched by the heat of the sun. It would have required rather high temperature for several months to hatch such an egg, and the presence of dinosaurs in a region would therefore indicate high temperatures and no cold periods. Because of various structures in the animal, it seems that it must have lived partially submerged in the water and that it could not have handled its huge bulk successfully on the land. As it was not a good swimmer, it probably waded about in water deep enough to submerge the body partially and to help support it. This also would account for the fine preservation of many specimens. When animals died, they might settle to the bottom and be covered by mud, but fewer than 1 in 10,000 might thus happen to be covered and preserved.

Stegosaurus. Stegosaurus, though not so large as the Brontosaurus described, was more specialized in some respects. It had huge bony plates on its back (Fig. 390), a specialization for which no reason is apparent. Some of the larger plates are too heavy for one man to lift.

FIG. 389. Above, Triceratops and Tyrannosaurus from the Upper Cretaceous. Below, Brontosaurus and crocodiles from the Jurassic. (From paintings by C. R. Knight, courtesy of Chicago Museum of Natural History.)

Its strange appearance was increased by its very small head, long, straight hind legs, and short front legs. Its teeth were well adapted for grinding vegetation. This dinosaur has the distinction of having the smallest brain compared to the size of the animal of any creature that ever existed. It is this fact that led to the erroneous statement that its brain was in the tail rather than in the head. The creature weighed perhaps 30,000 pounds and its brain weighed only about 10 ounces. The brain is so small in comparison to the rest of the animal that it would be possible to drag it backward into the tail region through the space for the spinal cord in the vertebrae. The space for nervous matter in the pelvic vertebrae is large enough for three or four such brains. As the greater part of the muscular control required to handle the huge tail, pelvis, and hind legs was in the tail region, the reason for such arrangement of nervous tissue is not difficult to see. The stupidity of such a creature can only be wondered at, not realized, and that such an animal could have evolved in spite of its poor mental equipment indicates extremely favorable living conditions.

Carnivorous Dinosaurs. Another type of dinosaur, a further development of one of the Triassic forms, had become larger and more voracious in the Jurassic. It walked on the hind legs, had small front legs, a large head, and long heavy tail. Its bones were hollow and it was a large-brained, active creature. It seems to have fed on the herbivorous types of dinosaurs.

Other Dinosaurs. More than 80 species of dinosaurs are known from the Morrison and the variety in size and kind was large. The size ranged from those 80 feet long to some not more than 2 or 3 feet long; brain capacity ranged from extremely small to relatively large; habits ranged from extremes of herbivores to extremes of carnivores. Most of them were egg-laying but it is possible that some were viviparous (the young were born alive). Some were light, agile, jumping, possibly almost flying, and others were of the clumsy type that lived mainly in the water. Imagine 80 of the most diverse kinds of mammals that you know from all over the world and the dinosaurs of the Morrison would be as varied as those 80 kinds.

Other Reptiles and Mammals. Although dinosaurs dominated, the picture of the life of the Upper Jurassic in western North America would not be complete without some account of the other creatures that were present. A few crocodiles, extremely rare lizards, and turtles constituted the rest of the reptiles. In spite of the large size and abundance of amphibians in the Triassic, all of them had disappeared before late Jurassic; at any rate, none of these fossils has been found. Mammals had come to America, but they were few in number and small. Professor Marsh kept two men collecting mammals from the Morrison in an area

FIG. 390. Armored dinosaur from the Jurassic. (From a painting by C. R. Knight, courtesy of Chicago Museum of Natural History.)

where they were known to occur, and the results of nearly two years of work by these men were less than a double handful of bones.[1] By the use of modern methods of collecting, a great many teeth of many kinds of mammals have been obtained from the Morrison. The mammals were no larger than rats and were extremely primitive, possibly of the egg-laying kind.

Ichthyosaurs. Ichthyosaurs (Fig. 391), descendants of the remarkable swimming reptiles of the Triassic, were present in the sea that came down in the Jurassic through northern United States from the Arctic Ocean.

FIG. 391. A fossil ichthyosaur, showing not only the skeleton but also the carbonized body, paddles, and fins. (*American Museum of Natural History.*)

In the field one may find ichthyosaur remains in one bed and dinosaur remains in the beds immediately above. One must have some rather thorough knowledge of these animals to distinguish them from fragmentary remains, although the ichthyosaurs were swimming reptiles with paddles for feet and the dinosaurs were land-living reptiles. The presence of ichthyosaur remains in a rock identifies it as marine, whereas the presence of dinosaur remains is almost as certain evidence that the rocks are continental, though a few dinosaur fossils have been found in marine strata where the remains had drifted out to sea.

As with the Triassic, the picture of Jurassic life gained from a study of American fossils is imperfect, and one must go to western Europe in order to complete it. Fossils that supplement those in America are found mainly in the Solenhofen beds of Bavaria, a marine deposit that contains also some well-preserved nonmarine forms. The Solenhofen beds are limestone of fine texture, which is quarried to be used as lithographic plates. The major part of the fossils come from the quarried blocks. Workmen in the quarries report the finds to paleontologists, and thou-

[1] Information from Professor Williston, who was associated with Professor Marsh at the time of collecting.

sands of specimens have been collected on the basis of their discoveries. Hundreds of almost perfect ichthyosaur specimens have come from the quarries and ichthyosaurs constitute the most abundant group found in the beds. Every museum of importance in the world contains ichthyosaurs from these quarries, but not more than 10 or 12 specimens have been found in the Jurassic rocks of America, and most of them are exceedingly fragmentary. Comparing this number with the thousands found in the Solenhofen beds probably does not give a true picture of the abundance of ichthyosaurs in the two seas, as the Solenhofen sediments were perfectly adapted for preserving fossils and those of America were not.

Flying Reptiles (Pterosaurs). Flying reptiles of the Jurassic evolved from the Triassic forms and geologists owe their rather complete knowledge of them to the remains preserved in the Solenhofen beds. The "pterosaurs," as they are called, were probably the most perfect flying vertebrates that ever lived, and their flying apparatus was distinctly different from that of birds or of the mammalian fliers, bats. Their bones were exceedingly light, a bone an inch in diameter having bony matter not much thicker than an eggshell. The wing developed by the great increase in length of one finger and the reduction of the others, which remained as small vestiges (Figs. 392 and 393). Some students of the group have thought it likely that the animals hung in trees by the use of the small fingers. The vestigial fingers may be 2 or 3 inches long and the one finger, which developed to support the wing membrane, 2 or 3 feet long. It is difficult to understand the mechanism by which such a change came about. The flying itself could not have induced the change as there could be no flight until there was some sort of wing. In order to be preserved in marine deposits, pterosaurs must have flown over the water. Many of them were probably fishers and were likely to meet disaster when they tried to catch fish out on the seas, as there were too many ichthyosaurs and other voracious reptiles to make diving for fish a safe occupation.

Birds. We found that during a time of great reptilian evolution in the Triassic not only did numerous kinds of new reptiles appear but much greater changes took place that gave rise to the mammals. During the Jurassic, reptilian evolution went on unabated, and still another widely divergent group, the birds, was developed. It was in the Solenhofen beds of Bavaria that the oldest bird remains were found, and only three specimens have been found in the Jurassic of the world. The oldest birds (Fig. 392) were so much like reptiles that had they not possessed feathers they would have been called "reptiles."

Birds with Teeth and Long Tails. The most striking difference between Jurassic and modern birds was the presence of teeth in the Jurassic

FIG. 392. Flying reptiles, birds, small dinosaurs, and primitive evergreens, from the Jurassic of Bavaria. (From a painting by C. R. Knight, courtesy of Chicago Museum of Natural History.)

specimens (Fig. 394).   The teeth were small but were well developed and
functional.   Probably the most impressive primitive character of these
birds was the presence of a long, bony tail.   Some modern birds are
described as having long tails, but the tail is entirely made up of feathers,
as in all modern birds the tail vertebrae are deformed and coalesced into
a small misshapen organ.   The Jurassic bird's tail was made of twenty-
odd vertebrae, which were not united.

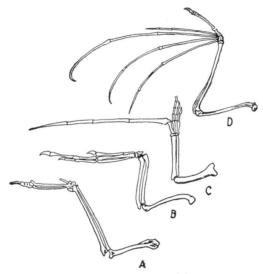

FIG. 393. (A) Wing of modern bird; (B) wing of Jurassic bird; (C) wing of flying reptile; (D) wing of bat.

FIG. 394. Head of a Jurassic bird, showing the teeth. (*From the restoration by Heilmann.*)

Primitive Bird Structures.   The modern bird's wing is highly specialized through the loss of some of the fingers and the union of others.   One
does not recognize the resemblance of modern birds' wings to the forefoot
of an ordinary animal, but the Jurassic bird had three well-developed
fingers.   The modern bird has the vertebrae in the shoulder region
firmly united and attached to the breast bone by means of the shoulder
girdle to form a rather perfectly boxed-in chest.   The Jurassic bird had
no union of the vertebrae in the shoulder-girdle region and therefore no
such protection as that possessed by the modern bird.   The modern bird

has the vertebrae united in the pelvic region and great specialization of the other pelvic bones, but the Jurassic bird had no union of vertebrae and no specialization of the other bones of the region. Probably the most fundamental difference between Jurassic birds and modern forms is in the vertebrae. The most primitive vertebrae, those of the fishes, were biconcave, *i.e.*, they were deeply hollowed out at each end. Before Triassic time all vertebrates, whether reptiles, amphibians, or fishes, had such biconcave vertebrae. Modern birds have very highly specialized vertebrae with no concavity, but the Jurassic birds had biconcave vertebrae like the reptiles of the Triassic and fishes of all time.

If Jurassic birds had not had feathers, they would have been considered as a peculiar lizard with forelegs strangely modified. Such structures as feathers are only rarely fossilized, but those of the birds from the Solenhofen beds are perfectly preserved to a minute degree, showing the barblets and scales on the features.

Fossil Birds Are Rare. Birds are among the rarest of fossils and the finding of only a few specimens in the Solenhofen beds does not indicate that they may not have been fairly numerous in their habitat on land. It was only accidental that they flew out over the sea, as they were not fishers like the pterosaurs.

Comparison of Records of Marine and Land Life. The record of sea life of the Jurassic is rather complete in western Europe. A study of the evolution of marine forms would show fairly steady progress with no marked gaps such as exist in the land life. It is the invertebrate marine life of which the record is fairly complete, but of the ichthyosaurs and many other marine vertebrates the continuity is no better than with the land vertebrates. It is likely that with the extension of geological studies to Asia, Africa, and South America, and with more extensive studies in North America, many of the gaps in the record will be filled.

MISCELLANEOUS

Climate. Jurassic climate seems to have been warm over most of the earth although there are some differences, possibly due to climate, between faunas as far north as Alaska and those in the United States. However, the ichthyosaurs, which must have been strictly warm-water animals, came into the interior of North America from the northern seas, and they must have lived as far north as Alaska.

Economic Products. In the United States, the Jurassic has only scant deposits of economic value. In California, the main gold deposits are partly in Jurassic rocks, where the gold veins were formed in a great series of slates that were intruded by igneous rock. For many years, California has been the main gold-producing state in the United States, and much of the gold came either from the Jurassic or from placer deposits derived from the Jurassic.   In Alaska, there are important coal deposits, which may in time become of economic value.

Close of the Jurassic.   The northern sea and the Gulf of Mexico gradually withdrew during the Upper Jurassic, and no great differential movements of the land accompanied the withdrawal.   The Pacific sea, however, may have been more abruptly drained off from the land as the first great uplift of the Sierra Nevada occurred in the late Jurassic. The uplift was accompanied by intense folding and by the intrusion of some of the largest magmas of the North American continent.   One of the batholiths resulting from magma stretches more than 800 miles north and south and reaches a width of more than 80 miles in some places. The Jurassic shales of eastern California were intensely folded and metamorphosed, so much so that many of them were changed to slates, and bedding planes and all other ordinary structures of sedimentary rocks were destroyed.   Some of the shales were metamorphosed to schists. There is some parallelism between the close of the second period of the Paleozoic, when the mountains of eastern New York and western New England were formed, and the second period of the Mesozoic with the formation of the Sierra Nevada.   A contrast between Paleozoic and Mesozoic exists in the Paleozoic marine rocks' being mainly in central and eastern North America and the Mesozoic marine rocks' mainly in the Rocky Mountains and western North America.

CHAPTER 25

UPPER MESOZOIC; CRETACEOUS PERIOD

The "Cretaceous" derived its name from *creta* (Latin for "chalk") on account of the large amount of chalk formed during the period. It was named from the chalk cliffs of western France, which stand out prominently along the coast. By many geologists the Cretaceous has been divided into two periods, and in some textbooks the Comanchean or Lower Cretaceous is given the rank of a period.

Sea Oscillations. As in the Triassic and Jurassic, the seas advanced first from the Pacific Coast, but the Sierra Nevada range stood as an impassable barrier and restricted the epicontinental seas to very narrow areas (Fig. 395). Almost at the beginning of the period, the Gulf of Mexico advanced through Texas and Oklahoma and, later in the first half of the period, extended northward as far as Wyoming. The Atlantic seas did not advance during the first half of the period. The Cretaceous seems to have been a considerably longer period than either the Jurassic or Triassic, and there were many more oscillations of the land and advances and withdrawals of the sea. The advances finally culminated in a sea that extended from the Gulf of Mexico to the Arctic Ocean and was more than 1,000 miles wide in its widest parts. Its eastern shore extended through eastern Texas, central Oklahoma, central Kansas, and thence eastward into Iowa and northward in a northwesterly direction to the Arctic Ocean. Its western shore was not far east of the Sierra Nevada. In this sea, deposits more than 20,000 feet thick were made in some places, although their average thickness was not more than 2,000 feet.

Methods of Working out Ancient Sea Margins. It may be well to review the ways of determining the extent of ancient seas, using Cretaceous as an example. Figure 396 is a diagrammatic cross section of Cretaceous deposits in Kansas, Colorado, and Utah as they have been worked out by numerous geologists in a long series of years. Figure 395 shows Cretaceous seas. In central Kansas the Cretaceous deposits are thin and patchy, *i.e.*, isolated outcrops occur here and there resting on Permian rocks (Fig. 396). The patchiness is due to erosion after the deposits were formed rather than to original deposition.

The Kansas Cretaceous rocks contain marine fossils of Upper Cretaceous time. The fossils have been determined as lower Upper Cretaceous
by finding them preserved in a series of rocks where the entire Cretaceous
section is exposed. Westward other Cretaceous rocks come in above

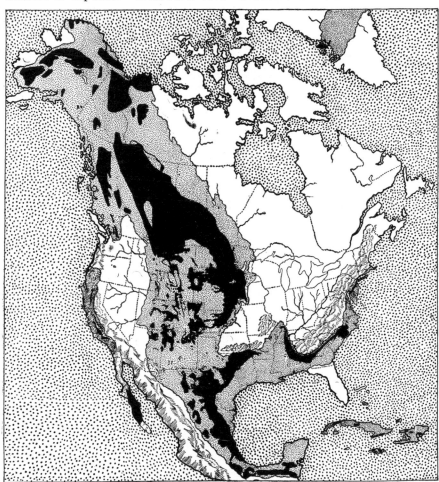

FIG. 395. Cretaceous seas at about maximum extent. Epicontinental seas in fine stipple; outcrops in
black. (*Seas modified from Schuchert.*)

those present in central Kansas. Those in the first location are represented by A on the diagram, and the ones coming in above are represented
by B. The geologist interprets this condition at the place where B begins
as the margin of a later Cretaceous sea, and, if he could trace the margin
of the outcrops northward and southward, he would be tracing the old sea
beach of that time. There is a considerable amount of uncertainty in
such tracing. In the first place, B may be covered almost every place by

C and it is difficult to determine the exact location of the margin of B. This margin may be exposed only where streams cut across it and these places may be many miles apart. Take a series of locations along the Pacific Coast, as represented in Fig. 395, mark them by crosses, and draw an outline of the coast from those locations. Comparing your outline with the actual coast line, you will find that the only places where your diagram is correct is at the crosses, but in spite of that you have represented the Pacific Coast in a roughly accurate way, more accurately than the Cretaceous map represents the Cretaceous sea (Fig. 395).

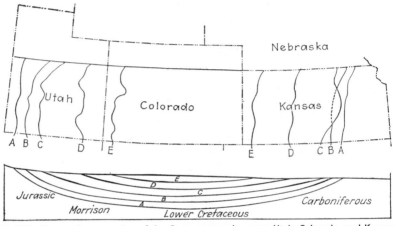

FIG. 396. Map and cross-section of the Cretaceous rocks across Utah, Colorado, and Kansas.

There is one other uncertainty associated with the geologists' determination of the old sea margin. The margin of the rocks that he finds may not represent the actual seashore. The marginal deposits may have been eroded before or after the overlying formation was laid down. Farther westward the margin of B is under C. A rests on the Morrison formation in Colorado and is the oldest of all the Cretaceous that the geologist is able to find by tracing the rocks over all of the area of deposition.

In Colorado and Utah, E comes in above D, and the margin of E has been made out by extensive geological study. The eastward migration of the margins from A to B, B to C, C to D, and D to E indicates shrinking of the Cretaceous sea. The western margin of A is in Utah; B shows small retreat of the sea eastward; D and E much greater retreats; and the sea in which E was deposited was narrow.

In making his investigations, the geologist is not able to follow the rock without interruption. If he could trace it along the outcrop and the rock remained the same from one place to another, the history would all work out rather easily, but neither one of these is true. Not only are there great distances between outcrops, but the rocks change in character from place to place. Under such conditions the age of the rock must be determined entirely from the fossil content. The fossils present must be known to the geologist, and he must be able to recognize them wherever he finds them. The fossils in each of the members must be distinct enough to differentiate it from all of the other members. In such a series it is not likely that all of the fossils will be different in each member. Most of them may be the same and the differentiation may be made on the basis of two or three species. Imagine in A such an assemblage of fossils as would represent the life in North America before its discovery by Europeans, and in B an assemblage that would represent the life in America today. Most of the species of the two periods are the same but the leading ones are different. All of the domestic animals were brought in by Europeans, and domestic animals dominate at the present time. Several of the species of pre-Columbian time are now extinct or almost so. Using the bison as an example, in A it was a dominating form, in B rarely ever found. Using the horse as an example of the other type, in A it was not present, but in B it is abundant. The geologists, after studying the fossils in A and B thoroughly enough to learn these two facts, could distinguish one from the other by bison and horses.

Geologists may identify formations by tracing them along the outcrops, a good way but with severe limitations because of scarcity of outcrops. He may identify the formations by the kinds of rock in them, which may be valuable or useless. As an example, chalk was formed in America during only a relatively limited time, and thus wherever it is found it indicates a rather definite age. Part of C in Fig. 396 is chalk and where the chalk is present in Texas, Kansas, and Nebraska it was formed in about the same epoch of time, but had C been made of shale, the kind of rock would have been useless in identification, as so many of the Cretaceous formations are shale.

Formation of Dakota Sandstone. We may now return to a consideration of the great Cretaceous sea that cut the North American continent in two from north to south. As this sea advanced northward from the Gulf of Mexico, it was very shallow near the margins and waves worked over the weathered material, sorted out the finer particles, and carried them into the deeper waters. Sands were deposited from the beach outward to a water depth of 200 or 300 feet, *i.e.*, as far outward as storm waves could strike the bottom rather vigorously. In many places there were doubtless sand dunes on the shore and the advancing seas encountered little fine material in addition to the sand. The objection may be raised that the seas would soon advance over a narrow strip of sand dunes and reach the normal mantle rock beyond. The seas were probably advancing at a rate of not more than 1 mile in 1,000 years, and it would not be at all difficult for sand dunes to form along the sea margin in belts 1 mile wide in 1,000 years, so that under some conditions the sea might advance over sand-dune areas for hundreds of miles, the dunes forming as fast as the sea advanced. However, the rocks would have to be composed of a sufficient amount of sand to furnish it for the dunes from their weathering. If the rocks were composed of shales without sand, no sand dunes could form except as the sand blew up from the sea; and this would not continue long as the source of sand would be exhausted with the advance of the sea over the shale area.

This beach and shallow-water sand formation extends from Texas nearly to the Arctic Ocean. It has been called the "Dakota sandstone" (Fig. 395) on account of its development in the Dakotas. Its eastern border is in Iowa, Nebraska, and Kansas, and its western in Nevada, Arizona, and Utah. It is A of Fig. 396 and is almost as extensive as the most widespread Cretaceous sea.

Alternation of Marine and Continental Deposits. The oscillations of the Cretaceous sea brought about alternation of sediments. Beds of coal may come between formations bearing marine fossils, and dinosaur tracks may occur in the muds associated with the coal, two evidences of continental deposition. Shells of fresh-water animals may be associated with the muds and sands above and below the coal, and these constitute still another evidence of continental deposition.

Other Cretaceous Deposits. The most typical of the Cretaceous deposits are in eastern Colorado and western Kansas and Nebraska, where the Dakota sandstone, at the bottom of the series, is followed by several hundred feet of shale, which, in turn, is overlain by limestone. Interpreting this, we may assume that the margin of the Cretaceous sea had advanced so far northward and westward that no more clays were being deposited in this part of the seas and that the only accumulation on the sea bottom was from shells and bones of sea animals and from chemically precipitated calcium carbonate. The lowest limestones contain clay, which was deposited while the land was near enough for fine sediments to be carried to the limestone-forming area. Above these limestones comes the chalk, which is extensive in western Kansas and Nebraska, eastern Colorado, and parts of Oklahoma and Texas.

Chalk. Chalk is a limestone of a type entirely different from any studied thus far. It is very soft, and some of it has been thought to be made up almost entirely of the remains of one-celled sea animals. Much chalk, however, is not so largely composed of such remains, and some of it has only a small proportion of fossils.

The softness of chalk is due to the poor cementation of the deposit and the minuteness of its fossils. Where the deposits are free from impurities, the chalk is as soft and free from grit as the crayon used on the blackboard. Until late in the nineteenth century, the crayons used were made from chalk, but now they are manufactured from neither limestone nor chalk, but from calcined gypsum.

Atlantic Coast Cretaceous. The early Cretaceous seas did not advance along the Atlantic Coast, but continental deposits of the nature of alluvial fans, flood-plain deposits, and landward sides of deltas formed east of the Appalachians, from Massachusetts to South Carolina, and in the last half of the period seas advanced to the base of the Appalachian Mountains and in the eastern Gulf region as a continuation of the great

FIG. 397. A slab of Cretaceous chalk from western Kansas, covered with specimens of a free-swimming crinoid. (After Moore.)

sea that covered the interior. The deposits along the Atlantic and Gulf coasts were thin (little more than 1,000 feet at the thickest) as compared with those of the western interior. Glauconitic greensands formed in many places, but most of the formations are clays, silts, and ordinary sands.

LIFE OF THE CRETACEOUS

In America the Cretaceous saw the culmination of Mesozoic plants and marine vertebrates and invertebrates. Invertebrate animals in Triassic and Jurassic had not been abundant in most of the American seas, but in the Cretaceous the seas fairly swarmed with great numbers and many kinds. In the main they were kinds with which the student is not familiar, and it will suffice to call attention to a few of the most striking things about them. Clams and cephalopods were the dominant forms. Crinoids, which were so abundant in late Paleozoic, were reduced to a few kinds, some of which were stemless (Fig. 397).

FIG. 398. Cephalopods from the Cretaceous. (*From U.S. Geological Survey publications.*)

Cephalopods. In the Cretaceous, cephalopods reached their culmination in complexity of partitions and number of species and their maximum size for the entire Mesozoic. This was true for America and not for Europe. However, the cephalopods were in old-age stages and showed very decided old-age characteristics. They did not evolve into new forms but acquired strange ornamentation and shapes. The beginning of coiled cephalopods was in the Ordovician. After that coiled

FIG. 399. Clams, a snail, and a sea urchin from the Cretaceous. (*From U.S. Geological Survey publications.*)

forms dominated, and the last of the straight forms disappeared with early Triassic. Until Upper Cretaceous, all of the complex partitioned forms had been coiled, but then they began to uncoil (Fig. 398). The oldest part of the shell was coiled and the youngest part straight. Some species almost tied their shells into knots, as shown in Fig. 398. Some became highly ornamented, a quality that accompanies old age or decay.

Clams. The clam group (Fig. 399) was at the height of its development and some of the kinds were large. Shells more than 4 feet across are not uncommon in the chalk of western Kansas. The oyster group, which appeared in the Triassic and increased in the Jurassic, became extremely abundant and developed many species in the Cretaceous. Some of them were several inches long and others were very small. More than 1,000 of the small ones have been found attached to one large clam shell.

Mosasaurs. The seas fairly swarmed with marine reptiles, and the numbers of fossils in the marine rocks were supplemented by the land reptiles and by birds that flew over the sea and became buried in the marine oozes, which finally formed the chalks. One of the great collecting grounds of the world for Upper Cretaceous fossils, particularly the vertebrates, is part of western Kansas. The most abundant animal in the chalk of the area is the mosasaur, a marine lizard with paddles instead of walking feet (Fig. 401).

FIG. 400. A chalk fence post containing fossil oysters, western Kansas. (Photograph by W. D. Keller.)

The first mosasaur specimen was found near the town of Maestricht, Holland, near the Meuse River. It became so well known that an invading army captured it and took it to Paris. Figure 401 is modified from a drawing by Professor S. W. Williston,[1] who did more than any other investigator to make the mosasaurs of North America known. The largest of the mosasaurs were about 60 feet long, a length comparable to that of small whales, although mosasaurs were more slender.

[1] It was probably the mosasaurs that made Professor Williston a paleontologist. He lived at Manhattan, Kansas, near the chalk beds and went with his professor of geology of the State Agricultural College to get fossils from the chalks. The finding of numerous bones in the chalk aroused his interest to such an extent that he went to Yale College to study vertebrate fossils under Professor Marsh, then the best-known student of Cretaceous vertebrates in the United States. At the time when Professor Williston first went to the chalk beds, bones were scattered widely over the surface where the chalk had weathered, but since then hundreds of collectors have worked over the exposures of chalk and have taken way all of the larger bones exposed on the surface. It is only as the chalk weathers and is eroded further that other specimens appear. It gives a collector a decided thrill to find a clean, perfect fossil bone

Flying Reptiles. Associated with the mosasaur fossils in the chalk are those of the final forms of the flying reptiles (Fig. 402). Greater specialization had created here a most perfect flying machine and the largest of the flying animals that ever existed (Fig. 403). The largest specimens had a wing spread of about 27 feet, but the whole framework of the animal weighed only a few pounds. Specialization was nearly all in the wings and head; the latter became greatly elongated and had a strong backward-projecting crest (Fig. 401), which served as an attachment for the wing muscles. The beaks came to acute points and the animals may have been able to spear their prey. As their remains have been found only in marine deposits they probably caught mainly sea animals. The earlier pterosaurs had long, strong teeth, but those of the chalk had evolved to a toothless stage. Pterosaurs[2] must have lived on the shores of all the seas of North America and they probably flew widely over the lands, but their remains have been found only in the chalks of western Kansas with the exception of one specimen in Washington. It seems remarkable that their bones are unknown from any other of the widespread Cretaceous deposits of North America.

Turtles. In the chapter on the Triassic the first appearance of turtles was mentioned. In the chalks three or four kinds of marine turtles are present. Some of these reached a length of 8 or 9 feet, and their skulls

---

lying on the surface of the chalk and then to locate other bones that are sticking out of the chalk. He may then take a pick or a knife, dig away the chalk and find more clean, hard bone. The collector never knows how much of a specimen he will find after he has located some part of an animal in the solid rock. The bone he is working on may be the last one present in the series, or the series may be complete from tip of snout to end of tail. After the animal died, it may have been torn to pieces by other voracious animals, and only under rare circumstances did a complete animal settle to the bottom and get covered with mud to fossilize in its entirety. Even if the entire animal were preserved in the chalk, the chance for some person to find it at the stage when none had been eroded away would be small. The chances are thousands to one that streams, while cutting valleys in the chalk, would have carried away or destroyed part of the bones of the specimen. Thousands of specimens of mosasaurs have been collected from the Kansas chalks, and, although good specimens are rare, nearly every important museum has at least one.

[2] In collecting from the chalks of western Kansas one should not expect to find pterosaur bones every day or even every week. One experienced collector found three specimens in 3 months. One of these consisted of a part of one wing, another of part of a head and one wing, and another of fragments of wing and body bones. The finding of the rarer fossils in the chalk is a matter of chance as well as perseverance. One collector had one day to spend in the chalk, and although he found nothing else worth while, he took out a very fine, small pterosaur, one of the most complete that has ever been collected. Another experienced collector, with one day to spend in the chalk beds, found and took out possibly the most perfect wing that has ever been discovered, but the same collector might work for a year without finding anything else comparable to it.

FIG. 401. Cretaceous animals of the chalk seas, western Kansas. Pterodactyls flying, mosasaurs and swimming birds in foreground, turtles at right, plesiosaur carcass on island.

were as large as the skull of a horse (Fig. 404). Their feet were paddles but not so perfect as those of the mosasaurs. Their backs were not covered with bones; in this respect they were like modern sea turtles but unlike modern land turtles.

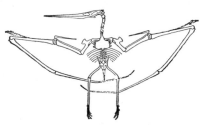

Plesiosaurs. At least one other marine reptile, the plesiosaur, was present in the seas in which the chalks were deposited. The extremely long, slender necks of the plesiosaurs have led to a rough description of them as animals with bodies like that of a turtle and neck

FIG. 402. Skeleton of a pterodactyl from the Cretaceous of western Kansas. (After Williston.)

and head like those of a snake (Fig. 405). Some of the animals became as large as the large mosasaurs. Plesiosaur remains are almost as rare as those of pterosaurs in the Kansas chalk, but in some other Cretaceous deposits they are fairly abundant.

FIG. 403. A Cretaceous pterodactyl. (Restoration by Herrick E. Wilson.)

Fishes. In spite of the abundance of reptile remains in the chalk, the collector finds fully three times as many fossils of fishes (Fig. 406) as

FIG. 404. A marine turtle from the Cretaceous. (After Williston.)

of all reptiles combined. In taking out the skeleton of one mosasaur he may destroy those of several fishes. This was the first time of great abundance of the bony fishes. Most of the kinds in the Age of Fishes were of the more primitive nonbony types. Some of these Cretaceous fishes were no mean antagonists of the reptiles. One species was 18 to 20 feet long and had its jaws armed with long, sharp teeth. Even the smaller species were well provided with teeth. Although the bony fishes dominated, some of the sharks of the Cretaceous were much larger, and at least one species attained the size of the large mosasaurs.

Birds. The collector of fossils from the chalk is never satisfied until he has found a fossil bird, the rarest of all the fossils.[3] Men have worked

[3] The first bird known from the chalk had a rather remarkable history. It was

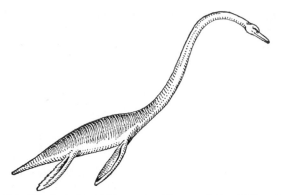

FIG. 405. A plesiosaur from western Kansas.   (After Williston.)

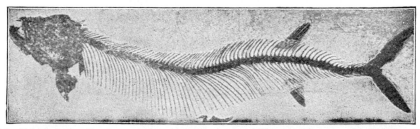

FIG. 406. Skeleton of a late Cretaceous tarpon.   Some specimens of this fish are 15 feet long. (After Moore.)

for years in the chalks without finding one bird bone.   Although all of the birds from the chalk had teeth, some of them were rather highly specialized in other respects.   Some still had the biconcave (fish type) vertebrae, but others had developed the highly specialized type of

collected by Professor Mudge of the Kansas State Agricultural College, who did not recognize it as a bird.   He boxed it up and directed it to Professor Cope of the Philadelphia Museum.   However, before he could ship it, a friend of his appeared who asked him to send it to Professor Marsh of Yale College.   Accordingly the direction on the box was changed and the specimen was sent to Professor Marsh, who later wrote a large book on birds of the chalk beds.   On receiving the specimen, Professor Marsh wrote a paper describing it and in an extra paragraph said that associated with the other bones of the bird were some little reptile jaws of a new type.   The paper hadn't been out long when Professor Marsh published a short correction saying that the so-called reptile jaws actually belonged to the bird and that birds with teeth had been found.   He was ridiculed in scientific papers, as well as in newspapers, as the man who had found birds with teeth.   However, other specimens were discovered soon after and all of them from the chalk had teeth.

Professor Marsh turned the tables on other geologists in a dramatic way.   The bird from the Jurassic of the Solenhofen beds had been known for a long time, but no teeth had been described from its jaws.   On going to the museum at Berlin, Professor Marsh asked for the privilege of examining the specimen and, using a sharp needle in preparing it, he was not greatly surprised to uncover teeth, which had been overlooked by the other paleontologists who had studied it.

vertebrae of modern birds.   One form had lost its wings and had developed webfeet (Fig. 407–1).   It was as truly water-living as the marine reptiles (Fig. 408).   Some of the other birds had as highly specialized flight organs as modern forms (Fig. 407–2).   One difference that is con-

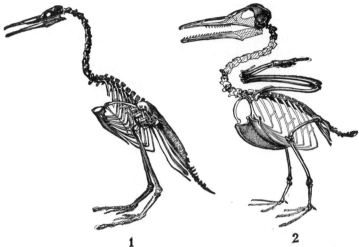

1   2

FIG. 407. Skeletons of Upper Cretaceous toothed birds.   (*After Marsh.*)

FIG. 408. Restoration of the swimming bird shown in Fig. 407 (1).   (*After Gleason.*)

stant between all Mesozoic and post-Mesozoic birds is the presence of teeth in the former and the lack of teeth in the latter.   The preservation of a bird seems always to depend upon some especially favorable type of sedimentation.   No birds are known from the Mesozoic of Europe except from the Solenhofen Jurassic beds, and only four are known in America outside of the Cretaceous chalks.

Dinosaurs. In the northern Rocky Mountain region, continental deposits developed over wide areas in the uppermost Cretaceous, and here we get the last picture of the dinosaurs (Fig. 409) and their associates. The first American picture of this group was in the Upper Triassic of the Connecticut Valley, the second in the Upper Jurassic of the Rocky Mountain region, and the third, and last, in the uppermost Cretaceous of the Rocky Mountain region. The largest of the dinosaurs had disappeared and peculiar specializations had taken the place of mere bulk, although dinosaurs were still by far the largest animals that lived on the land. One form had developed a very large head (in some specimens 9 feet long by 5 feet broad) with two or three horns on it (Fig. 389). Its body was relatively low, broad, and heavy. It was named "Triceratops" on account of the three horns of the first one discovered. One of the Jurassic dinosaurs had the distinction of having the smallest brain for the size of the animal of all creatures, but Triceratops (Fig. 410) had the smallest brain compared to the size of the head of any known animal. On a recent expedition of the American Museum to Mongolia, the discovery of what seemed to be ancestors of the Triceratops type was made. Dozens of skulls like those of the Triceratops were found. They ranged in size from above 1 foot long to almost the length of the American Triceratops. A unique discovery in connection with these animals was their eggs. Although Triceratops has been known for 50 years, the 2 years of collecting in Mongolia produced more specimens than have come from all of North America.

A carnivorous dinosaur that walked on its hind feet and had very short, almost useless front legs was the last of its type and reached the culmination of its kind in size and ferocity (Fig. 389). It was named *Tyrannosaurus rex,* "king of the tyrant reptiles." As it stood on its hind legs it was some 25 feet high. Its head was more than twice the size of a horse's head, and its teeth were long, sharp, and strong.

Another peculiar species was the duck-billed dinosaur (Fig. 409). It, too, walked on its hind legs and had very weak front legs. The front of its head was flattened and widened so that it looked very much like the bill of a huge duck. It had flat teeth, adapted only for feeding on plants.

These descriptions may seem to be altogether of the peculiar types of dinosaurs, but they were the dominant ones. The race was rapidly moving toward extinction, and the latest dinosaurs known in America were present here. There is some disagreement as to whether the top of this dinosaur-bearing formation should be called "Cenozoic" or "Mesozoic," and on the interpretation of some geologists dinosaurs persisted into the Cenozoic, but according to the majority they disappeared near the close of the Mesozoic.

FIG. 409. A group of Upper Cretaceous dinosaurs. (From a painting by C. R. Knight, courtesy of Chicago Museum of Natural History.)

FIG. 410. Several types of Cretaceous horned dinosaurs.   The best-known genus, Triceratops, is shown in 3.   (After Berry.)

CRETACEOUS PLANTS

The most significant advance toward modern conditions in the early Cretaceous was the appearance of flowering plants in the Atlantic Coast region.   Plants of simpler types had been abundant since the Middle Paleozoic, but flowering plants were unknown until the Lower Cretaceous. They then evolved rapidly and soon spread westward from the Atlantic Coast to the localities of the western-most Cretaceous deposits.   In the Rocky Mountain region they were preserved first in the Dakota sandstone (Fig. 411) of the Upper Cretaceous, where they are exceedingly abundant. Probably no other formation is better known for its plants than the Dakota sandstone.   Maple, cottonwood, oak, walnut, sassafras, willow, and many other present-day types of plants were common, but none of the modern species had appeared.   One result of the appearance of flowering plants was that insects could evolve the process of honey making from blossoms and that various kinds of animals could develop the special diet of nectar, fruits, and other products of flowering plants.

MISCELLANEOUS

Climate of the Cretaceous.   Large reptiles and subtropical plants have been found in Cretaceous rocks in high latitudes, indicating mild temperatures over all the world.   There is no evidence of extreme aridity any place during the period, but aridity is a condition dependent upon local conditions and likely to be present in every period.   It is only where it is extreme and widespread that evidences of it are likely to appear in the rocks.

Economic Products.   The economic value of Cretaceous mineral products is greater than that of such products of all the rest of the Mesozoic, and equal to the value of those products of some periods of the Paleozoic.

The great coal deposits of the Rocky Mountain region and the area eastward are mainly Cretaceous. Coal of this period is comparable in amount to that of the late Paleozoic in eastern United States, although the quality is by no means so high. Most of it is low grade bituminous coal or lignite. As coal deposits are extensive in the Cretaceous rocks, swamps containing luxuriant vegetation must have extended over wide areas several times during the period.

FIG. 411. A piece of Dakota sandstone (Upper Cretaceous) containing two fossil leaves.

This vegetation was mainly flowering plants rather than the types that formed the coal of the late Paleozoic. The coal reserve in the Cretaceous rocks is more than 200,000,000,000 tons and is being mined only sparingly. Next to coal, petroleum is the most valuable Cretaceous product. The oil fields of parts of Texas, Wyoming, Montana, New Mexico, Mississippi and Mexico are Cretaceous in age. Sixteen per cent of present world production is from Cretaceous rocks.

Close of the Cretaceous. In late Cretaceous nearly all of the Rocky Mountain ranges were uplifted and folded, so that western North America, from being an area of deposition, became one of erosion, with great numbers of mountain ranges. Mountain making was in progress from Alaska to Cape Horn and was even more intense in South than in North America. Uplift was general over North America, and the Appalachian Mountains rose again. Since their origin in late Paleozoic, they had undergone almost constant erosion and were nearly peneplaned before the uplift at the close of the Cretaceous.

CHAPTER 26

THE CENOZOIC ERA

The Greek compound "Cenozoic" means "recent life." The rocks of the Cenozoic era contain species of animals and plants which are living today. No modern species are found in Mesozoic rocks, but even early Cenozoic rocks contain some modern species of invertebrate animals. Species as distinct as the modern ones could not have originated from Mesozoic types without transitional forms. Since these are not found, there must have been a considerable interval of time between the deposition of the highest Mesozoic and the lowest Cenozoic fossil-bearing beds.

Divisions of the Cenozoic. The Cenozoic era has lasted no longer than did some of the Paleozoic and Mesozoic periods. It has been divided into six time sequences, each of which is better considered as an epoch. These are:

Recent, present time and the preceding 25,000 years
Pleistocene, meaning "most recent," the glacial epoch
Pliocene, "more recent"
Miocene, "less recent"
Oligocene, "little of the recent"
Eocene, "dawn of the recent"

These six epochs constitute the single period of the Cenozoic. No widespread invasion of the seas over the continents has yet occurred within the era, and we seem to be living during an interval between periods.

Early Cenozoic Land. Mesozoic and older rocks in the Appalachian region and in the mountains of the West lie in truncated folds covered by horizontal Eocene beds. This condition gives evidence of the erosion which occurred before the Cenozoic seas overlapped the Mesozoic and older rocks, as they must have done to produce the known relationships between Cenozoic and Mesozoic rocks. The early overlap was not on the areas that had been formed into mountains in the closing stages of the Cretaceous but rather on the low-lying areas. If the seas were to start to encroach on the North American continent at the present time, on account of the general rise of sea level, they would first overlap the lowlands at the mouths of the Mississippi and other rivers, and it would be a long time before they would reach far enough inland to rest directly on consolidated rock of previous periods. The land is probably not so

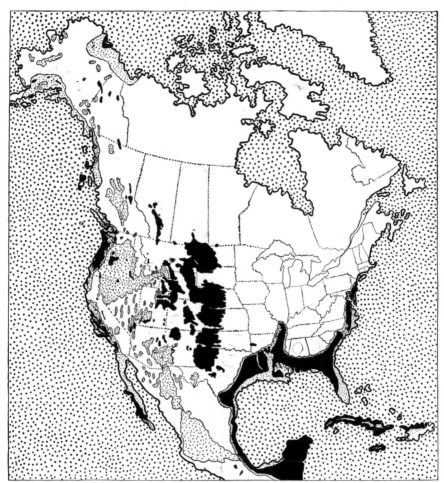

FIG. 412. Cenozoic seas and rocks. Epicontinental seas in fine stipple; igneous rocks in inclined dashes; outcrops of sedimentary rocks in black.

emergent now as it was when Cenozoic history began, and the mountains have been eroded to a much greater degree.

Eastern Cenozoic Seas. The Atlantic and Gulf coastal areas have been somewhat unstable during Cenozoic time. During each of the epochs, seas encroached upon narrow areas near the existing coast lines and withdrew after relatively short periods. The oscillations were much smaller and less numerous than those that occurred during the Cretaceous period.   Mexico and Central America were more largely inundated than the rest of North America (Fig. 412).

The seas were shallow and the sediments were nearly all of near-shore types, alternating sands, silts, and clays.   Each epoch is represented by a few to about 500 feet of sediments, except in the Gulf of Mexico region, where more than 12,000 feet of Cenozoic sediments are known.   Slight unconformities separate the rocks of each epoch.   Early in the Cenozoic, the sea advanced from the Gulf as far north as southeastern Missouri. In parts of the Gulf region, the seas may have remained without withdrawing at the close of epochs, but the sediments of the region show many alterations of subaqueous and subaerial conditions, as one would expect in a delta.   Coal formed in some of the delta swamps, and, even along the Atlantic Coast, nonmarine beds alternate with marine formations.

Although Central America was under the sea several times during the Cenozoic and many thousand feet of sediments were deposited, it seems to have formed a land bridge between North and South America in the middle and later part of the era.

Pacific Cenozoic Seas.   The Pacific sea invasions (Fig. 412) were no larger than those of the Atlantic, but sediments accumulated to a much greater thickness.   More than 25,000 feet of strata were deposited, though no single section is that thick.   The sediments are coarse, volcanic ash makes up no inconsiderable part of them, and lava flows alternate with sediments in many places.

In the Puget Sound region, a great delta formed and more than 100 coal beds alternate with other sediments.   In California, diatoms (one-celled plants) make up formations more than 1,000 feet in thickness. These diatoms seem to have accumulated in shallow water though diatoms ordinarily live in deep water far from shore.

Continental Deposits.   To most geologists the greatest interest in Cenozoic strata of North America centers about the continental deposits of the Rocky Mountain region and that to the west.   The main reason for this interest is the preservation in those deposits of fossils that give a key to an understanding of the development of many types of animals.

As the Upper Mesozoic seas were withdrawing from the Rocky Mountain region, they were partially filled with deltas built by extended consequent streams which crossed the newly emergent land.   This land was irregular in topography.   The irregularities were not large, however, but resembled those of the surface of the delta of the Mississippi at the present time.   In the depressions, rank vegetation flourished and much of this finally became coal.   Alluvial fans from the higher lands formed over the tops of the deltas and merged with the top beds of deltas to form widespread nonmarine deposits, the oldest of which were the youngest of the continental Cretaceous rocks. The later deposits of the same kind, formed after the seas had withdrawn from the continent, were the oldest of the Cenozoic deposits. These deposits were most extensive in Montana, Wyoming, and North and South Dakota, and the amount of coal in them is very large.

Contact between Mesozoic and Cenozoic Rocks. You will readily see that the contact between Mesozoic and Cenozoic rocks could not be sharp under such conditions and that geologists would find difficulty

FIG. 413. Cenozoic nonmarine sediments above and below a lava flow, near Tower Falls, Yellowstone National Park. (*Photograph by Carl C. Branson.*)

in determining just where to draw the boundary between the eras. The change from one type of sediment to another would not be significant. When we contrast this contact with the line of demarcation between eras as we have considered them before, this seems the wrong place to draw the line, but such relationships must have developed in some places between the latest deposits of every era and the earliest of the succeeding era. The Mesozoic-Cenozoic relationship is better preserved over larger areas than the others because, owing to the short space of time that has elapsed, there has been much less chance for its destruction by erosion. The contact between Cenozoic and older rocks produced when the Cenozoic seas advanced over the eroded lands is one of unconformity.

Cenozoic Volcanism. During the Cenozoic there was a great amount of volcanism. In Washington, Oregon, Utah, and Idaho, lava ranging in thickness from a few to 5,000 feet flowed out over an area of more than 200,000 square miles. The surface of the Columbia River Plateau is made up of basalts formed at this time (Fig. 412). Near the Pacific

Coast in both North and South America, numerous volcanic mountains formed. In Arizona, New Mexico, Colorado, Utah, and Montana, many dikes, necks, sills, and larger intrusive masses of Cenozoic age have been exposed by erosion, and many areas are covered with lava flows, mainly basalt. In late Pleistocene time Yellowstone Park was the scene of a great deal of volcanism (Fig. 413).

Cenozoic Mountain Making. The mountains of western North and South America had various degrees of uplift during the Cenozoic, and many of them owe most of their elevation to Cenozoic movements. The Pliocene and Pleistocene epochs witnessed direct elevation without folding of most of the Rocky Mountain ranges and coast ranges. The Appalachian Mountains experienced several upwarpings during Cenozoic time, and most of their height above sea level is due to Cenozoic uplifts, although all of the folding preceded Cenozoic.

Basins between the Mountains. The Rocky Mountain ranges formed at the close of the Mesozoic but were not then uplifted to their present heights. Between the various mountain ranges there were basins in which extremely irregular continental deposits formed. Where streams have cut through them, so that they may be observed, one sees thick beds of sandstone gradually grading to shales along the beds. Sandstones and shales alternate from top to bottom, so that one formation may have many beds of sandstone and many beds of shale. The materials of the sandstones and shales are not well sorted because rivers do not sort materials thoroughly except in their large deltas, where they spread over wide areas. If one visualizes the sort of deposit formed on a wide flood plain, where the stream working laterally builds up one side and cuts down the other, cuts off meanders, abandons oxbows, probably fills the oxbows with fine muds at times of flood, cuts across old oxbows and fills the crosscuts with sand, gets gravels from the bluffs and alternates them with sands and clays in some places, he has some idea of the complexity of the river deposits of the Cenozoic.

The sites of deposition were not in the same places throughout all of the Cenozoic era. In southern Colorado and northern New Mexico, a considerable area was covered by deposits during the first part of the era, but this site ceased to receive sediments during the last three epochs. Several basins might be receiving sediments at the same time but be entirely disconnected.

LIFE OF THE CENOZOIC

During the closing stages of the Mesozoic the typical reptiles, birds, and mammals were dying off or undergoing great changes, and with the earliest Cenozoic the animals contrasted strikingly with those of late Mesozoic. Whereas Mesozoic is known as the "Age of Reptiles,"

Cenozoic is known as the "Age of Mammals." None of the large and highly specialized reptiles of the Mesozoic remained, the dinosaurs, flying reptiles, and many kinds of swimming reptiles having disappeared. In place of the reptiles, mammals (few and small in the Mesozoic) became the dominant type of Cenozoic land life. In the oldest of the Eocene continental deposits, remains of primitive[1] generalized mammals (all small) have been found, but they are rare.

An Example of Early Eocene Life. Try to imagine a landscape such as may be found at present in southern California hemmed in by low mountains, vegetation luxurious and subtropical palm trees common, the animal life consisting mainly of generalized types of mammals, most of them small. If you could have caught and examined one of them, you would have found it unlike anything that you had ever seen or read of. It might have resembled a small horse or might have looked more like a dog. You might really have been examining an ancestral horse. In the oldest Cenozoic deposits, horses were no bigger than small dogs; they had four toes, walked flat-footed, and only remotely resembled modern horses (Fig. 414). Another of these animals looked something like a cat and more like a dog, but it was neither. It did not have sharp shearing teeth or well-developed canine teeth, and it did not have claws. It was a primitive type of carnivore, or flesh eater; one of the ancestors of the carnivores of the present time (Fig. 415). Among the trees you would have missed the variety of birds that are present almost every place in modern time. Birds were present but of few kinds and probably few in numbers. However, birds are preserved with great difficulty

---

[1] By "primitive types," it is meant that the forms were like those from which you would expect the more specialized species to develop. By "generalized," we mean that the animal has characteristics that become distributed in the higher forms. One of the higher forms will have some of the characteristics of the generalized type and lack others, so that in a large number of species of the higher types one would find all of the characteristics possessed by the generalized types.

For instance, all of these mammals had four or five toes, whereas with the progress of evolution many of them lost one or more of the toes. Man is primitive in respect to number of toes. All of these mammals had 44 teeth, but during the progress of evolution most animals lost some of their teeth. Man has 32 teeth and is somewhat specialized in that respect. Some mammals have become very highly specialized in respect to teeth, having lost all of them. Specialization does not necessarily mean advantageous progress. It may even mean degeneration.

The early Cenozoic mammals were all flat-footed, *i.e.*, none of them walked on the ends of their toes as many mammals do at the present time. All of them had generalized teeth; they were not specialized for eating grass, flesh, insects, or fruit. Nearly all mammals of the present have some such specialization of teeth. Hogs' teeth are not specialized for any particular kind of diet and so may be said to be "generalized" or "primitive."

None of those primitive mammals had developed the burrowing habit of the rodents or the swimming specializations of many modern mammals.

and are always rare as fossils no matter how abundant they were; hence, we may be incorrect in considering that the number of birds was small.

You would have seen few reptiles although it may be that modern types of reptiles played a more important part than we suppose. Turtles, crocodiles, lizards, and snakes were present but not in great numbers or of many kinds.

FIG. 414. An ancestral horse from the Eocene. The front feet had four toes, the hind feet three. (After Scott.)

FIG. 415. An ancestral carnivore of the Eocene. (After Scott.)

Rapid Changes in Animals. Conditions for rapid changes of mammalian species were favorable. Many types of highly specialized mammals appeared, great numbers developed, large forms evolved from small ones, and all of the main types of mammalian life were present by the end of the Eocene. Several kinds of mammals reached elephantine size during the Cenozoic (Fig. 416). Before the close of the first epoch one kind had attained a height of 5 feet. Its head was large and many-horned, and upper canine teeth of the males were large and curved. As its remains were found first near the Uinta Mountains, it was named "Uintatherium" (Fig. 417). One of the striking peculiarities of the animal was that it had the smallest brain for the size of its body of any known mammal.[2] Most mammals are large-brained, and the proportion of brain to size of body is always larger than in other types of animals. The large mammals of the early Cenozoic were herbivores that had developed forms with generalized teeth.

Horses. Probably the history of the horse group is better known than that of any other. We have already considered the horse that occurred in the oldest Cenozoic formation, an animal no larger than a small dog, four-toed, walking flat-footed, having 44 teeth not differentiated or highly specialized, hoofs not well developed. In later Eocene many changes took place in the horse. The animals become larger

[2] Recall that one of the Mesozoic animals had the smallest brain compared to size of body among all animals (page 420), and that another had the smallest brain compared to the size of its head (page 442).

FIG. 416. Titanotheres, tortoises, and primitive carnivores from the Oligocene. (From a painting by C. R. Knight, courtesy of Chicago Museum of Natural History.)

FIG. 417. Uintatheres and four-toed horses. (*From a painting by C. R. Knight, courtesy of Chicago Museum of Natural History.*)

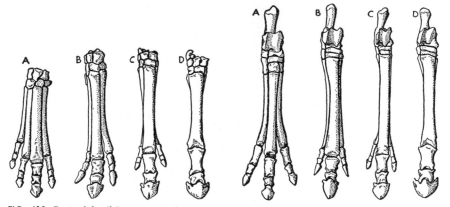

FIG. 418. Feet of fossil horses and of the modern horse, forefeet at left, hind feet at right. (A) Eocene horse; (B) Oligocene horse; (C) Miocene horse; (D) modern horse. (*From Romer, "Vertebrate Paleontology."*)

(about the size of Shetland ponies) and the number of toes was reduced to three on each foot[3] (Fig. 418).

The loss of toes, accompanied by changes that caused the animal to walk more on the ends of the toes, forced other modifications in the foot (Fig. 418). The change from flat-footedness to walking on the ends of

[3] The reduction of toes seems to have come about by the animal's starting to walk on the ends of the toes. Illustrate this with your own hand by placing it flat on the able with the forearm erect. Now start to raise the hand so as to rest it on the ends

the toes caused alterations in muscles and in relationship of the feet to the legs. A striking change was in the elongation of the tarsal bones, which assumed an erect position and attained an increase in length that was greatly out of proportion to the other increase in size of the animal.

Only one of the five tarsal bones remains in the one-toed stage, and it has increased greatly in length: from 2 inches in the earliest horse to 18 inches in some of the larger horses. The foot lengthened to 20 or 22 inches, and had a single line of bones extending from the ankle[4] to the hoof.

All parts of the horse were changing all of the time, but some parts more rapidly than others. The lengthening of the foot required decided changes in other parts of the body. The horse was becoming a grazing animal; and with an increase in the length of the foot that brought its head 18 inches farther from the ground, an adjustment was necessary unless it was to get down on its knees or lie down in order to feed. The horse's head and neck both elongated at the same time as the foot increased in length, so that there never was a time that it could not readily reach the ground with its mouth.[5]

In the early stages the horse could not be a grazer because grass had

---

of the fingers rather than on the flat of the hand. As the hand comes up, the thumb ceases to connect with the table. Keep on raising the hand until the little finger also ceases to connect with the table. You now have the condition of the three-toed horse, with the middle toe bearing the greater weight and the side toes resting on the ground and helping bear the weight. It has really become an odd-toed creature, the middle toe being largest (Fig. 418). As the first toe ceased to touch the ground, it gradually atrophied or ceased to develop, and, as we observed, in the oldest horse it was already missing, assuming that this four-toed form had developed from an original five-toed animal. During the Upper Eocene the same thing happened to the fifth toe, the little finger as represented by your hand; every vestige of that toe had disappeared before the end of Eocene time.

Continue to raise your hand into a still more erect position so that the arm and hand are in a straight line from the elbow to the tips of the fingers. The fingers on either side of the middle drag backward as your hand is raised and finally cease to touch the table. This seems to have happened to the horse as it began to walk on the middle toe, and by glacial time it had lost all but that toe. The other two, however, remained as mere splints or vestiges and are present in the modern horse (see part D of Fig. 418).

[4] People unfamiliar with the anatomy of horses are likely to call the ankle the knee. The part of the horse about the height of the knee of man, which seems to function like the knee of man, is really the ankle, and the knee is up against the body.

[5] Such discussion of changes does not imply that geologists know what caused them, which came first, which was the most important in the evolution, or anything further than that the changes actually took place. As biologists working with modern forms are usually unable to tell what causes variations, geologists are absolutely helpless in working out causes of changes in forms that lived so long ago.

not developed. First, it had to eat shrubs and branches of trees. As grasses developed, the horse formed the habit of eating them, but its teeth were not well fitted for the purpose. They were small and too much alike in hardness throughout each tooth to make them effective grinders of grass. The later evolution of the teeth was as striking as that of the feet. They became large and elongated but, most essential of all, developed very complex patterns of enamel alternating with a softer material called dentine (Fig. 419). We found from studying the

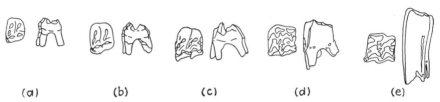

(a)   (b)   (c)   (d)   (e)

FIG. 419. Evolution of horses' teeth. (a, b) Eocene; (c) Oligocene; (d) Miocene; (e) Pleistocene and recent. (After Osborn.)

rocks that hard layers stood out as soft layers wore down and that where alternating layers of hard and soft rocks were exposed the topography consisted of ridges and valleys. The tooth of the horse, by having harder and softer layers on edge, remains rough as long as such layers exist. By increasing the length of the short teeth, the animal's length of life could thus be increased greatly, for the wear caused by eating grasses reduces teeth rapidly. Possibly, the Pleistocene horse lived several times as long as the early Cenozoic horse, although such a conclusion is not susceptible of proof.

Many species of horses developed from early Cenozoic to Pleistocene. More than 60 species have been described from North America alone, and it is probable that as many more will be found. Seven or eight species lived at the same time, and horses may have been as abundant as the bison were on the great plains 100 years ago. However, horses entirely disappeared from both North and South America long before the coming of Europeans to the continents.

Horses are known as odd-toed ungulates (hoofed animals) because the usual number of toes was three or one. A four-toed horse was mentioned but it was a temporary stage between five-toed and three-toed. Many other odd-toed ungulates appeared during the Cenozoic.

Rhinoceros. After the horse, the most abundant odd-toed ungulate in North America was the rhinoceros, along with which the tapir and the horse are the only odd-toed ungulates extant. The rhinoceros lived in such great numbers in parts of Nebraska and Kansas that some Cenozoic deposits there consist almost entirely of its bones. Several kinds existed, but three main types roamed North America at the same time. One of these, a large heavy-limbed form like the modern African species, lived in low-timbered regions. Another was a light-limbed, slender, grass-eating type, and a third was intermediate between the two in size and habits (Figs. 420 and 421).

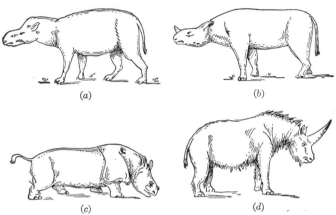

FIG. 420. Cenozoic rhinoceroses. (a) Oligocene; (b) Miocene; (c) Pliocene; (d) Pleistocene. (After Osborn.)

Tapir. The tapir is a three-toed form with modern representatives only in Africa and the American tropics. In Central and South America, it is the largest of the wild animals living today, but the evolution of the feet has not gone beyond the clumsy three-toed type (four on the

FIG. 421. Woolly rhinoceros, with antelope and mammoth in the distance. A midwinter evening in northern France on the steppes near the close of the glacial epoch. (*From a painting by C. R. Knight, courtesy of American Museum of Natural History.*)

front), and none of the fine adjustments of elongated tarsal bones has come about in its evolution.

Even-toed Ungulates. The general consideration of the odd-toed ungulates leads up to the study of the much more numerous even-toed ungulates, which are represented by hundreds of species and by the most valuable of modern animals with the exception of the horse. Cattle, sheep, deer, antelope, camels (Fig. 422), and goats are some of the even-toed ungulates. Instead of having one, three, or five toes they have two or four toes.[6] They seem to have branched off from the odd-toed ungulates very early in Cenozoic time. Several species of camels developed in North America during early Cenozoic, and they seem to have flourished until about the time of the glacial period.

FIG. 422. Oligocene camel at the left, Miocene-Pliocene camel at the right. (After Berry.)

Carnivores. Carnivorous mammals appeared in large numbers and many species, culminating in size in the huge saber-toothed tiger, which was very abundant in the late Cenozoic. Not only was this cat very large but the great size of its upper canine teeth readily distinguished it from all of the other large cats (Fig. 423). A remarkable occurrence of the remains of the saber-toothed tiger is at Rancho la Brea in Los Angeles, California, where large seepages of oil occurred, the volatile parts of which evaporated, leaving an asphalt lake. Animals coming to the lake to drink were mired in the asphalt. Thousands of specimens of the saber-toothed tiger have been taken from these lakes. Their flesh was not preserved in the asphalt but only their bones.

Primates (Apes and Man). Man and the apes form the group called

[6] If you will again use your hand to illustrate the foot of the primitive lower Cenozoid flat-footed mammal, you can see the process through which the even-toed ungulates passed as they changed to two-toed forms. As before, have the forearm erect, the hand flat on the table. Raise the hand slightly until the thumb is off the table and the weight of the arm and hand rests on four fingers. The thumb now is useless; gradually the toe, thus represented, atrophied in the even-toed ungulates and the animal came to walk on four toes. Continue to raise the hand to a more erect position, but bring the weight to bear on the two middle fingers instead of on the middle finger. The outer two fingers now become useless; gradually, in the even-toed ungulates the outer toes ceased to develop and two-toed forms, such as cattle, goats, and sheep, resulted. The splints of the other toes remain as vestiges of the former structures in almost all forms. Many of the earlier species of the even-toed ungulates had four functional toes and several of the living forms have four toes, although the outer two are not functional. The evolution of the rest of the foot paralleled that of the odd-toed ungulates. Two palm bones functioned in the same way as one in the horse, and the ankle of the animal is in the same position as that of the horse. The head and neck of the large species lengthened at the same time that the foot elongated. They, too, became grazing animals and their teeth became modified in much the same way as those of the horse. Specialization in teeth went even farther than in the horse, as some of the even-toed ungulates lost all of the teeth from the front part of one jaw.

"Primates," and in the oldest Cenozoic formations fragmentary remains of primitive, generalized apes have been found.   Small apes were scarcely distinguishable from some other primitive types of mammals.   In North America, apes were neither numerous nor highly developed; the rise of the higher types of primates came mainly in Africa and Asia.

FIG. 423. Eocene cat at the left; Pleistocene saber-toothed cat at the right.   (*After Scott.*)

Elephants.   Eurasia was favorable for mammalian evolution in the Cenozoic.   Odd-toed and even-toed ungulates, carnivores, and many other forms were much like those of North America.   The elephant group, however, was entirely distinct and was well developed and large before it migrated to North America.   It seems to have originated in

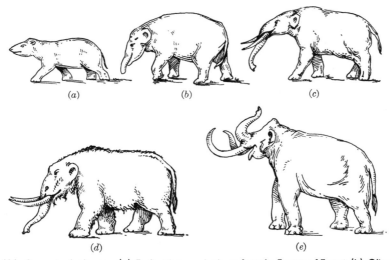

FIG. 424. Cenozoic elephants.   (a) Earliest known elephant, from the Eocene of Egypt; (b) Oligocene elephant; (c) Miocene elephant; (d) Pliocene elephant; (e) Pleistocene elephant.   (*After Osborn.*)

Africa, and members of the first elephantlike species were small and resembled modern hogs (Fig. 424a).   This was only a superficial resemblance, however, one of shape rather than structure.   The oldest elephants lived in early Cenozoic time.   They had protuberant snouts but neither trunk nor tusks.   With the progress of Cenozoic time they increased greatly in size, and the snout elongated and became prehensile (Fig. 424b).   Unlike the horse, the elephant did not reach the ground by an elongation of the neck and head; instead the elongation of the trunk allowed the animal to drink from the low-lying pools and to browse from the tops of trees.

The outer incisor teeth increased in length in both upper and lower jaws and finally developed into tusks. In some species only the upper incisors enlarged, in others only the lower, and in still others both upper and lower. The females of many of the species lost the incisors and were tuskless. Unlike their development in the horse, the feet of elephants remained large and clumsy. The earliest known elephants had somewhat specialized teeth, but the tendency was for teeth to become large and have alternating vertical layers of enamel and dentine (Fig. 425), such as are present in the horse. As the mouth and head did not keep pace with the rest of the body in size, it was necessary that the mouth should be an effective food gatherer in order to provide the animal with the food that it needed. The small teeth of the early forms could not perform that function and with the progress of time the number of teeth became greatly reduced and their size greatly increased. In the final stages of development, the elephants have only one functional tooth in each jaw, not counting the tusks. A peculiarity of the teeth is that another one comes in behind the one that is functioning and gradually pushes it up and out, so that elephants shed their teeth several times during life. The pain caused by the incoming tooth is known to animal keepers as "elephant toothache"; it sometimes drives the animals nearly frantic.

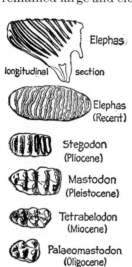

FIG. 425. Evolution in size and grinding surface of elephant teeth. (After Moore, modified from Lull.)

About Middle Cenozoic time, before the North American animals migrated into South America, elephants came across some land bridge between Asia and North America and finally crossed the Isthmus of Panama into South America. They spread all over North America, and the remains of the two main types, mastodon (Fig. 426) and mammoth, have been collected from every state in the United States.

Domestic Animals. It is remarkable that all of the domestic animals of the Americas were brought by Europeans, save only the small camels of South America. Horses, camels, dogs, all had been early denizens of North America, but none survived until the white man arrived. All of the present-day forms originated from old-world species.

South American Mammals. North America was separated from South America by a water barrier until rather late Cenozoic time. South

America was thus left as an isolated region and peculiar types of animals evolved there, entirely independent of the animals of other regions. Some

FIG. 426. American mastodon from the Pleistocene of New York. (*From a painting by C. R. Knigh:*, courtesy of Chicago Museum of Natural History.)

remnants of this development are still present in South America; it is there that the sloths (Fig. 427)—clumsy, awkward, stupid creatures— occur. Huge birds of peculiar types, some of which reached a height of 7 or 8 feet and were wingless, appeared late in the era and lived almost to the present.

Late in the Cenozoic, after land connec- tion had been established between North and South America, some of the South American animals came into southern United States. Among them were the sloths, one of which (Fig. 427) was described by Thomas Jefferson, who seems to have been the only president of the United States who ever dabbled in paleontology. He found remains

FIG. 427. A giant sloth from the Pleistocene.

of this animal in North Carolina, collected them, and named the genus. A very large armadillo-like animal had flourished in South America and it came as far north as the Missouri River. North American mammals went south into South America and flourished, but South American types never gained much of a hold in North America.

Animals of Isolated Areas. Islands and other isolated areas are favorable for the origin of peculiar types. This is strikingly brought out by Alfred Russel Wallace in his book called "Islands and Island Life." Darwin was greatly impressed by the development of peculiar types in the Pacific islands. In Australia many kinds of primitive mammals survive.

Aquatic and Flying Mammals. In the evolution of reptiles of the early Mesozoic, you will recall how some forms took to water and developed swimming appendages, others to the air and developed wings, some became climbers, and others burrowers. Parallel development took place among mammals in early Cenozoic. Mammals with wings, such as those of the bat type, came in early but were always rare. Flying mammals never reached the importance of flying reptiles, and they are among the rarest of all fossils. The water has always been a favorite habitat for animals and no sooner does the evolution of a particular group start than some of them become aquatic. The land animal that we have been considering did not live in surroundings favorable for the adoption of an aquatic habitat, but where the seas came over the land on the Atlantic and Gulf coasts mammals had ample opportunity to take to the water. Before the close of the Eocene, several types had so adjusted themselves as to be entirely at home in water. Primitive whales inhabited the water along the Atlantic and Gulf coasts and in a comparatively short time they developed into very large animals.[7]

Many other types of swimming mammals were developing throughout the Cenozoic. Everyone is familiar with several of the modern descendants, such as seals, sea lions, and walruses. As with the reptiles, the adaptation to living in the water was best shown in the modification of the feet and legs, which became paddles. In some the legs disappeared, and the animal swam mainly by means of the tail. No air-breathing animal has evolved water-breathing organs.

---

[7] The bones of fossil whales were objects of curiosity to early settlers in the Carolinas and were interpreted as remains of huge animals that had succeeded in reaching those places at the time of the Deluge. One enterprising citizen collected and put together enough bones to make an animal about 125 feet long. With these he traveled over the country, displaying "the great reptile," as he called it, for an admission fee. He named the animal "Basilosaurus," and finally took the specimen to England, where it was purchased by the British Museum. Experts there found that several animals were represented in the one specimen. The owner had collected as many bones as he needed and put them together to make an animal of large size for exhibition purposes. The experts also found that the animal was not a reptile, as was indicated by the name "Basilosaurus," but a primitive whale, and it was renamed in accordance with its true nature.

Fossil Fishes. When the Union Pacific Railroad was built through western Wyoming, numerous fossil fishes were found in the Green River formation of the Eocene in one cut and the place was named "Fossil" on that account. Ever since that time these fossil fishes have been an object of curiosity for tourists and have been sold at various towns along the railroad. At present, one man makes it his business to quarry out these fossils and sell them. The fishes are preserved in a fine-grained limestone, which probably was formed as a chemical precipitate on the lake floor. Every detail of the structure of the hard parts is preserved and the fossils occur in such quantities that a person knowing nothing about them can collect many fragments if he happens to go to the right place. The rock is quite different from the lithographic limestone of Bavaria, which we have mentioned as ideal for the preservation of fossils.

The fishes from the Green River formation are much like modern forms, indicating that most of their evolution had taken place before early Cenozoic. However, the differences are great enough to distinguish all of them from species of the present. Along with the fishes occur huge palm leaves and parts of other subtropical plants, evidences that the climate was considerably warmer during that period than at present. Fossil insects are abundant in the same beds as the fishes.

MISCELLANEOUS

Climate. The climate of the Cenozoic fluctuated considerably. Evidences of glaciation have been found in Eocene deposits of Colorado; in the Green River deposits of the same period in western Wyoming, subtropical plants were abundant. Coal formed in Alaska and on islands within the Arctic Circle. Fossil palms have been found in Greenland. In Pliocene, the climate became cooler and that epoch closed as the great ice sheets spread over the continents. Within the glacial epoch, climates became so mild during glacier retreats that subtropical plants grew as far north as southern Canada. The glaciers disappeared, and at present we do not know whether climate is growing colder or warmer, drier or wetter.

Economic Products. The Cenozoic rocks furnish more than half of world oil production. In North America most of this oil comes from California, Texas, and Louisiana. A great deal of coal formed in the early Cenozoic in northwestern United States, but little is mined. The igneous intrusion of the period gave rise to many rich deposits of gold, silver, copper, lead, zinc, and other metals.

CHAPTER 27

THE PLEISTOCENE OR GLACIAL EPOCH

All the geological epochs except the Pleistocene, now under consideration, are based on advances and retreats of the seas. After the last important sea invasion, the climate became so cold that extensive glaciation was produced in many middle latitudes of the world. When this was first realized, it was supposed that here was the first extensive glaciation that had taken place in geologic time and that it constituted a real geologic period. Had the earlier glaciations been known as they are now, it is probable that the Pleistocene would have been considered as merely an epoch of another period, and it is so considered in this book.

Glaciers Form. The Pleistocene was initiated by decrease in temperature, particularly in the northern hemisphere. This decrease gradually brought on an excess of snowfall over waste in the northern half of North America and Europe. Such excess could occur only where the amount of snowfall was considerable. Glaciers do not form in arid regions no matter how cold. In North America, glaciers advanced southward from three centers of dispersion and at their greatest extent reached about to the Missouri and Ohio rivers. The front of the glacier extended from Long Island to the Rocky Mountains of northern Montana. The ice edge was sinuous but resembled a reasonably regular shore line (Fig. 428).

In Iowa, four epochs of glaciation have been recognized by the presence of four drift sheets. Four times glaciers covered all or part of the state, and four times they melted away. During the time between advances of the ice was more weathering than has taken place since the last ice retreat, indicating that the time between the retreat and readvance was longer than the time since the last glaciation.

Indications of two to four ice advances have been found in many areas in North America and Europe, and students of glaciation recognize four glacial epochs in the Pleistocene. The oldest glacier of the Pleistocene was the most extensive and advanced more than 1,000,000 years ago. The last glacier withdrew from the Niagara Falls region 40,000 to 50,000 years ago if our Niagara Falls timepiece is to be trusted.

Ice Covers Mountains and Enters the Ocean. The ice of the main glaciers must have been 4,000 feet or more thick in the centers from which it advanced and have thinned to less than 100 feet at the edge. Most of the New England mountains were covered by ice, as were, also, the Adirondacks in New York and various ranges in Canada. Along the New England coast and part of New York, the ice pushed out into the shallow

FIG. 428. Map of North America showing area covered by glacial ice during some part of the Pleistocene epoch. (*After T. C. Chamberlin.*)

part of the ocean and built its terminal moraines under the sea. It left the area over which it advanced mantled with ground or terminal moraine and dotted with large and small lakes. The basins of all the Great Lakes were formed largely by glaciation, mainly by filling and irregular damming of old valleys, but in part by scouring. The glaciation left waterfalls and streams entirely out of adjustment with the underlying solid rocks.

The Great Lakes. The history of the lake region, from the time when the last glacier retreated so as to allow the lakes to begin to form, is well known. The first outlets were south, from Lake Erie and Lake Michigan to the Ohio and Mississippi (Fig. 429). The Chicago Drainage Canal, which carries the sewage from Chicago, was excavated in one of these old outlets and restores the southward drainage. At a later stage of ice retreat a lower margin was uncovered, the one through which the waters run over Niagara Falls.

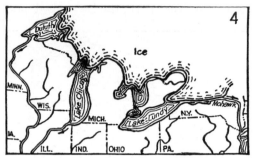

FIG. 429. A late stage in the formation of the Great Lakes. (*From Taylor and Leverett, U.S. Geological Survey.*)

During this history the margins of the lakes changed considerably, and some of the lakes remained at different levels long enough to create old beaches and even well-developed sea cliffs and wave-cut terraces. South of Lake Erie and Lake Ontario old beaches and barriers may be followed for many miles. The first railroads in northern Ohio were built on the old beaches. The first wagon roads also followed these beaches and the farmhouses were built near them. Away from the beaches the mantle rock was largely lake deposits of silt and clay, which made road construction very difficult. Silt and clay might be 10 feet or more thick, and when wet formed a deep mud, with the result that vehicles mired down. The beaches and barriers were built of sand and gravel and made natural roads. The results of early selection of this ready-made type of road are still apparent in the alignment of villages along the old beaches, and the main roads are still there.

Glaciation and Economic Development. The effect of glaciation on early settlements is shown by other trade routes. The construction of the Erie Canal would probably never have been undertaken had it not been that a valley had been formed by a stream draining the Great Lakes. A canal running from the west end of Lake Erie southwestward through Ohio and Indiana follows an old outlet valley. Cleveland became a railway center because of preglacial valleys through the highlands to the southeast. These valleys were abandoned by their streams with the readjustments of drainage that came about when the glacier retreated. Niagara Falls was due to changes of drainage brought about by glaciation, and the great electric plants developed there thus owe their location to glaciation. The side of a great valley was formed in the Paleozoic rocks east and west of Niagara.   The tributary streams to this valley were in harmony with the main stream and had cut through the side cliffs so that they entered the main valley at the level of the main stream.   The glaciers filled up the old valleys with drift, and a new stream draining Lake Erie took a new course, after the glaciers retreated, through the lowest place over the glacial topography.   This new drainage stream missed the old valleys, came to the cliff over high land, and thus formed the original Niagara.   If it had happened to strike through one of the preglacial valleys, the entire history and development of that part of the United States would have been different.

Old Lakes Filled with Peat.   Nearly all of the peat bogs of Canada and of northeastern United States originated in glacial lake basins.   The peat bogs of Ireland and of western Europe also developed in such lake basins.   We do not think of glaciation as creating conditions favorable to the beginning of coal beds, but the peat in the bogs could become covered with silt and sand and, in course of time, change to coal.   Such coal beds would be small and irregular and would not compare in thickness or extent with the coal beds of late Paleozoic or late Mesozoic.   However, in Ireland and western Europe, peat is used extensively as fuel and the peat bogs are thus of real value to the inhabitants.   In New Jersey, peat is gathered, cut into briquettes, and used as fuel.   Some of the old bogs that have filled with plant remains and clay are used for growing garden truck.   The celery gardens of New Jersey and eastern New York are largely in these old bogs.

In some places, however, the bogs are not advantageous to man. Some of the earlier railroad builders, particularly in Canada, had great trouble from them.   The railway engineers did not realize the character of the material and so built railroads directly across the bogs or "muskegs," as they called them.   As soon as the railroads were used, the tracks began to settle, and in spite of the use of thousands of tons of rock as ballast, they continued to settle, in many places compelling relocation of the road.

Western Lakes.   Some other lakes of Pleistocene and later times should not be passed without mention.   Great Salt Lake was a body of fresh water many times as large as at present.   It drained northward into Snake River through a valley that has been little changed since the stream ceased to flow through it.   Along with increase in temperature in the Rocky Mountain region, decrease in precipitation must have come, for Great Salt Lake has actually dried down to its present state (Figs. 430 and 431).   That means that it has changed from a lake covering 20,000 square miles to one covering less than 2,000, from extreme depths of more than 1,000 feet to an average depth of less than 20 feet, and from normal river water containing only 1 part common salt in 20,000 parts

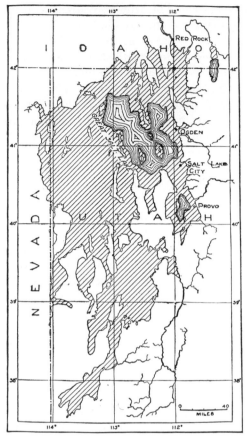

FIG. 430. Map of Lake Bonneville (shaded), the vast fresh-water lake ancestral to Great Salt Lake. (*After Gilbert, U.S. Geological Survey.*)

FIG. 431. Shore-line terraces of Lake Bonneville.   (*After Gilbert.*)

of water to a water that contains 1 part common salt in 5 parts of water. Other salt lakes of the same kind were present in the Rocky Mountain region and westward, but Lake Bonneville, the ancestor of Great Salt Lake, was the largest. Lake Agassiz (Fig. 79, page 88), another very large Pleistocene lake, covered considerable areas in Canada, Minnesota, and North Dakota. It was shallow and became nearly filled with sediments, mainly sand and coarse clay, before it was drained by the lowering of the northern outlet upon withdrawal of the glaciers. The deposits cover nearly flat areas that constitute the extensive wheatlands of the region where the lake existed. At one time this lake drained southward into the Mississippi, but, with the disappearance of the ice at the north, the northern margin became lower than the southern, and it drained northward through the Nelson River.

Valley Glaciers. While the continental glaciers covered so much of the northern part of America, alpine glaciers were much more extensive in the mountains than they are at present. Glaciers 25 miles long stretched out on to the plains from the Uinta Mountains in Utah, where no glaciers now exist. Every mountain range of the Rocky Mountains and westward presents similar phenomena. Between the moraines of the continental glaciers in Montana and the terminal moraines of the mountain glaciers of the Rocky Mountain front ranges, there is a wide nonglaciated area. The Appalachian Mountains were not high enough to have local glaciers, but some of the mountains of northern New England had alpine glaciers.

Boundary of Glaciated Areas. As described in the chapter on glaciation, the margin between the glaciated and nonglaciated areas is not well marked in all places, the oldest glacial deposits having been so greatly eroded by streams that none of the original glacial topography remains. Under such conditions the former presence of glaciers can be recognized only by the occurrence of materials from remote regions in places where they could not have been deposited by streams. This is true along the margins of the old drift near the Missouri and Kansas rivers in Kansas and Missouri.

Nontransported soils correspond in a general way to the underlying rock, but in glaciated regions the soils are irregular and do not correspond to the underlying rocks. A good soil map is likely to show the contact of glaciated and nonglaciated areas by the soils represented.

Drift Becomes Tillite. The wide occurrence of glacial drift over North America and the similarity of the drift from one place to another allow its recognition with very little question. Drift is a continental deposit as widespread as many of the rocks that were formed beneath the sea, which geologists trace over very wide areas, and, with their fossil contents, form the basis for working out historical geology. With the progress of time much of the drift is likely to be washed away by streams and reworked to form stream, lake, and ocean deposits. Should seas advance over the area of drift and deposit other materials above it, cementation might change the drift to solid rock so that it would be preserved. In Canada this solid rock, or tillite, might be on pre-Paleozoic deposits, in New York on Paleozoic, in Montana on Mesozoic, in some other place on Cenozoic, and its age could not be determined from the rocks on which it lies.

How to Determine the Age of Drift. If the Pleistocene consolidated drift in Canada should happen to overlie the pre-Cambrian tillite, the two might be so much alike as to make the distinguishing of them difficult. The materials for both would have come from the pre-Cambrian rocks, and glaciers in the pre-Cambrian must have made their deposits in the same way as they did in the Pleistocene. There is some likelihood that the pre-Cambrian drift would be somewhat metamorphosed, but, if neither were metamorphosed beyond the stage of being firmly cemented, they might be indistinguishable. It would be possible that the pre-Cambrian drift had been entirely eroded away from one place and Pleistocene drift deposited directly on granite or pre-Cambrian schist or gneiss. In a near-by area it would be possible that the pre-Cambrian drift would lie on the same kind of rocks with no Pleistocene drift over it. A geologist working in the field would find it difficult, then, to tell the age of the two drifts. Either might be Pleistocene; either might be pre-Cambrian. One fossil might serve to solve part of the problem. If even a fragment of bone were found in the drift, it could not be pre-Cambrian, as animals with bones did not live at that time. A mastodon tooth, a mammoth tooth, the tooth of a horse, or any recognizable bone of Pleistocene mammal would be adequate proof of Pleistocene age. However, if the age of one drift were proved in this way, and no fossils were found in the other, it would not on that account be pre-Cambrian. It might be Pleistocene but nonfossiliferous. The Pleistocene drift would be difficult to identify from one locality to another on the basis of fossil content, because fossils are so rare. Conditions for burying and fossilization of animals were not favorable.

It might be possible to solve the question of the age of the drifts by tracing them laterally. If one could find Paleozoic rocks overlying one drift and underlying the other, he would then have proved the wide difference in age of the two, and, as only the two series of drifts have ever been found in southern Canada, he might assume with a considerable degree of certainty that the one drift is pre-Cambrian and the other Pleistocene.

Effects of Glaciation on Plants and Animals. As the margin of the glacier moved northward, plants covered the ground left bare by the retreating ice, but at times the ice retreat was fast enough to leave great areas of barren ground exposed. Some geologists suppose that such barren ground, covered with the mixed glacial flour and weathered material, furnished the winds with the fine material that finally formed loess. As you will recall, loess contains a large amount of nonchemically weathered fine material which could have originated from the ground-up rock of the glacier.

The fluctuation of temperature between advances of the ice went beyond what we now consider normal. In some of the interglacial stages plants of types that grow no farther north than Florida at the present time grew in southern Canada, *i.e.*, southern Canada, seemingly, was subtropical. It is possible that we are now living in an interglacial stage, although there is no sure evidence to indicate this. As has been pointed out, most gla-

FIG. 432. A Pleistocene woolly rhinoceros.

ciers are retreating at the present time, indicating either a lessening of the amount of precipitation or a rising of temperature. However, even the retreat of the glaciers does not show that we are living in an interglacial stage. The climate has not become so warm as it was in some interglacial stages of the Pleistocene.

Glaciation had profound effects on the life in and beyond the glaciated regions. As the cold climate came on and glaciers advanced from the north, the warmth-loving animals and plants migrated southward.

FIG. 433. (a) Pleistocene mastodon; (b) Pleistocene mammoth; (c) Pleistocene elephant. (*After Scott.*

Many of the plants were destroyed. Animals that could not adjust themselves to increasing cold gradually disappeared or inhabited only the more southerly areas. Some animals lived at the margins of the glaciers or inhabited the hills that stuck up through the ice and some developed protective coverings. The woolly rhinoceros (Figs. 421 and 432) and the hair-covered mammoth (Figs. 421 and 433) lived on the glaciers and along the glacial margins.

In general the animals and plants of the Pleistocene were not greatly different from those of the present, although some of the more prominent animal species have died out.

In North America, many species of horses, deer, antelope, bison, bear, cats, and dogs of various types mingled with some boreal forms and some tropical species, and all moved northward with the coming of the warmer climate. The mastodon (Fig. 426) and mammoth were common until after the retreat of the last glacier from the United States. Their remains have been found in bogs of the youngest moraines. Horses were rather abundant, but they disappeared from North America between the time of the retreat of the ice and the coming of Europeans. The disappearance of horses, mammoths, and mastodons is hard to explain. The mammoth lived until a relatively recent time. Its remains with flesh intact have been found frozen in the ice of Siberia.

MAN

The Pleistocene epoch might be called the time of the rise of man to dominancy. We are naturally much interested in the history of man, but from the geological point of view less is known of him than of most other animals. Man's history has been worked out only from imperfect, widely scattered specimens, whereas the well-known horse history is based on thousands of fossils.

Pithecanthropus, the Ape Man of Java. In 1892 a specimen was discovered in Java that seemed to be intermediate between the highest type of ape and man. Apes have large brain capacity compared to their size, though this proportion is very much less than in man. Man's brain capacity is greater than that of any other animal in comparison to his size. The Java specimen does not have the brain capacity of man but seems to have a greater one than any ape. As a matter of fact only part of the skull of the "Java man" is known, and measurements of brain capacity vary to a considerable extent. The teeth of the Java specimen are somewhat more like those of apes than of man. Only one limb bone is known, a femur, and it indicates an erect-walking creature, much more like man than ape. It is not known that all of the associated bones found in Java belong together, so that though this creature is called "the ape man of Java," so many uncertainties are connected with it that it furnishes little help in tracing the descent of man (Fig. 434A).

As far as can be determined, the Java remains came from the Pliocene, the epoch immediately preceding Pleistocene, and they constitute our earliest record of man, if the creature was really man.

The Heidelberg Man. The next oldest remains were found in Germany, near Heidelberg, and consist of one lower jaw, which is heavy and retreating. Though the teeth are much more primitive than those of modern man, they are not apelike and by no stretch of the imagination could the jaw be considered as belonging to anything but man.

The Piltdown Man.   In 1911, part of a skull was found in a gravel pit near Piltdown, England, and near it but not associated with it a tooth and some other bone fragments.   The skull is primitive in many respects, and the teeth also are considerably different from those of modern man. The brain capacity, so far as can be determined, is smaller than that of

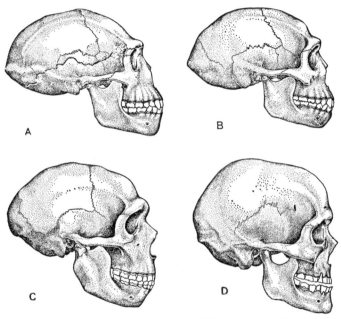

FIG. 434. Skulls of fossil human types.   (A) Java man; (B) Peking man; (C) Neanderthal man; (D) Cro-Magnon man.   (*From Romer, after McGregor and Weinert.*)

ordinary man, although not smaller than the smallest brains known among modern people.   As the remains were scattered, it was not possible to determine the position of some of the teeth.   Had this not been the case the specimen might have helped to solve the problem of the relationship of the remains to those of modern man.

The Peking Race.   In 1928, fossils of man more advanced than the Pithecanthropus were found near Peking, China, and since then several other finds have been made (Fig. 434*B*).   At the present time, paleontologists are not agreed as to whether the race represented by the Peking fossils is older or younger than the Piltdown race.   Some students of fossil man believe that the Peking man was closely related to the Neanderthal man of Europe.   The Piltdown man seems to have lived about the third interglacial stage and the Heidelberg man probably the second interglacial stage.   In the fourth interglacial stage cave dwellers had established themselves in western Europe and their remains are rather well known. All are plainly types of men comparable to some present types.

Ancestors of Man. The Neanderthal men, as they are called, throw no light on the way of man's development (Fig. 434C). The Grimaldi, a negroid type that lived at the same time, was not in the line of development of modern man and cannot be considered directly ancestral to modern man. Another race, known as the "Cro-Magnon" (Fig. 434D), was one of the finest physically that ever lived. They were large, had large brain capacity, and their civilization had progressed to a high stage. It was they who painted in colors the well-known pictures in some of the ancient caves of France. But none of the three types gives any real clue as to the descent of modern man. We are left with the firm conviction, the certainty as a matter of fact, that man has developed from lower animals in the same way that other modern animals have developed from ancient forms, but we do not know the precise steps in the development of man or from what ancestor he came.

Man's way of taking care of his dead has made him the rarest of all fossils, and, though it is likely that more fossils of man will be found and probable that man's ancestry may be roughly traced at some time, at present we must consider the matter as unsettled and allow the future to take care of the problem.

Pleistocene Man in Europe. In western Europe, man was a cave dweller during the late Pleistocene. Not only his bones but his implements and drawings have been found in the caves and in deposits below glacial drift in other places. In the caves, his bones are associated with those of the cave bear, saber-toothed tiger, mammoth, and other Pleistocene animals, and his drawings depict Pleistocene species. The drawings are more convincing than the bones, as man's bones might have become mingled with older bones in the caves, but he could not have drawn animals that he had never seen. Artifacts such as those found in the caves have been found in interglacial deposits at no great distance from the caves and constitute a means of matching the cave time with glacial time.

Pleistocene Man in America. Man was present in Europe during the later part of the glacial period and probably during the earlier, but it is still a point in question as to whether he was present in America. Many finds of implements made by man and of actual human bones have convinced some investigators of his presence before the last ice advance, but in every case there has been enough uncertainty to leave the less easily convinced skeptical. No scientist says that man was not present in America during the Pleistocene, and recent discoveries tend to strengthen belief in his presence.

We may raise the question as to what would be sufficient evidence of his presence.   At Viro, Florida, bones of man were found with those of animals that lived only during the Pleistocene.   They were not very far below the surface, and some investigators said that they might have gotten mixed up with the bones of the Pleistocene animals by falling into a hole where a tree had been uprooted from above the deposits that contained the other animals, or by a small stream cutting a little valley through the deposits and the valley becoming filled by deposits in which the bones of man were preserved and the other bones weathered in from the sides or carried in from a short distance away.   Or it was possible that all of the bones had been carried and deposited in that place later than Pleistocene times.   The Viro deposit is evidence in favor of man being present at the same time as the other animals, but it is not absolutely convincing.

Near Lansing, Kansas, human remains were found below some 40 feet of river deposits, and for a time this was held as proof of man's early occupancy of America.   But students of river deposits soon pointed out that the river may shift its deposits very quickly and that 40 or 50 feet of sand and clay could be piled up in one place within a few years.

Recently, in Oklahoma and Texas, the remains of man have been found in seemingly undisturbed sediments along with bones of mastodon and other animals not known to have lived beyond the Pleistocene. These finds, too, have not proved convincing to some geologists, and the question still remains open, although evidence seems to point more and more positively toward man's early occupancy of America.   The finds in Oklahoma and Texas are outside of the glaciated area and so are not associated with glacial deposits.   In Minnesota bones of a woman were found below laminated clays, indicating burial in Pleistocene time. However, this occurrence is not positive evidence of her presence there in Pleistocene time.   When man's implements or bones are found below a considerable thickness of undisturbed glacial drift, *i.e.*, where there can be no question of their ever having been moved, geologists will be completely convinced of the presence of man in America during the Pleistocene.

INDEX

A

Abrasive action, by ice, 61, 62, 239–247
  by water, 61, 97–99
  by wind, 61, 268–269, 272–273
Adirondacks, 226, 465
Adjusted shore line, production of, 169–176
Agassiz, Louis, 239, 265–266
Agate, 141
Age, of drift, determination of, 470
  of mammals, 451
  of topographies, 101–103
Air, as chemical agent of weathering, 63–65
  composition of, 64
Air-breathing animals, first appearance of, 373–374
Alabaster, 199
Albrecht, W. A., 47
Algae, 146, 337
Alluvial deposits, 117–124
Alluvial fans, 117–118, 124
Alternation of sediments, 344–346
Aluminum, 8–10, 48, 57, 68, 69, 73–75, 77, 156, 225
Amazon River, 123
Ameba, 337
Amorphous substances, 5–6
Amphibians, Paleozoic, Middle, 372–373
  Upper, 384–385
  Triassic, 406–407, 408
Anhydrite, 187, 198
Animals, air-breathing, first appearance of, 373–374
  generalized types of, 451
  of isolated areas, 462
Anthracite, 202, 289, 393
Anticlines, 287–288, 293, 358–361
Apes, 458–459, 472
Appalachian Geosyncline, 342
Appalachian Mountains, 295–296, 333, 382

Appalachian Mountains, formation of, 380–381
  growth of, 445
Appalachian Trough, cross-section of, 343
  end of, 380–381
  sedimentation in, 341–344
  shallow-water deposits of, 379, 380
Arbuckle Mountains, Oklahoma, 146, 333
Archeozoic era, 332–338
Arenaceous (sandy) shale, 189
Argillaceous (shaly) sandstone, 189
Armor, 369, 371
Armored fishes, 369, 371, 372
Artificial levees, 121
Asbestos, 336
Assam earthquake, 305, 306, 313–314
Astronomic geology defined, 4
Atacama Desert, 84
Atoms, 5–7
Aulosteges, 383
Australia, 177, 279
Azoic rocks, definition of, 337

B

Bacteria, 202
Badlands, 110–113
Bar, 167–169
Barchanes, 276–278
Barents Sea, 177
Barrell, Joseph, 326–327
Barrier beaches, 166, 168
Basalt, 46, 47, 51, 52, 74–75, 231, 404
Basalt porphyry, 51, 52, 231
Basaltic lava, 53
Basaltic (gabbroid) zone of earth, 13
Base level, 101–102
Basilosaurus, 462n.
Batholith, 17, 21–22, 52, 54, 427
Bauxite, 76, 77
Bayous, 106
Beaches, barrier, 166, 168
  as place of active wave work, 158–159